The BIGGEST book of Party Games Ever!

THIS IS A CARLTON BOOK

This edition published in 2001

Copyright © Carlton Books Limited 2001

A CIP catalogue record of this book is available from the British Library

ISBN 1 84222 310 0

Editor: Kerrin Edwards
Designer: Vaseem Bhatti
Production: Lisa French

Printed and bound in Great Britain

The BIGGEST book of Party Games Ever!

CONTENTS

ATHLETIC PURSUITS

MUSICAL INTERLUDES

NOT IN FRONT OF THE VICAR

IN FULL SWING

TIME FOR BED

TRICKS

PRACTICAL JOKES AND TRICKS

CARD TRICKS

PUB TRICKS

TRICKS WITH EVERYDAY OBJECTS

DRINKING GAMES

MONEY GAMES . . . .

DICE GAMES

TONGUE-TWISTERS & WORD GAMES

INTRODUCTION

It is one of life's great dilemmas. You've sent out the invitations, spent half the day baking enough sausage rolls to feed the entire street and put all breakable ornaments into the spare room. Now only one further matter needs to be addressed before you can be sure that your party will be a roaring success – that is, do you arrange some activity to keep your guests entertained, or simply leave them to their own devices? The latter would be easier, but how do you then prevent your best friend from being cornered by Uncle Sidney and his interminable stories about his career in the tax office or stop nice Mr Wilkins from down the road being eaten alive by man-hungry cousin Wilma? The answer is to involve them in games and show-off a few tricks.

What follows in this fun-packed volume are more than 750 of the best party games, most amusing tricks and practical jokes and finest drinking games. The Party Games range from old favourites like Blind Man's Bluff to Squeak-Piggy-Squeak and Postman's Knock (everyone knows these games, but perhaps a few just need to 'refresh their memories') to somewhat less well-known games such as Name That Ghost and Fan The Kipper!

There are tricks and practical jokes that will impress and humiliate in equal measure. Amaze your friends with clever cards tricks like The Lady Vanishes and Double Dealing and embarrass your enemies with messy practical jokes such as Egg On Their Face and Lager Shower.

And as for the drinking games and pub tricks, you can begin the evening by demonstrating the careful flicking of coins into glasses before moving on to such essential japes as Fuzzy Duck and Drink Don't Think. Unless you are a real expert in this field there's a kind introduction to more obscure games like Mexico and Speed Dice. Whichever one you select, these capers are bound to quicken the evening's precedings and get everyone very much in the mood to party!

So throw open your doors, let in the hordes and may the party begin! (Of course you could take this fine tome down to your local if you are fearful for the well-being of your home.) But either way, no self-respecting party-organizer can be without the information within these pages. So read up and party on!

PARTY GAMES

All the very best party games are gathered together in the next 300 or so pages. These are guaranteed to liven up any party, be it a sedate after-dinner gathering accompanied by chocolate mints or the sort of wild carry-on where time is forgotten in the pursuit of pushing through to dawn!

There are thoughtful pencil and paper games; games designed to help all the guests get to know each other; races and romps; word games; saucy games; acting games; and games that are just plain silly.

There are games for intellectuals and for those whose only qualification is a certificate for the 50 metres backstroke; there are games for the energetic and games for those who prefer more peaceful pastimes; there are games for flamboyent extroverts and for shy individuals who habitually spend the entire evening in the kitchen minding the food. Whether you wear a medallion or an anorak, whether your opening line at a party is 'You've got to be Cindy Crawford's younger and prettier sister', or 'Did you know this is the driest October for 82 years?', there are plenty of games here to suit your taste.

Some of the games do need a little preparation, but the majority require nothing more than a group of willing participants. And so that you can choose games that suit the personalities of your guests and their physical and mental state at any stage of a party, a list of helpful symbols accompanies each game. By following these guides, you can avoid creating undue exertion on ageing limbs or causing unnecessary suffering to sensitive souls.

Enjoy the party!

SYMBOLS

 A gentle game

 Guaranteed to upset the neighbours

 Best played after a few drinks

 Danger of structural damage to the home

 Only to be played when blind drunk

 Physical Contact game

 More than one brain cell needed

 Possible grounds for divorce

 Intellectually demanding

 May upset the neighbours

 Liable to cause hideous personal embarrassment

BREAKING
THE ICE

VALENTINES

Players: Any even number

You will need:

Small pieces of card or paper

What better way for your guests to get to know each other than by searching for their spiritual partners? Before the party, the host writes down on pieces of paper or card pairs of famous or infamous lovers corresponding to the number of guests expected. When the guests arrive, they are handed their new identities whereupon Napoleon immediately sets out to find his Josephine while Minnie Mouse hunts down her Mickey. They do this simply by chatting away in character although if a male guest is seen swinging from the light fittings, it is a fair chance that Esmerelda is about to locate her Quasimodo. If there are more women expected than men, this can be balanced out by the inclusion of a Henry VIII or Warren Beatty. Similarly, if there is a surfeit of women, Liz Taylor or Patsy Kensit will prove invaluable.

WHOSE BABY?

Players: Any number

You will need:

Guests' baby photos, paper, pencils

Each guest is asked to bring along a photograph of themselves as a baby or youngster. These are then either pinned to a board or laid out on a table with a number above each photo. The players must try to determine which photo is of which guest, writing down the answers on a piece of paper. The winner is the one who comes up with most correct answers. This game is probably best played by a group of people who know each other's names.

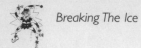

WHO AM I?

Players: Any number

You will need:

Pieces of paper, safety pins

This popular ice-breaker is a good way of keeping the early arrivals occupied while you're still waiting for late-comers. After writing down the names of famous people on slips of paper, pin one on the back of each player. The players have to find out who they are by questioning each other, but these questions can only be answered by 'yes' or 'no'. Time permitting, the game continues until everyone has solved their personal identity crisis.

MATING CALLS

Players: 8-14

You will need:

Blindfolds

Players are divided into pairs, boy and girl. Each couple agrees upon a distinctive ornithological call sign – such as 'Tweet-Tweet', 'Too-Wit-Too-Woo' or 'Squawk-Squawk'. The male partners then leave the room to be blindfolded and, on their return, have to find their mate as quickly as possible. With all the hens chirruping away at the same time, this is easier said than done. To help him, the female is allowed to make her call, but no more than three times. When the pair are finally united, it is the girl's turn to be blindfolded.

TIED IN KNOTS

Players: 10 or more

You will need:

String, scissors

Cut up over 60 pieces of string in different lengths and secrete them about the house. Working in pairs, players hunt out the pieces of string, knotting them together as they go. The winning pair are the ones with the longest continuous length of string within the pre-arranged time limit.

HIDDEN AGENDA

Players: 12 or more

You will need:

Small objects, sticky tape or safety pins, pencils, paper

The host prepares a list of a dozen or so small items – things like a button, a paper clip, an elastic band and a feather. On their arrival, the guests are then taken individually into a quiet room where one of the objects is pinned or taped to their body. The best places are visible yet difficult to spot immediately, such as on socks or belts or under collars. The players are then given copies of the list of the items for which they have to search and they then circulate, examining their fellow guests and, upon discovery, writing down the object next to the name of the person on which it was concealed. The winner is the first person to locate every object or, if you prefer a short game, the one with most correct answers in five minutes.

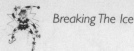
SQUEAK-PIGGY-SQUEAK

Players: Any number

You will need:

A blindfold, a cushion

One player is blindfolded and given a cushion in the centre of the room while the other guests sit in a circle around the outside. The game begins with the blindfolded player being turned around three times to remove any last hint of co-ordination. He or she must then place the cushion on another player's lap and sit on it. In doing so, the blindfolded player calls out 'squeak-piggy-squeak', in response to which the person who is being sat on squeaks like a pig. If the blindfolded player correctly identifies the owner of the squeak, the two change places. If not, another lap must be found. Once a new person is blindfolded, the players all swap positions. This is an excellent way of getting your guests acquainted and making fools of themselves at the same time.

BLIND MAN'S STICK

Players: Any number

You will need:

A blindfold, a stick or cane

This less embarrassing version of 'Squeak-Piggy-Squeak' involves a blindfolded person trying to identify fellow players from the noises they make. While one player is blindfolded and given a stick, the others move slowly around the room. When the blindfolded person touches someone with the stick, that player is asked to imitate a noise – something like a trumpet, a car engine on a cold morning or a creaky door. The blindfolded player has three guesses at the name of the impersonator. If the guess is correct, the two players change places; if the guess is wrong, the blindfolded player takes up the stick again and searches out someone else.

CINDERELLA'S SLIPPERS

Players: Any number

No sooner do they walk through the front door than guests are asked to remove a shoe. Ladies take off their left shoe; gentlemen their right shoe. When everyone has arrived, the host gathers all of the shoes in the middle of the room and invites the guests to pick up one shoe (obviously not their own) and, in true Cinderella fashion, to find the person whose foot it fits. If there is a lack of women, the sight of the local bank manager trying to fit a size 11 Doc Marten on to the foot of a 16-stone bricklayer can detract from the game's essentially romantic flavour. The winner is the owner of the last shoe to be fitted. The prize is a sip of champagne from the shoe of the victor's choice – but be sure to remove any Odour Eaters first.

CHINESE OPERA

Players: Any number

You will need:

Pieces of paper

On separate slips of paper, write down a line or two from well-known songs. There must be two slips for each song and one slip for each guest. Each person takes a slip and, after reading his or her lyrics, tries to find the other guest with lyrics to the same song.

CHAIN LINKS

Players: Any number

You will need:

Paper, pencils

Prior to the party, write a chain of instructions – one per player. Each instruction has two lines. The first line reads something like 'You are a cream cracker' and the second line may be 'Find a hair dryer'. The next instruction therefore begins 'You are a hair dryer' followed perhaps by 'Find a dog biscuit' and so on until the chain is completed with 'Find a cream cracker'. Each instruction is written on a separate slip of paper and handed to a guest, together with pencil, paper and orders to find the second article on their slip. Players do this by asking each other, 'Are you a dog biscuit?' or whatever the article is they are seeking. If the answer is 'no', the player asks someone else. If the answer is 'yes, I am a dog biscuit,' that person will add, 'Find a toilet brush' or whatever the second article is on their slip. As players find each link in the chain, they write down the name of the object on their paper.

The winner is the first to complete the chain in correct order. The following list may be used for 12 players:

YOU ARE A CREAM CRACKER	FIND A HAIR DRYER
YOU ARE A HAIR DRYER	FIND A DOG BISCUIT
YOU ARE A DOG BISCUIT	FIND AN INFLATABLE DOLL
YOU ARE AN INFLATABLE DOLL	FIND A CORN PLASTER
YOU ARE A CORN PLASTER	FIND A SMELLY SOCK
YOU ARE A SMELLY SOCK	FIND A RUBBER DUCK
YOU ARE A RUBBER DUCK	FIND A CHEESE GRATER
YOU ARE A CHEESE GRATER	FIND A STOMACH PUMP
YOU ARE A STOMACH PUMP	FIND A ROTTEN EGG
YOU ARE A ROTTEN EGG	FIND A TEA BAG
YOU ARE A TEA BAG	FIND A TOILET BRUSH
YOU ARE A TOILET BRUSH	FIND A CREAM CRACKER

Note: If somebody comes up to you and says, 'Find a mouth freshener', it may have nothing to do with this game but more to do with the fact that you have just eaten garlic.

PIN-UP PARTNERS

Players: Any even number

You will need:

A notice-board, a sheet of white paper, magazines or newspapers, drawing pins

This adaptation of Pin the Tail on the Donkey is a novel method of pairing off unattached couples for party games. The host cuts out a selection of newspaper and magazine photos of glamorous celebrities (anyone from Pamela Anderson to Lassie) and gives them to guests of the appropriate sex. Each cut-out has a drawing pin through the head and its guest's name on the back. In turn, each guest is blindfolded, swung round three times and aimed at the sheet of paper on the notice-board. According to where the cut-outs land, the nearest male and female pin-ups become partners for the following game... and maybe the rest of the evening.

FIRST IMPRESSIONS

Players: 12 or more

You will need:

Pencils, pieces of card, safety pins or sticky tape

On arrival, guests have a blank card pinned or taped to their back. As they mingle, they write a brief, two- or three-word description or first impression of each other on the card. Thus people will be walking around with comments like 'nice eyes' or 'terminal dandruff' pinned to their backs, although it is best not to be too insulting, particularly if you intend staying at the party. After 10 minutes, the host asks the players to read out the card of the person standing next to them.

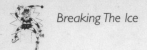

SOAP STARS

Players: 6-12

You will need:

Sticky labels, pencils, paper

Stick a numbered label to each guest and give them the identity of a well-known character from Coronation Street, EastEnders, Emmerdale, Brookside, Neighbours or The Archers. As they circulate, they must talk in character (the host will provide helpful hints if a guest is unsure about the finer points of, say, Percy Sugden) and at the same time try to discover the identities of their fellow players. They can make as many guesses as necessary and when a player admits that, yes, she is Mandy Dingle from Emmerdale, the answer is written down next to that player's number. The winner is the first player to unmask all of the characters. The sound of Mavis Wilton trying to engage Grant Mitchell in intelligent conversation is not to be missed.

MR AND MRS

Players: Any even number

You will need:

Pencil, paper

Based on the long-running TV series, this game can be played by partners who are total strangers as well as by those who have known each other for years. The players are split up into couples and one person from each couple leaves the room. The remaining players are then asked a series of pre-planned questions about their partner, spouse or date and try to answer them in the way they think their partners would reply. These answers are written down. The missing players then return and are asked the same questions. If their answer matches that given by their partner, they score a point. In the next round, the partners' roles are reversed. The winning pair are the first to reach five points. Although seemingly innocuous, this game can turn nasty when couples who have been together for years disagree over fundamentals such as 'who snores the loudest?'

AMNESIACS ANONYMOUS

Players: Any number

You will need:

Paper, pencils

Guests are asked to come to the party with something about them which suggests a lapse of memory – such as odd socks, one earring (for a woman), a watch worn upside down, a shirt buttoned up incorrectly or, for the true exhibitionist, no trousers. As the players mingle, they write down the perceived errors. The winner is the one with most correct answers within a time limit of 10 minutes.

PAIRS

Players: Any even number

You will need:

Pieces of paper, safety pins, pencils

This game presents another excellent opportunity for guests to mingle. The host cuts out a series of pieces of paper – the number of slips being equal to the number of guests – and folds each in half. On the inside of each folded piece is then printed a Christian name and an unconnected surname of a famous person – for example Eric (Cantona) and (Benjamin) Disraeli. Each name is then given a number. With 20 players, the Christian names will be numbered from 1 to 20 and the surnames from 21 to 40. One piece of paper is then pinned to the back of each player in such a way that the names are hidden from view. Armed with pencil and paper, the players proceed to circulate in an attempt to match up the pairs. After asking a fellow guest for permission to raise their flap (who knows what this could lead to later in the evening!) and noting the contents by number, players must lower the flap again in order to prevent others getting a free look. The winner is the first to pair up all the numbers of first names and surnames correctly.

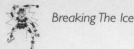
PUPPET ON A STRING

Players: Any even number

You will need:

Balls of string

Another string game which serves as a good ice-breaker is 'Puppet on a String' although it is not strictly necessary to emulate Sandie Shaw by playing barefoot. The drawback from the host's point of view is that it involves turning parts of the house into a war zone with lengths of impenetrable string wrapped around every conceivable item of furniture. You need one length of string for every two guests. The lengths should then be wound around backs of chairs, table legs and so on to form a vast web leading into an adjoining room. For the particularly adventurous, the second room could even be upstairs. Care must be taken not to create knots, however. The male guests go into the first room and the girls go into the second, everyone taking an end of string. They then set about winding it up until the pair with the same length of string meet somewhere in the middle with a kiss. The beauty of the game is that, if the string has been looped around cleverly, it is not until the last moment that you find out who you are going to kiss. This may or may not be good news.

NAME THAT GHOST

Players: 6-12

You will need:

Sheets, chairs, pencils, paper

All the men leave the room and in their absence the women sit down on numbered chairs and cover themselves completely in sheets. When the men return, they have to identify the various ghosts, jotting down their answers on paper. To help in the identification, the men may ask the ghosts to groan. The ghosts must respond accordingly but must never speak any words. Additionally, the man is permitted to feel each ghost's hair, eyes, nose and ears but, unless it is a particularly friendly party, it is advisable that he restricts his investigation to above the shoulders and keeps his hands outside the sheet. The winner is the man with most correct identifications after five minutes. The roles can then be reversed with the men becoming ghosts.

MATCH THE PROVERBS

Players: Any number

You will need:

Pieces of paper or card, a hat or basket

Think up a list of proverbs, one for each guest. The two halves of each proverb are written on separate cards. Thus 'Too many cooks' would be on one card and 'spoil the broth' on another. All of the first halves are mixed into a hat; the second halves are scattered around the house, face down. Players draw their proverb from the hat and then have to hunt out the second part. Only those who are able to produce both cards will be adjudged to have completed the game.

DINGBAT

Players: 4-10

You will need:

Pieces of card

A good way of getting people into the swing of things is to play your own version of the popular board game. You need to prepare in the region of 30 cards and illustrate them with picture writing which represents a phrase. For example write a small letter b and a small letter c inside a large letter u. This translates as 'Be seein' you'. Or write the word 'QUICK' immediately above the word 'DRAW' for 'Quick on the draw'. Make sure that you hold each card up high enough so that all of the players can see. When someone shouts out the correct answer, move on to the next card. This can either be played as a competitive game, with a prize going to the player with most answers, or simply as an enjoyable getting-to-know-you exercise.

MATCHMAKING

Players: Any number

You will need:

Matchsticks or cocktail sticks

Give each guest 10 matchsticks or cocktail sticks. As the players circulate, they take some of their sticks in hand and, with clenched fist outstretched, accost each other with the question, 'Odd or even?' If the second player guesses correctly, he or she receives one stick from the first player. The roles are then reversed with the second player demanding, 'Odd or even?' When that transaction is over, both parties go their separate ways in search of another 'victim'. The winner is the player with most sticks when time is called.

THE MISSING GUEST

Players: 10 or more

You will need:

A blindfold

All of the guests stand in a circle with one chosen person in the middle. That person is given five seconds to memorise who is there before being blindfolded. Everybody else mills around the room except for one guest who sneaks out. The blindfold is removed from the person in the middle who then has a minute to reveal the identity of the missing player. If at this stage of the game, guests are unfamiliar with each other's names, an accurate description will suffice. Should the guess prove correct, it is the missing player's turn to be blindfolded. If not, the guesser has another turn in the middle.

ADVERBIAL ANSWERS

Players: Any number

You will need:

Slips of paper

Before the party, think up a selection of unusual adverbs and write them down on slips of paper, one for each guest. On arrival, the guests are handed their adverb and must spend the rest of the evening talking in that fashion. This game can certainly set the tone for the party as those who have been given 'hideously' or 'aggressively' are likely to have made fewer friends than those with 'delightfully' or 'sexily'. At the end of the evening, by which time 'claustrophobically' has probably gone for a walk and 'murderously' is helping the police with their inquiries, all of the guests try to decipher each other's adverbs.

FIND YOUR PARTNER

Players: Any number

You will need:

Slips of paper, safety pins

Prepare as many pieces of paper as there are men at the party and write a different male guest's name on each slip. As each girl arrives, pin one of these slips to her back and tell her that she has to quiz the men present to find out whose name she bears. She is only allowed to ask questions which can be answered 'yes' or 'no' and is not permitted to ask obvious questions about clothes, size or appearance, such as 'Am I wearing a balaclava?' or 'Have I got a massive whitehead on my chin?' By the use of subtle interrogation, she will eventually track down her prey. This game is best played with groups of people who know each other reasonably well so that questions can be asked about work, drinking habits, hobbies etc.

MYSTERY GUEST

Players: Any number

You will need:

Pencils, paper

An innocuous game in which players mingle merrily in a bid to find out as much about each other as possible, taking notes as they do so. After 15 minutes, the host reads out a list of facts about one of the gathering who has been chosen as the mystery guest (favourite foods, hobbies, birthday, where he or she went to school, job etc) and the first person to shout out who the mystery guest is wins the game.

FLOWER POWER

Players: Any number

You will need:

Pieces of paper, sticky tape or safety pins, pencils

On separate pieces of paper (one per player) print the names of well-known flowers with eight letters – such as foxglove, snowdrop, bluebell, daffodil, geranium, hyacinth, primrose, lavender, larkspur and marigold. One of these slips is then attached to the back of each player who is told the number of letters in their flower. Their task is to discover the name of the flower on their back by asking fellow players about the letters. Thus a player may inquire of another: 'Do I have a B?' If the answer is yes, that is written down. Even if there are two of the same letter, only one may be revealed at a time and players may not ask the same player two consecutive questions. They must move on to someone else – it is all part of the attempt to boost circulation. Having found all the letters, players sit down and try to solve the anagram, the winner being the first to do so. When playing this game, it is advisable to cover up all mirrors to discourage cheating.

FALLING LEAVES

Players: Any number

You will need:

A pack of playing cards, two wastepaper bins

The players are divided into two teams each of whom are issued with 13 playing cards of one suit. To make identification easier, it is probably helpful if one team has a black suit, the other a red. The first player of each team stands over their respective bin and holds a card in such a way that its long edge is touching the tip of the player's nose. From that position, they allow the card to fall downwards in the hope that it will land in the bin. After the captains have dropped their 13 cards, they pick up those cards which have not fallen into the bin and hand them to the next team members. The game continues until one team has safely binned all 13 cards. This is much more difficult than it sounds — unless your name happens to be Pinocchio.

NUMERICAL ORDER

Players: 10 or more

You will need:

Paper, pencils, sticky tape

Cut up small squares of paper, numbered 1 to 25, and arrange them around the house. They can be secured under an ornament or stuck to a surface, but the whole number must be visible. The players receive answer forms with 25 spaces but each form varies slightly. The first is numbered 1 to 25, the second 2 to 1, the third 3 to 2 and so on to make sure that each player has a different starting point. The object of the exercise is to enter the name of the article to which the number is attached in the appropriate space on the form. The first to complete all 25 is the winner. However the list must be done in precise numerical order. For example if a player finds number 1 and sees number 3, he cannot enter that until he has found number 2, by which time, of course, he may have forgotten where number 3 is. Any player suspected of cheating can be challenged by a fellow competitor and if the challenge is upheld, the culprit loses a mark. If the challenge is rejected, the accuser loses a mark. The challenge rule has the effect of bringing the guests into contact although it may mean that they take an instant dislike to each other rather than strike up a friendship!

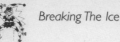

GUESS THE WEIGHT

Players: 5-10

You will need:

A selection of household articles, kitchen scales

Before the party, scour the house for a number of different-sized everyday articles such as a cushion, a pen, a paperweight, a saucepan, a comb and a mixing bowl, and weigh each one. Make a note of the weights and arrange the articles on a table. Then ask the players to write down their estimated weights of the various objects. They are allowed to pick up the articles to assist in their calculations. The player with the closest estimates overall wins the game.

BAGS OF FUN

Players: Any number

You will need:

Paper bags, pencils, paper, a selection of small objects

One of the simplest party games, this is nonetheless a hardy perennial. Players are confronted with a series of numbered paper bags and have to do nothing more arduous than guess the contents. This they are allowed to do only by sense of touch. Anyone caught peering inside a bag is liable to be shown the red card and ordered to do the washing up. The answers are written down on a piece of paper and, when the allotted time is up (15 minutes is usually enough), the winner is declared to be the one with the most correct answers. When choosing items, you should avoid anything sharp and concentrate instead on things like a bottle top, a safety pin or nail clippers. Liquids are not advisable either. This game can also be played using a pillowcase instead of paper bags.

TIP THE LEMON

Players: Any even number

You will need:

Spoons, lemons

This is an ideal game to play while guests are still arriving. It is a contest between two standing players, both of whom hold a spoon in either hand. The right spoon contains a lemon. The aim is to knock off your opponent's lemon while keeping yours intact. You can have as many rounds as you wish or, for the truly sporting, the whole event can be staged in the form of a knock-out tournament where you will probably lose to the German guest in the semi-final.

HOW MANY?

Players: 5-10

You will need:

Various household objects

In this guessing game, players are confronted with a series of items on a table and have to estimate specific information about each object without touching it or picking it up. This could include:

> The number of pages in a closed book
> The number of cards in an incomplete pack
> The number of matches in a partly-filled box
> The number of beans in a jar
> The number of paper clips in a half-empty pack
> The number of elastic bands in a pile

Naturally enough, the player with the closest guesses is the winner.

33

DESPERATELY SEEKING SUSAN

Players: 8 or more

You will need:

Pieces of card, pencils

Each female guest writes a brief description of herself and the outfit she is wearing on a blank piece of card. The only name on the card is Susan. The cards are then mixed around in a hat after which each man draws a card and seeks out his 'Susan' from the description. When he finds a likely target, he reads out the words on the card whereupon she will either say 'Yes, I'm that Susan' or 'Sorry, wrong Susan.' The game is over when everyone is paired up correctly. To avoid making the man's task too easy, it is best if the descriptions are fairly vague. 'I'm the one with the purple hair, nose-stud and Mad Dog tattoos' can be a bit of a giveaway – especially at an over-60s party.

EARTH, WATER, AIR

Players: Any number

This ever-popular game is another good one for getting a party going. All the players sit in a circle except for one person who stands in the centre. That person issues commands by pointing at any of the other players and shouting either 'Earth', 'Air', 'Fire' or 'Water'. If 'Earth' is called, the player must name an animal; if 'Air' is called, it must be a bird; if the shout is 'Water', a fish must be named. All answers must be given by a count of three or the player concerned takes centre stage. If 'Fire' is called, the player pointed at must remain silent. The same animal, fish or bird cannot be named twice.

PERSONAL BINGO

Players: 6-12

You will need:

Large pieces of card

Prepare a large bingo card for each player. The cards should each have nine spaces arranged in three rows of three. The players are asked to remove nine small objects from their pocket, wallet or purse and place them on the spaces on the card. Choose a player to start and ask that player to take an article off his or her card, hold it up and call out, for example, 'key-ring'. All players with a key-ring on their card can then remove it. Going round in a clockwise direction, the next person repeats the process and the game continues until someone shouts 'Bingo!' having removed all of their items. If this proves too time-consuming, victory can be bestowed upon the first player to complete a line. To ensure a variety of objects, it is a good idea for the host to ask the guests to bring a selection of small items to the party. It also allows a rare glimpse of daylight for that boiled sweet which has been in your pocket for the past 18 months.

NEXT IN LINE

Players: Any number

There is no more forceful way for party guests to memorise each other's names than to play 'Next in Line'. The guests are seated in a circle and are asked to call out their first names. The host, who is in the middle of the circle, suddenly points at one of the players and demands, 'Who's Next?' If the host points with the right hand, the player must immediately call out the name of the person to their right; if the host points with the left hand, it must be the person to the player's left. The second player repeats the process, pointing to someone else in the circle with either hand. The same rules of right and left apply. And so the game continues at a frantic pace. Any player guilty of going in the wrong direction or forgetting a name is disqualified.

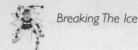

SKELETONS IN THE CUPBOARD

Players: 10 or more

You will need:

Pieces of card, pencils

On small cards, prepare a series of clues, one relating to each guest. Each clue will offer vague details of a hobby or other highly individual trait of one of the guests. For example it might say, 'Plays in a band'. By talking to the other guests, the players, each of whom is given a card at the outset, attempt to fill in the name of the band and the person concerned. Then they try to find the answers to the remainder of the clues. The winner is the player with most correct answers in the given time.

If there are 10 players, the cards could read:

Plays in a band.
Name of band:
Name of person:

Has a terrible phobia.
Name of phobia:
Name of person:

Is a county sports champion.
Name of sport:
Name of person:

Has been on TV.
Name of programme:
Name of person:

Has a rare collection.
Type of collection:
Name of person:

Owns a sports car.
Make of car:
Name of person:

36

Has had a book published.
Name of book:
Name of person:

Once spent the night in jail.
Type of offence:
Name of person:

Lives next door to an undertaker.
Name of undertaker:
Name of person:

Left his wife for another woman.
Name of mistress:
Name of person:

At this point it is probably best to end the game.

PENCIL AND PAPER REQUIRED

WORDBUILDER

Players: 2 or more

Players are given the same word, preferably something long like 'INTELLIGENT' or 'HYPOTHETICAL', and have 10 minutes in which to write down as many words as they can using the letters of the starter word. Words must be at least four letters long and foreign words, plurals, abbreviations and proper nouns are not allowed. A letter can only be used in a word as many times as it appears in the starter word. The winner is the player with most acceptable words – in case of disputes, it is advisable to keep a dictionary handy.

TELEGRAM

Players: Any number

Each player calls out a random letter of the alphabet until there are a dozen in all. The players then have 15 minutes to compose a telegram, each word beginning with the chosen letters and in that order. So if the letters shouted out were S.S.E.H.I.P.C.E.A.P.A.Z., the telegram could be SEVEN SWEATY ELEPHANTS HAVE INVADED PITCH. CROWD EXTREMELY AGITATED. PLEASE ADVISE. ZEBEDEE. The winner is the player adjudged to have come up with the cleverest offering. An alternative method of play is to select a word from a newspaper or magazine and to build a telegram, each word beginning with the letters of the chosen word and in that order. Thus RESTORED could end up as RANDY EARL STARTS TO OGLE RETIRED ENTOMOLOGIST'S DAUGHTER.

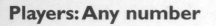

SCRIBBLE

Players: Any number

Players are given a sheet of paper and a pencil and instructed to scribble a line of any shape they wish. However the line should not be too long as this can prove restrictive. Having completed the scribble, they pass the paper to the player on their left, at the same time receiving a sheet from the player on their right. When all the papers have been passed, each player draws a picture of which the original scribble must be an integral part. A prize goes to the artist who produces the funniest drawing.

CATEGORIES

Players: 2 or more

The players jot down a list of a dozen categories such as Fish, Flower, Fruit, Vegetable, Animal, Bird, Country, Town, River, Boy's Name, Girl's Name and Famous Person. A letter of the alphabet is then chosen at random and the players have five minutes in which to write a word for each category beginning with that letter. For example with a chosen letter of B, the list could be Barbel, Buddleia, Blackberry, Beetroot, Bison, Bittern, Bulgaria, Basingstoke, Bure, Brian, Beth and Beethoven. The players read out their lists in turn. Each word which is not on any other player's list scores a point. The winner is the player with most points. Of course, if you really want to make the game a challenge you could come up with categories such as Characters From Dickens, French Impressionist Artists or British Tennis Champions.

GUGGENHEIM

Players: 2 or more

For those who find 'Categories' too easy, this variation presents a sterner test. A list of categories is chosen and each player writes that list down the left-hand side of their sheet of paper. A keyword of five or more letters is then selected and the letters of that word are spaced out across the top of the paper. Everybody must then write down one word beginning with each letter of the keyword for each category within a time limit of 10 minutes. With a keyword of STRAW, the grid might look like this:

	S	T	R	A	W
Bird	Starling	Tern	Redwing	Auk	Wheatear
Country	Sweden	Turkey	Rumania	Austria	Wales
Flower	Spiraea	Tansy	Ragwort	Anemone	Wallflower
Town	Swansea	Taunton	Rochdale	Auckland	Wrexham
Food	Spinach	Tangerine	Radish	Apple-pie	Waffles
Boy	Sean	Thomas	Roland	Andrew	Winston
Girl	Samantha	Tessa	Rachel	Alison	Winifred
Rock band	Supergrass	Troggs	R.E.M.	Ash	Wurzels

As with 'Categories', players score a point for each word which nobody else has on their list.

CASCADE

Players: Any number

Everyone writes down the same word, ideally one of four, five or six letters, at the top of the paper. By changing just one letter at a time, players construct a cascade of words beneath the original word. For example if the first word is 'think', this could be followed by 'thick, trick, trice, price' etc. The same word cannot be used more than once. A time limit is set for the game, the winner being the player with most words in the given time.

TRANSFORMATION

Players: Any number

This game is a variation of 'Cascade' but here the players begin by writing down the same two words, one at the top of the paper and the other at the bottom. Both chosen words must have the same number of letters. The aim is to change the first word into the second word by altering just one letter at a time and each time forming a new word. As a simple example, 'hot' could be changed to 'cab' via 'hob' and 'cob'. The winner is the player who completes the transformation in the fewest number of words.

666

Players: Any number

This is the ideal game if you are holding a Pythagoras theme party or just want peace and quiet for an hour or two. Each player writes down 13 numbers, from 0 to 9, with no number featuring more than three times, and then passes the list to the player on his or her right. By combining some of the numbers, a new set of numbers is formed, none of which must exceed three digits. Thus if player one chose the numbers 6, 9, 8, 1, 3, 3, 4, 5, 7, 2, 9, 2, 0, player two may elect to re-group them into 79, 6, 8, 133, 4, 5, 7, 2, 20. Taking one starting number (such as 133), player two must use all of the remaining numbers once only and by means of addition, subtraction, multiplication and division, arrive at 666. Multiplication with 0 is not permitted but the use of brackets is. The winner is the first person to complete the equation or alternatively the one who has not lost the will to live by the end of the time limit.

FIRE!

Players: 5-10

You will need:

Sticky tape

The object of this game is for players to reveal which six items they would rescue from their home in the event of fire… and why. Before the party the host draws up a list of items, six per player, and writes each item on a separate slip of paper. These slips are then numbered 1 to 6, folded, sealed with sticky tape, to prevent anyone from seeing the contents, and scattered around the house. At the start of the game, each player is given a form headed: 'In the event of fire I would rescue…' Each form is numbered 1 to 6. On the left-hand side is space for the six objects, and on the right-hand side, after the word 'because', is space for the six reasons. Players are then asked to fill in the six reasons… even though at this stage they don't know which items they are referring to. When the forms have been completed, the host shouts 'Fire!' (not too loudly for fear of alarming the neighbours) and each player collects six of the sealed slips, one of each number. Opening the slips, they then match the object named with the corresponding numbered reason for rescuing it. Therefore, object 1 is placed in the space alongside reason 1 and so on. The end results can be quite illuminating. A typical form might read:

In the event of fire I would rescue…

1. The grand piano because I always have it in bed with me at night.
2. My false teeth because they used to belong to my grandmother.
3. My rubber duck because I think it's worth a lot of money.
4. My toupee because it's the best thing I've got for cleaning the windows.
5. A stapler because I've really become attached to it.
6. My pet hamster because I love a tasty snack before bedtime.

Pyromaniacs will probably derive great pleasure from this game.

WORD BEGINNINGS

Players: Any number

The host prepares a list of 20 clues, the answers to all of which are words with the same prefix. If the prefix is 'Imp', you could have, 'The Imp that is unlikely' (Improbable) or 'The Imp that you can't get through' (Impenetrable) and so on. Other suitable prefixes are 'Int', 'Dis', 'Pan', 'Sub', 'Mis', 'Pre' and 'Con'. But the word must have a proper prefix. Thus 'Disgrace' is perfectly acceptable but 'Dishwater' is not even though it begins with 'Dis'. The player with most correct answers in a 15-minute time limit is the winner. Access to dictionaries is strictly forbidden.

NAME THE NOISE

Players: Any number

You will need:

Assorted props

The rules of this game are simple – players merely have to try and identify a series of everyday noises. The noises can either be pre-recorded on tape by the well-organised host, or made out of sight (for example behind a chair). The players then write down their answers. The one with the most correct responses wins. Suggestions include pulling a cork from a bottle, rubbing two pieces of sandpaper together and running fingers along a comb. Of course, an adventurous host may opt to pre-record the mating call of the Lesser Amazonian Warbler in the hope of catching everyone out.

THE FAME GAME

Players: Any even number

You will need:

A bowl

Everybody writes the names of 10 famous people or characters on strips of paper. Fold the strips so that you can't read the names, put them into a bowl and mix them up. The players are then divided into two teams. Alternating between the two groups, each player takes out a strip and describes the famous person without naming them. The other team has to guess the identity. When all the strips have been used they are re-folded and placed back in the bowl. In round two, the same process is repeated but this time players can only use three words to describe the famous person. For the third round, players are only allowed one word of description and in the fourth and final round, the names have to be acted with no speech permitted.

ADVERTISEMENTS

Players: 4-10

You will need:

Magazines

Cut out a series of product advertisements from old magazines and colour supplements and remove all brand names, logos or other means of identification. Numbering each advert, arrange them on a table or board and allow players 10 minutes to write down the names of the various products being advertised. The player with most correct answers wins.

WHERE ON EARTH?

Players: Any number

You will need:

An atlas

Using an atlas, trace the outlines of 12 countries on to paper and cut them out. Number each outline and ask the players to write down the names of the respective countries. Depending on the intelligence level of your guests, places like Australia or Wales may be too easy but landlocked countries such as Bulgaria or Switzerland offer a far greater challenge.

WHAT'S IN A NAME?

Players: Any number

This is a soccer quiz in which a list of former English and Scottish League club names is written down. Players have to write what the club is called today. Here are some examples: L & Y Railway FC (Manchester United), Dial Square FC (Arsenal), St. Mary's YMCA (Southampton), St. Jude's Institute (Queens Park Rangers), Thames Ironworks (West Ham United), Pine Villa (Oldham Athletic), Black Arabs (Bristol Rovers), Singers FC (Coventry City), Heaton Norris Rovers (Stockport County), New Brompton (Gillingham), Shaddowgate United (Carlisle United), Brumby Hall (Scunthorpe United), Sunderland and District Teachers AFC (Sunderland), Bainsford Britannia (East Stirlingshire), Excelsior FC (Airdrieonians) and Ferranti Thistle (Meadowbank Thistle).

STAIRWAY

Players: Any number

A letter is chosen at random and the players are given 10 minutes to build a stairway of words, each beginning with that letter. The stairway begins with a two-letter word, then a three-letter word, four-letter word, five-letter word and so on. No plurals are allowed. The winner is the player who comes up with the longest word provided no steps have been skipped en route. For example, if you are unable to think of a 12-letter word your list ends there, even if you can come up with a 13-letter word. A stairway for the letter D might read:

D
DO
DAB
DENT
DANCE
DOLLAR
DOUBLET
DREADFUL
DRAMATIST
DISTRAUGHT
DRAUGHTSMAN
DISCREDITING
DEVELOPMENTAL
DISINCLINATION
DOLICHOCEPHALIC

NICKNAMES

Players: Any number

Draw up a list of 20 nicknames of famous people and, if possible, photocopy it so that each player has a copy. The players are then given 10 minutes to write down the name of the person next to the appropriate nickname. Why not try some of the following: The Iron Duke (Wellington), Good Queen Bess (Elizabeth I), The Cheeky Chappie (Max Miller), Captain Sensible (Ray Burns), The Rumble of Thunder (Luigi Riva), The Desert Fox (Rommel) or The Italian Stallion (Sylvester Stallone).

SOCCER NICKNAMES

Players: Any number

If your guests are sportingly inclined, get them to pair off two jumbled lists of football club nicknames. Put a list of 15 clubs in the left-hand column and a list of 15 nicknames in the right-hand column. The players have to match the nickname with the club. Try these for size: Darlington (The Quakers), Montrose (The Gable Endies), Rotherham United (The Merry Millers), Millwall (The Lions), West Bromwich Albion (The Baggies), Queen of the South (The Doonhamers), Bury (The Shakers), Bolton Wanderers (The Trotters), Arsenal (The Gunners), Arbroath (The Red Lichties), Exeter City (The Grecians), Southend United (The Shrimpers), Clyde (The Bully Wee), Chesterfield (The Spireites) and Luton Town (The Hatters).

SHORT STORIES

Players: Any number

Players have to write down the longest sentence they can in three minutes using only words of three letters or less. All words must be spelt correctly. It sounds easy but it's not. An even tougher assignment is to compose a sentence solely of three-letter words.

SQUARES

Players: Any even number

You will need:

Graph paper

This classic pencil and paper game can be adapted into a team contest for a party, particularly when everyone is too tired and emotional to play anything physically and mentally demanding. The game is played on graph paper, and the two teams should have different colour pencils. On their turn, the players simply mark one side of a square. Whoever draws the line which closes a single square wins it and should fill it in with the team colour. That team must then make the next move. The border of the paper is deemed to be one long line. At the end of the game, which can develop into a mean tactical battle, the victorious team is the one which has completed most squares. As a variation from single squares, the game can be played with any shape which is able to be closed with one move.

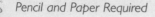

SQUEEZE

Players: 2-10

You will need:

Graph paper

Each player takes it in turns to draw a square or rectangle on the graph paper. The shape can be any size, but the borders must not be either those of an existing shape or the edges of the graph paper. Although the rectangles or squares may not share the same border, they are permitted to overlap. The object of the exercise is to squeeze your opponents out of space so that they have no room to draw a new shape. Any player unable to construct a shape is eliminated. When all possibilities – and players – have been exhausted, the last to build a shape successfully is declared the winner.

CONNECT

Players: 2-10

A series of 36 dots are marked on a piece of plain paper in six rows of six. The object is for each player, on his or her turn, to connect two or more dots with one straight line – either vertically, horizontally or diagonally. The first player begins anywhere on the grid but, thereafter, any line must start from either end of the previous player's line and must not, of course, retrace an existing line. Any player unable to draw another line is out of the game. The winner is the last person who can draw a line.

CONSEQUENCES

Players: Any number

For this classic game, players are given a long sheet of paper and told to write down certain information. After they have done so, they fold the paper over to hide what they have written and pass the sheet to the player on their right while simultaneously receiving a different folded sheet from the player on their left. Thus players are adding new lines to the story without knowing what has been written previously. There are 13 stages, at the end of which the results are read out... sometimes to the acute embarrassment of those present.

The stages are:

An adjective describing someone's appearance or character
The name of a girl or woman – real or fictitious, dead or alive.
The word 'met' followed by another adjective describing appearance or character.
The name of a man – real or fictitious, dead or alive.
The word 'at' and the place where they met.
The words 'He wore', followed by his mode of attire.
The words 'She wore', followed by hers.
The words 'He said to her' followed by whatever he said.
The words 'She said to him' followed by what she said.
What he did then.
What she did then.
The words 'And the consequence was', followed by whatever the consequence happened to be.
The words 'And the world said', followed by whatever it said.

The end result could be along the lines of:

Varicose-veined
Madonna
met
Glamorous
Jack Duckworth
at
Heckmondwhite's Pickle Factory
He wore a Lycra jump suit
She wore a suit of armour
He said to her, 'Do you think you could handle this?'
She said to him, 'My mother went down on the Titanic'.
Then he did an impression of Tommy Cooper
Then she spontaneously combusted
And the consequence was, they were both picked for the Olympic synchronised swimming team.
And the world said, 'He only wants her for her collection of gerbils.'

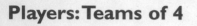

PICTURE CONSEQUENCES

Players: Teams of 4

This is a game for the artistically inclined or those with a colourful imagination. At the top of the paper, the first artist draws the head of a person down to the neck. The paper is then folded back in such a way that only the beginning of the neck is visible to the next team member. The second artist then draws the torso down as far as the navel. The paper is folded once more and handed to the next player, again with only the edges of the previous drawing visible. The third artist draws from the navel to the knees before folding the paper and handing it to the last member of the team who completes the figure by adding on the legs and feet. When the finished drawing is opened out, it may reveal something like a bespectacled granny with a chest like Giant Haystacks, legs like Bugs Bunny and wearing cycling shorts and flippers. A prize should be awarded to the most bizarre creation.

ANAGRAMS

Players: Any number

Choose a category (such as Countries, Singers, Animals, Actors, Statesmen) and make anagrams of 10 words belonging to that category. Photocopy the list and hand one to each player who then has 10 minutes to unscramble as many of the anagrams as possible. Likely anagrams for animals are TAMMEROS, FLAFOUB, ROANKOGA, FEARFIG, PLEATHEN, EGGEDOHH, GREIT, HEPTARN, MALCE and APRODLE which when unscrambled make Marmoset, Buffalo, Kangaroo, Giraffe, Elephant, Hedgehog, Tiger, Panther, Camel and Leopard.

NEWSPAPER COLUMNIST

Players: Any number

You will need:

A newspaper

Each player is given a page from a newspaper and, working from the top of the first column, is asked to find a word beginning with A. That player circles the first word located beginning with A and makes a note of the word on a piece of paper. This process continues down the column right the way through the alphabet except for the letters X and Z. At the end of five minutes' search, the players are given another three minutes to make a reasonably sensible sentence from the words they have found. The words can be used in any order. Any player who did not find all 24 letters has to make do without the missing ones. Players then read out their offerings, the winner being the one who has used up the greatest number of words from their list in a proper sentence.

DEAR DAPHNE

Players: Any number

You will need:

Two hats or bowls

Players are given slips of paper and asked to write out an imaginary question to an agony aunt named Daphne. This could cover anything from fears about your partner's infidelity with the local lollipop lady, to concerns about getting piles. The questions are put into a hat, mixed up and drawn out again. Each player then uses another slip of paper on which to write the agony aunt's advice to the question he or she has drawn. Then the two slips are folded, placed in separate hats – one for the questions and the other for the answers – and thoroughly mixed once more. Finally the players take it in turns to draw a slip from each hat and read out the question and answer. With luck, the advice should be gloriously irrelevant to the problem. Here is an example of the misunderstandings that can arise when two vastly different problems become mixed up.

'Dear Daphne,

I have to make a maiden conference speech next week and am absolutely terrified at the prospect. Can you offer me any advice?'

'Dear Writer,

The first time is always nerve-racking. You may find it best to lie down with the lights off. And don't forget to wear a condom.'

'Dear Daphne

My girlfriend is pressuring me into having sex. I'm still a virgin and am worried whether I will be able to satisfy her. Can you help?'

'Dear Writer,

It is bound to be worrying the first time you perform in front of 300 people, but don't forget John Major used to do it four or five times every day. Take your time, give a slow, purposeful delivery and I'm sure you'll rise to the occasion. And if you're lucky, you'll never have to do it again.'

BATTLESHIPS

Players: Any even number

The familiar game of battleships can be adapted into a party game between two teams. Large square playing areas are marked out on two sheets of paper, one for each fleet. The squares are divided into 100 smaller squares, 10 across by 10 down. The squares across are labelled A to J and the squares down 1 to 10. Amid enormous secrecy, each team plots the positions of their fleet which consists of a battleship, two cruisers, three destroyers and four submarines. The battleship occupies four squares, the cruisers each occupy three squares, the destroyers each occupy two squares and the submarines occupy one square apiece. The squares forming a ship must be in a continuous straight line – vertically, horizontally or diagonally – and there must be at least one empty square between ships. When both teams have drawn their fleets, battle begins and the players take it in turns to attempt to sink the enemy fleet. Each player fires a shot at the enemy by calling out a square, for example J7. The opposing team examine their chart. If J7 is not occupied by a ship, they call out 'miss' but if it is, they call out 'hit' and say what type of ship has been struck. For future guidance, the attacking team either marks J7 on their chart with a dot (in the case of a miss) or with a letter identifying the type of ship (in the case of a hit). In order to sink a ship, all of the squares which form it must be hit. The game continues with the teams firing alternately until all of the ships in one fleet have been sunk.

KIM'S GAME

Players: Any number

You will need:

A tray, assorted small objects, a cloth

A favourite game of Baden Powell, founder of the Boy Scouts, 'Kim's Game' is the ultimate memory test and an inspiration for the famous conveyer belt of prizes at the end of The Generation Game. Place in the region of 20 different small objects on a tray (things like a clothes peg, an elastic band, a corkscrew and a pair of scissors) and cover the tray with a cloth. Then gather the players around the tray and remove the cloth for 30 seconds. After replacing the cloth, ask the players to write down as many objects as they can remember in five minutes. Players score a point for every item they remember but lose a point if they name an object which was not on the tray. The player with most points is declared the victor.

THE TRICK TRAY

Players: Any number

You will need:

A tray, assorted small objects, a cloth

This is an even more cunning variation of 'Kim's Game'. The host's assistant (it could be one of his children or a neighbour) removes the cloth to enable the players to examine the tray of objects for 30 seconds. But the catch comes just as the assistant leaves the room with the tray. The players are told that, instead of writing down a list of the items on the tray, they have to try to remember as many things as they can about the assistant — such as clothing, hair colour and jewellery etc.

PREFIXES

Players: Any number

This alternative to 'Word Beginnings' does not involve clues but instead requires players to name as many words as they can with a given prefix in 20 minutes.

WHAT'S MISSING?

Players: Any number

You will need:

A tray, assorted small objects, a cloth

In this variation of 'Kim's Game', the players gather round to study the 20 or so items on the tray for a period of 30 seconds. The cloth is then replaced and the host surreptitiously removes one article. The cloth is then removed again and the players have to write down which item has vanished. The routine is repeated over 10 rounds with one object being removed each time. After each round, the articles should be moved around a little to stop the players becoming too familiar with their whereabouts. Also a devious host may opt to remove the same item for two successive rounds. At the end of the 10 rounds, the player with most right answers is the winner.

POLITICAL CORRECTNESS

Players: Any number

In the age of political correctness comes the eternal quest for yet more convoluted phrases to replace seemingly innocuous everyday words. Now that 'short' is 'vertically challenged' and 'poor' is 'economically disadvantaged', it can be fun trying to think up ridiculous PC alternatives for other adjectives. So see who can write down the best translation for the following: bow-legged, stupid, ignorant, jug-eared, repulsive, lazy, pig-headed, two-faced, homicidal, drunk, randy and foul-mouthed. If all of these apply to one of your guests, assure him or her that your choice of words was purely coincidental.

THREE-WORD VERSES

Players: Any number

You will need:

A hat or a bowl

Each player writes three words on separate pieces of paper. These are then folded and put into a hat or a bowl. The slips are shuffled and each player draws out three. The aim is to compose a four-line rhyme incorporating all three words in any order. Obviously this is not too demanding if the words are something like 'pretty', 'girl' and 'blue', but it is quite a different matter with 'dodecahedron', 'liquescent' and 'prestidigitator'.

ANIMAL ANSWERS

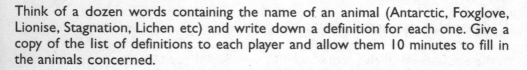

Players: Any number

Think of a dozen words containing the name of an animal (Antarctic, Foxglove, Lionise, Stagnation, Lichen etc) and write down a definition for each one. Give a copy of the list of definitions to each player and allow them 10 minutes to fill in the animals concerned.

HIDDEN QUADRUPEDS

Players: Any number

Another game where the names of animals are hidden, but this time in sentences. Try your guests with the following and see whether they can spot all the animals in two minutes.

In America the most popular sport is baseball.
The forecast says it will be a very hot day.
The defendant insisted there was nothing to add.
When the sergeant arrives, the private jumps to attention.
We heard the band in good form.
In the bathroom there is soap and a towel.
Which are the principal ports of Belgium?
A voice called out, 'Do get a move on!'
To span the river, the locals built a fine bridge.
If the robber is caught there will be a reward.

Answers: 1. Cat 2. Beaver 3. Toad 4. Stoat 5. Dingo 6. Panda 7. Hare 8. Dog 9. Panther 10. Bear

The game can also be played with other subjects such as birds, flowers, towns and trees.

DRAWING IN THE DARK

Players: 2-6

You will need:

Blindfolds

Players are blindfolded and asked to draw a picture of their house, adding on such accessories as a car, a few flowers and trees, clouds in the sky and perhaps even a passing postman and dog. When the drawings are finished, the blindfolds are removed and the fascinating results examined.

NAME THE TUNE

Players: Any number

You will need:

A tape recorder

Before the party, compile a tape featuring a few bars of a dozen songs, following on quickly one after another. Give each player pencil and paper and switch on the tape. Ask them to write down as many titles as they can recognise, the winner being the one with most correct answers. Unless your party is composed of record producers and rock stars, it is only fair to make most of the tracks fairly distinctive although it is always tempting to slip in a Moira Anderson album track to sort out the men from the boys.

PICK A LETTER

Players: Any number

Select a letter and get the players to go through the alphabet writing down pairs of connected words, the second word of which must always begin with the chosen letter. Thus if the letter is S, the list could be:

Able Seaman
Brain Surgeon
Calcium Sulphate
Dover Sole
Extra Sensory
Film Star
Gordon Sumner (aka Sting)
Hazy Sunshine
Ink Spots
Jay Silverheels (who played Tonto in The Lone Ranger)
King Solomon
Leather Shoes
Milk Shake
Night Shirt
Open Sesame
Prime Suspect
Quiz Show
Rail Strike
Smoked Salmon
Tom Sawyer
Urine Sample
Virtual Standstill
Word Search
Xmas Spread
Yard Stick
Zebra Stripes

At the end of the 10-minute time limit, players read out their lists and delete any answers that have already been given. The player with the greatest number of original pairings is declared the winner.

LOVELY WORDS

Players: Any number

Players are given five minutes to write down as many English language words as possible which contain the word 'love' ('clover, glove, plover, lovely, slovenly, beloved, lovelorn' etc). When the lists are read, each player checks their answers for duplicates. A player with a word not on anyone else's list scores a point, the winner being the one with most points.

SINGING CHARADES

Players: Any even number up to 12

'Singing Charades' requires players to guess song titles depicted in drawings. Guests are divided into two teams of five or six each and one person from each team goes forward to receive the title of a song from the host. Those two players then go back to their respective teams and draw a picture which suggests the title. No words can be spoken or written by the artist. The first team to guess the right answer and sing the song (not in its entirety) wins. The game continues until every player has had a turn at being the artist. The following titles can make for an interesting – if lengthy – encounter:

'The Lunatics Have Taken Over the Asylum'

'Calling Occupants of Interplanetary Craft'

'Does Your Chewing Gum Lose Its Flavour (on the Bedpost Overnight)?'

'Gilly Gilly Ossenfeffer Katzenellen Bogen By The Sea'

'I Saw Mommy Kissing Santa Claus'

'My Boomerang Won't Come Back'

'Subterranean Homesick Blues'

'Wombling Merry Christmas'

'Boom Bang-a-Bang'

SALES PROMOTION

Players: 5-10

Here is a game for would-be advertising copywriters, the sort of people who lie awake at night trying to think up a catchy slogan for corn plasters. Players are asked to fill in a form promoting the virtues of a new product… without actually knowing what the product is. Beforehand, the host draws up the form with spaces for the brand name of the article, what it is made of, when and how to use it, its promotional slogan and the name of a celebrity who swears by it. A copy of the form is handed to each player who uses his or her imagination to come up with some suitable answers – the more bizarre the better. When all of the forms are completed, players are given a card bearing the name of the product which they are supposed to be promoting. This name is added to their form in the space for Article. Then each player reads out their finished form. A typical example might be:

Brand name: Whizzo

Article: Nostril-hair removal cream

Made of: Sun-ripe tomatoes, mangos and pineapple

When to use: Only during a full moon

How to use: Dip the affected area in concentrated sulphuric acid

Slogan: You'll feel twice the man with Whizzo

Celebrity who uses it: Attila the Hun

Other articles which may prove useful for this game include: Drain-clearing rods, toupee, thermometer, pneumatic drill, soldering iron, dental floss, circular saw, carving knife and a pair of Y-fronts.

CROSSWORDS

Players: 5 or more

Crossword buffs will enjoy this opportunity to create their own puzzle even though the finished product may not be quite as complex as the one they are used to doing on the 8.22 to Waterloo. Before the game starts, each player has to draw a grid of squares – the same number across as down – on a sheet of paper. The size of the grid depends upon the number of players. For five players, seven squares across and seven down is ideal, but with more participants a bigger grid is necessary. Each player in turn then calls out any letter of his or her choice whereupon the other players must enter that letter somewhere in their own grids. Once that letter has been entered, it cannot be moved. The object of the game is to form words either across or down, the game finishing when all of the squares have been filled. One point is scored for each letter in an acceptable word – abbreviations, proper nouns, one-letter words and foreign words do not count. A letter may not be shared by two or more words in the same line or column. For example, if a player's line reads RAMPSTO, the maximum number of points he or she can score for that line is five for RAMPS. There are no extra points for RAM, AMP or AMPS. If a player has a word which fills an entire row or column, he or she receives a bonus point. The player with the highest total score is the winner. For example:

```
R   O   U   N   D   L   Y   8
A   N   K   L   E   F   X   5
N   E   B   O   A   K   T   6
C   W   L   Z   D   M   H   0
H   A   L   F   I   N   D   6
B   I   T   G   P   S   0   5
L   T   0   N   G   U   E   6
5   7   2   0   4   0   3   3
```

Total: 57

THE LYRIC GAME

Players: Any even number

Before the party, go through your collection of CDs and old vinyl and write down two lines of lyrics from a dozen different songs. It is best to stick to songs which have actually been hits and to bear in mind the age range of your guests. There is little point in including Blur or Oasis tracks at an OAPs gathering while conversely the classic Major Lance lyrics 'Um um um um um um' from 1964 will be wasted at a party where the oldest guest is 25. Players are divided into two teams and the first team to guess the name of the tune from which the lyrics are taken and the artist who recorded it scores two points. If a team only gets half the answer right, they score one point. Be prepared for a great deal of argument and shouts of, 'That was never from "Agadoo"'!

FOUR-LETTER WORDS

Players: 5-10

This game involves players trying to work out a rival's chosen keyword by a process of elimination. Each player chooses a four-letter word and writes it down without letting any of the other competitors see it (this is to prevent players illegally changing their word mid-way through the game). Going in a clockwise direction, players take it in turns to try to discover the chosen word of the player on their left by coming up with a succession of guess words. If player one has selected MASH as his or her keyword and player two volunteers CALF as his or her guess word, player one must respond with how many letters in the guess word correspond to those of the keyword. In this instance, the only letter featured in both words is an 'A' so the reply would be one letter. Whilst player two is trying to ascertain player one's keyword, player three is attempting to discover player two's and so on. If a player has chosen a keyword with a double or treble letter (such as TWIT or EPEE), his or her reply to the guess word must reveal how many letters have been scored out of the four, including duplicates. So with a keyword of EPEE and a guess word of HATE, the answer would be three letters as there are three Es in the keyword. The trick is to find out whether the 'three' refers to three different letters, two the same or three the same. Thus testing for duplicates is all important. Artful players often prefer to choose anagrams as their keywords. With MASH, player two might have discovered all of the letters, but he or she still has to get them in the right order. For the keyword could also be SHAM. The extra go needed to solve that problem could allow another player to win.

SCAFFOLD

Players: Any number

Each player is given the same three letters of the alphabet picked at random from a newspaper and has 10 minutes in which to think of as many words as possible featuring those three letters in the order given. Players score a point for each word but no plurals are allowed. For example, if the letters selected are P, R and S, among the eligible words are: Purse, Pursue, Praise, Perish, Parish, Persecute, Prose, Appraise, Sparse, Parsnip, Parsimony, Persist, Press, Suppress, Surprise, Precious, Pernicious, Reprise, Person, Personally, Personification, Persuasion, Persevere, Parsonage, Parsley, Prosaic, Process and Priest. For those seeking a tougher challenge, try playing the game with four selected letters, such as M, N, T, Y which could yield Minty, Monetary, Monthly, Elementary, Amnesty, Mandatory, Misanthropy etc.

HOLLYWOOD TRAILERS

Players: 5-10

You will need:

A hat or a bowl

The American movie industry is not in the habit of underselling anything – they would make a screen version of the Vauxhall Nova car manual sound like the greatest story ever told if they thought it would make a buck or two! So here is a chance for each of your guests to don the mantle of a Hollywood trailer writer by composing short, snappy, sensational pieces to promote a new film adaptation of a classic book. Prepare a selection of titles, each on a separate slip of paper, and mix them up in a hat or bowl. Ask each player to draw a slip and give them five minutes to write their pieces. The most ingenious trailer wins a prize. Here are a few books which have inexplicably escaped the clutches of Hollywood to date, but which might be ripe for the big screen:

The Concise Oxford Dictionary

Knitting for Beginners

The South Lincolnshire Telephone Directory

Modern Sewage Methods

101 Things to do with Raffia

The Goldfish – a History

TERMINATIONS

Players: Any number

The host draws up a list of 20 words ending in the word 'nation' and supplies clues for each word. Each player is given a copy of the list and has to fill in the answers in 10 minutes, the one with most correct replies being the winner. Examples include:

> The nation of light (illumination)
> The nation of political murder (assassination)
> The nation of clove-scented flowers (carnation)
> The nation of explosion (detonation)
> The nation of riddance (elimination)
> The nation of journey's end (destination)

HANGMAN

Players: Any even number

Habitually played at school during boring maths lessons while the teacher's back is turned, 'Hangman' makes a good team party game. The aim is simple – to try and guess the other team's word in fewer than 11 attempts. The first team think of a word and write down a series of dashes, one for each letter. The second team then starts guessing the letters in the word, calling out one at a time. If the letter occurs in the word, it is written above the appropriate dash. If the same letter appears more than once in the word, every occurrence must be noted. Thus if you call out an E and the word is ESSENTIAL, two Es will be put in the correct spaces. If the second team's letter does not occur in the word, the first team draw part of the Hangman picture, depicting a hapless individual on the scaffold. There are 11 sections in all – base, upright, crosspiece, support, rope, head, body, left arm, right arm, left leg and right leg – and they must be drawn in that order. Should the first team complete the picture before the word is guessed, they win the game. To avoid repetition, all incorrect letter guesses are recorded beneath the dashes. It is worth remembering that shorter words like ORYX, ZEBU or LYNX are more likely to result in the successful hanging of your opponent.

CITIES

Players: Any number

Prepare a list of clues for 20 words ending with the word 'city' and ask the players to fill in the answers within a 10-minute time limit. Listed below are a few suggestions:

    The city of bizarre behaviour (eccentricity)
    The city of speed (velocity)
    The city of wisdom (sagacity)
    The city of deception (duplicity)
    The city of currents (electricity)
    The city of numbers (multiplicity)

COMBINATIONS

Players: Any number

If you feel your party is degenerating towards tabloid sleaze, here is a game guaranteed to raise the tone. Strictly for spelling experts, it requires players to find words containing various combinations of letters. First draw up a list of a dozen letter combinations – four of two letters, four of three letters and four of four letters. Each player is given the same list, for example:

SY	NIS	PLA
EX	AWN	POLI
IB	IEN	UPTU
JU	BEC	ROVO

They then have 10 minutes to build the longest words possible containing those letters, excluding plurals. But the combinations must appear within the words, not at the beginning or end. Thus, from the above list, answers such as POLITICIAN OR EXTRAORDINARY would be ruled out. When the time limit is up, the players read out their words, calculating their totals by adding up the letters in each acceptable word. If a word features the required combination twice (such as STOMACHACHE for CH), the points score for that word is doubled. The player with the highest total is declared the resident brain-box and will probably be shunned for the remainder of the evening.

Answers for the above list could be:

MONOSYLLABIC	12
DEXTERITY	9
FLIBBERTIGIBBET	30
PREJUDICIAL	11
RECOGNISED	10
MULLIGATAWNY	12
COMEDIENNE	10
BARBECUED	9
ESPLANADE	9
TRAMPOLINE	10
VOLUPTUOUS	10
PROVOCATIVE	11
TOTAL	143

SIMILES

Players: Any number

You will need:

A variety of small objects, pieces of card

Think up a list of everyday objects that are used in similes ('as bright as a button', 'as neat as a new pin' etc) and place these articles on a table on a series of numbered cards. Players have to write down the simile suggested by each object. Other items which could come in handy for this game include a beetroot ('as red as a beetroot'), the ace of spades ('as black as the ace of spades'), a wine glass ('as clear as crystal'), a whistle ('as clean as a whistle'), two pieces of wood ('as thick as two short planks') and a table tennis bat ('as blind as a bat'). You may have problems finding a newt to put on the table but by the end of the party that could be the most apt comparison of all.

DESERT ISLANDERS

Players: 5-10

Armed with pencil and paper, players are asked to write down the six items which they would take with them to a desert island, and why. The answers should be as truthful as possible although any husband who names 'the blonde next door' is liable to receive a few dirty looks from his wife. There are no winners, as such, to this game although a prize could be awarded for the most amusing list.

CELEBRITY DESERT ISLANDERS

Players: 5-10

In this less traumatic adaptation of 'Desert Islanders', players have to write down a list of six items which a well-known personality might choose to take to a desert island. Each player is handed a card bearing the name of a different famous person, dead or alive, true or fictional, anyone from Ethelred the Unready to Deputy Dawg. This game is excellent therapy for exorcising pet hates. For example you might decide that Chris Evans should do a great public service by taking with him to a desert island Shane Richie, Noel Edmonds, Freddie Starr, Emlyn Hughes and The Fugees.

PSEUDONYMS

Players: Any number

Flick through the books on your shelves to compile a list of 20 people who were born with a different name to that with which they eventually found fame. Hand a copy of the list to each player and give them 10 minutes to come up with as many correct identifications as possible. The following are worthy stand-bys in case you get stuck:

Archibald Leach (Cary Grant)
Frances Gumm (Judy Garland)
Diana Fluck (Diana Dors)
Charles Lutwidge Dodgson (Lewis Carroll)
Karol Wojtyla (Pope John Paul II)
Stuart Goddard (Adam Ant)
Mary Anne Evans (George Eliot)
Ruby Stevens (Barbara Stanwyck)
Sandra Goodrich (Sandie Shaw)
Jean François Marie Arouet (Voltaire)
Lewis Winogradsky (Lord Grade)
George Panos (George Michael)
Vladimir Ilyich Ulyanov (Lenin)
Marion Morrison (John Wayne)
Michael Barrett (Shakin' Stevens)
Israel Balin (Irving Berlin)
Issur Danielovitch Demsky (Kirk Douglas)
Paul Raven (Gary Glitter)
Helen Porter Mitchell (Dame Nellie Melba)
James Lablanche Stewart (Stewart Granger)

POTTED PROVERBS

Players: Any number

Each player is given a piece of paper with a potted proverb written on it – that is, a proverb minus all its vowels with the consonants joined together. After 30 seconds, the host calls out 'change' and, regardless of whether or not they have solved the riddle, the players pass their papers to the person on their left. The game continues in this way until the slips have travelled full circle and the players have worked on every proverb. A point is scored for each correct answer. The sort of proverbs which could be used are: STTCHNTMSVNN (A stitch in time saves nine), LKBFRYLP (Look before you leap) and NPPLDYKPSTHDCTRWY (An apple a day keeps the doctor away).

ALLITERATION

Players: Any number

This is another intellectual game whereby each player selects a letter from the alphabet and sets out to write a news item, a poem or a short story in which every word begins with his or her chosen letter. This can be tough going even for those with more than a GCSE in woodwork so it is advisable to allow 25 minutes' playing time. By then, it is a fairly safe bet that everyone will have had enough. When the results are read out, a prize can go to the author of the longest or most imaginative piece.

ABBREUIATIONS

Players: Any number

Think up 20 abbreviations (some reasonably well-known, a few more obscure) and write them down on a sheet of paper. Hand a copy of the list to each player and allow them 10 minutes to work out which each set of initials stands for. If they don't know some of the answers, encourage them to make something up – their invented answers may be more appropriate than the genuine article. Who knows what a well-oiled party guest might think up for F.A.N.Y. (First Air Nursing Yeomanry)? At the end of the time limit, the player with most correct answers wins. There could also be a prize for the guest with the best made-up answer. Here are a few suggestions for abbreviations – there is usually a good list in the back of a dictionary.

A.C.A. (Associate of the Institute of Chartered Accountants)
A.S.L.E.F. (Associated Society of Locomotive Engineers & Firemen)
B.R.C.S. (British Red Cross Society)
C.B.E. (Commander of the British Empire)
E.T.A. (Estimated Time of Arrival)
F.B.I. (Federal Bureau of Investigation)
F.R.S.G.S. (Fellow of the Royal Scottish Geographical Society)
G.M.T. (Greenwich Mean Time)
I.C.I. (Imperial Chemical Industries)
L.C.P. (Licentiate of the College of Preceptors)
L.T.A. (Lawn Tennis Association)
M.I.C.E. (Member of the Institution of Civil Engineers)
N.A.T.O. (North Atlantic Treaty Organisation)
N.C.O. (non-commissioned officer)
R.C.M.P. (Royal Canadian Mounted Police)
R.W.S. (Royal Society of Painters in Water Colours)
S.P.E. (Society for Pure English)
T.W.A. (Trans-World Airlines)
V.H.F. (Very High Frequency)
Y.H.A. (Youth Hostels Association)

EPITAPHS

Players: Any number

Dorothy Parker wanted 'Excuse my dust' put on her headstone, while W.C. Fields said that his epitaph should be: 'On the whole I'd rather be in Philadelphia.' Here, players are given the task of writing a witty epitaph either for a celebrity, or for someone else in the room. Depending on how well you know your fellow guests, it might be advisable to make the suggestions reasonably good-natured. Headstone comments such as Robert Benchley's suggested inscription for a movie star ('SHE SLEEPS ALONE – AT LAST') may not go down too well in certain company...

WORD SEARCH

Players: Any number

Draw up a list of a dozen distinctive word features and give the players two minutes to come up with one example of each.

Here are some suggested categories:

> Words ending in 'x' (onyx)
> Words containing three 'e's (telephone)
> Words ending in 'ic' (traffic)
> Words of more than four syllables (encyclopedia)
> Words beginning with 'ven' (ventriloquist)
> Words containing three 'a's (aardvark)
> Words with a 'q' in the middle (pique)
> Words ending in 'sm' (prism)
> Words beginning with 'mic' (microphone)
> Words containing three 'i's (imagination)
> Words of more than 14 letters (monographically)
> Words beginning with 'z' (zenith)

DRAWN FROM MEMORY

Players: 4-8

You will need:

Pieces of card

Draw six simple sketches on separate pieces of card. These can be something like a square with four different patterns, a boat with two sails, a house with a driveway and car or a ball with five spots. Number the cards and allow the players to study them for a total of a minute and a half. Then ask them to draw each sketch to the best of their recollection. The results will show just how much attention they were paying to detail. Award a prize to the most accurate set of reproductions.

MAD LIBS

Players: 4-8

Write a short story about the people at your party, or a nursery rhyme or fable and then remove key nouns, verbs, adjectives, adverbs and people's names. For these are to be filled in by the players who have absolutely no idea what the text is about. Give each player a pencil and paper and simply call out 'adjective', 'noun', 'exclamation' or whatever. At the end of the piece, collect the various answers and read them out, inserting the players' chosen words in the spaces in your text. The results can be somewhat illuminating. For example your story could be:

THE GIRL OF MY DREAMS

'The girl of my dreams has ADJECTIVE blonde hair and ADJECTIVE eyes which remind me of PLURAL NOUN. Her skin is as smooth as a (an) ADJECTIVE NOUN and is scented like PLURAL NOUN. Her legs are shaped like a NOUN and she looks really sexy when she's wearing her ADJECTIVE NOUN. In fact I think she's got a figure like NAME OF MAN IN ROOM. When I look into her PLURAL NOUN, I want to say, "I would really like to VERB you one day." I would ADVERB give up all my PLURAL NOUN for one night with this ADJECTIVE girl. Her name is NAME OF GIRL IN ROOM.'

This may end up as:

'The girl of my dreams has mouldy blonde hair and hideous eyes which remind me of dried prunes. Her skin is as smooth as a geriatric camel and is scented like Brussel sprouts. Her legs are shaped like a grand piano and she looks really sexy when she's wearing her grey gas-mask. In fact I think she's got a figure like Mr Appleby the butcher. When I look into her nail clippers, I want to say, "I would really like to garrote you one day." I would miserably give up all my pork scratchings for one night with this lice-infested girl. Her name is Mrs Ollerenshaw.'

Or alternatively you could try:

THE WEDDING

'The wedding took place yesterday of the ADJECTIVE NAME OF MALE CELEBRITY and the ADJECTIVE FEMALE CELEBRITY. The bride's dress was made of NOUN and had a ADJECTIVE neckline. On her head she wore a NOUN. She looked quite ADJECTIVE. When the groom slipped the NOUN on her PART OF BODY, there wasn't a dry NOUN in the house. Later at the reception the bride's mother, a ADJECTIVE woman, wiped away a NOUN and said, "This is the most ADJECTIVE day of my life." With that the ADJECTIVE couple cut the NOUN with a NAME OF CUTTING IMPLEMENT. Among the presents they received were a NOUN, a NOUN and the world's largest collection of PLURAL NOUN. "They will look lovely on our NOUN," said the bride. After the reception they set off by MEANS OF TRANSPORT for a ADJECTIVE honeymoon in PLACE.'

This could produce:

'The wedding took place yesterday of the turbo-charged Murray Walker and the repulsive Imelda Marcos. The bride's dress was made of tin and had a crude neckline. On her head she wore a potty. She looked quite ghastly. When the groom slipped the axe on her neck, there wasn't a dry toilet seat in the house. Later at the reception the bride's mother, a vindictive woman, wiped away a moth and said, "This is the most excruciating day of my life." With that the argumentative couple cut the vicar with a scythe. Among the presents they received were a frying-pan, a cotton bud and the world's largest collection of moose droppings. "They will look lovely on our dinner plate," said the bride. After the reception they set off by donkey for a nauseating honeymoon in Castleford.'

EYE TEST

Players: Any even number

This is a game that could get you into big trouble with your partner. Participants are divided into sexes and each man is instructed to talk to any one woman for a minute. When the time is up, the women are sent from the room and each man has to write down a description of what the woman he was talking to was wearing. The most detailed and accurate description wins. But beware. It may not always be wise to eulogise about the length (or lack of it) of a girl's skirt or the tightness of her jeans if the person in question is not your partner. The roles are then reversed with the women talking to the men for a minute before noting down in as much detail as possible what the man they were talking to said. Similarly if it was a chat-up line, it might be best to draw a discreet veil over the conversation. Whoever devised this game obviously believes that women have nothing worthwhile to say and men never wear anything worth mentioning. The only drawback is that after a few pints, most men can't remember what they've just been talking about either so when playing this game they are advised to stick to a prepared text about their job or whatever. Besides, what woman could resist an opening gambit of 'I'm in sewage'?

WHICH TOWN?

Players: 5-10

This game is a picture version of 'Charades'. The host – or a particularly artistic guest – draws a series of quick sketches, each depicting the name of a town. The other players have to study the drawings and work out the names of the towns. Popular ideas include:

    A drawing of an off-licence (STOCKPORT)
    A grave digger at work (BURY)
    A plate-full of food (NUNEATON)
    A bank robber demanding money (ANDOVER)
    A man walking towards a very low bridge (MINEHEAD)
    The numbers 2, 4, 8, 16, 32 (DUBLIN)

LITTLEHAMPTON should be avoided at all costs...

WHAT'S THE LINK?

Players: Any number

Think up a list of 20 pairs of famous people who have a common link. For instance with Robert the Bruce and Miss Muffet, the link would be spiders. Give each player a copy of the list and allow them 10 minutes to fill in the missing links between the various pairs. The one with most correct answers wins the game. Here are some possible examples:

1. William Tell and Sir Isaac Newton
2. Tab Hunter and Donny Osmond
3. Jeremy Brett and Douglas Wilmer
4. Jim Bowen and Schubert
5. Henry VIII and E.M. Forster
6. Dave Webb and Andy Linighan
7. Edward Heath and Sir Francis Chichester
8. Mrs Arthur Daley and Maris Crane from Frasier
9. John Cleese and Jeffrey Archer
10. Ben Turpin and Ken Dodd
11. Henry I of England and King John
12. Norman Tebbit and Tony Hancock
13. Wolf and Zodiac
14. Ann Packer and Mary Peters
15. Mick Jagger and Bing Crosby
16. Peter Adamson and Peter Baldwin
17. James A. Garfield and William McKinley
18. Annie Lennox and Jocky Wilson
19. Billy Bunter and Frank Spencer
20. John Lennon and Jackie Wilson

Answers: 1. Apples. William Tell is supposed to have fired his crossbow at an apple on his son's head while Sir Isaac Newton is said to have started thinking about the laws of gravity after seeing an apple fall in an orchard. 2. Both had number one hits with the song 'Young Love'. 3. Both played Sherlock Holmes on television. 4. Both once worked as school teachers. 5. The fifth of Henry VIII's wives was Catherine Howard who was executed; Howard's End is a novel by E.M. Forster. 6. Both scored the winning goals in FA Cup final replays, Webb for Chelsea against Leeds United in 1970 and Linighan for Arsenal against Sheffield Wednesday in 1993. 7. Sailing. Both were keen sailors. 8. Neither TV characters have ever been seen. 9. Both were raised in Weston-Super-Mare. 10. Insurance. Boss-eyed silent film star Ben Turpin was insured for $100,000 against the possibility of his eyes ever becoming normal again and similarly Ken Dodd insured his distinctive teeth, the result of a schoolboy cycling accident, for over £10,000. 11. Food. Both died from over-eating. Henry perished from a surfeit of lampreys (small eel-like creatures) and John died after devouring a quantity of peaches and cider. 12. They both once had jobs as assistants in menswear shops. 13. Both appear on the TV show Gladiators. 14. Both won Olympic track and field gold medals for Britain, Ann Packer in the 800 metres in 1964 and Mary Peters in the pentathlon in 1972. 15. Both sang hit duets with David Bowie. Crosby and Bowie reached number three in the UK charts with 'Little Drummer Boy' in 1982 and Jagger and Bowie got to number one in 1985 with 'Dancing in the Street'. 16. Both were killed off in Coronation Street – Adamson as Len Fairclough, Baldwin as Derek Wilton. 17. Both were U.S. Presidents who were assassinated in office. 18. Fish. Singer Annie Lennox and darts player Jocky Wilson both used to work in Scottish fish factories. 19. Michael Crawford, who played Frank Spencer, was one of the boys in the TV version of Billy Bunter in the 1950s. 20. Both had posthumous number one hits.

PICTORIAL PROVERBS

Players: Any even number up to 12

This 'Picture Charades' game involves players doing drawings which portray well-known proverbs such as 'Make hay while the sun shines', 'A bird in the hand is worth two in the bush' and 'A nod is as good as a wink to a blind horse.' It is best played as a team game with a player from each team being told which proverb to illustrate by the host. They return to their respective groups and, without speaking or writing any words, perform their mime via a drawing. The first team to guess correctly wins the round, the game continuing until every player has had a stint as the artist. The game can also be played with films, TV programmes and book titles.

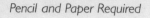

HEADLINES

Players: 4-10

Have you ever wondered how The Sun would have reported the Battle of Hastings or how The Mirror would have covered the Roman invasion of Britain? Well here is your chance to find out. The host prepares a list of historical events and asks the players to think up tabloid headlines to fit them. This is probably best played as a non-competitive game with players having as many goes as they wish since some will prove more adept at this task than others. Here are a few suggestions but no doubt you can do much better:

IT'S ONE IN THE EYE FOR HAROLD

– WILY WILLY SHOOTS 'EM DOWN (Battle of Hastings)

NELSON IN DEATH-BED SNOG SCANDAL (Battle of Trafalgar)

M.P. KILLED AT RAILWAY OPENING

– DIDN'T EXPECT TRAIN TO BE ON TIME (Death of William Huskisson)

CATCHPHRASES

Players: Any number

Think up a list of a dozen catchphrases used by famous people and characters past or present and jumble them up. The players have to pair the right person with the right catchphrase. These may prove helpful:

'Let's meet the eight who are going to generate' (Bruce Forsyth)

'Don't embawass me' (Lenny the Lion)

'You've never had it so good' (Harold Macmillan)

'Awight?' (Michael Barrymore)

'Yabba Dabba Doo' (Fred Flintstone)

'Book 'em, Danno' (Steve McGarrett)

'Heavens to Murgatroyd' (Snagglepuss)

'Yus, m'lady' (Parker)

'Just the facts, ma'am' (Sergeant Joe Friday)

'Who loves ya, baby?' (Theo Kojak)

'Before your very eyes' (Arthur Askey)

'You lucky people' (Tommy Trinder)

A QUESTION OF TASTE

Players: Any number

You will need:

Blindfolds, plastic cups, assorted liquids

This game is probably more enjoyable played when the guests have warmed up a bit – in other words, had a few drinks – because it tests their sense of taste. A series of plastic cups are filled with different drinkable liquids – including washing-up liquid may seem like a fun idea at the time but might not make you terribly popular. The players are blindfolded and take it in turns to sniff and sip the liquids, writing down their guesses as to the contents as they move along the line. You want to select as great a variety of liquids as possible while slipping in a couple of closely-related wines (say a Chardonnay and a Sauvignon Blanc) to test the connoisseurs. An ideal line-up might comprise: Bovril, Marmite, Ovaltine, grapefruit juice, pineapple juice, cocoa, drinking chocolate, Bisto gravy, tap water, bottled spring water, Chardonnay and Sauvignon Blanc. The winner is either the one with most correct answers or the last to throw up.

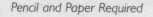

BEHEADED

Players: Any number

Each player has 10 minutes to go through the alphabet listing a word beginning with each letter which, when the first letter is removed, still makes a proper word. For example if your first word is 'ago', after deleting the 'a' you still have the word 'go'. Other examples are 'broom' ('room'), 'crook' ('rook'), 'drake' ('rake'), 'eastern' ('astern') and ending in 'yearn' ('earn') and 'zany' ('any').

THE NUMBERS GAME

Players: Any number

Prepare a list of phrases, sayings, song titles, movie titles etc, each containing a number. Copy the list and give the players a minute to fill in the appropriate numbers. For example:

The Magnificent——————— (7)

The —— Steps (39)

—— Red Balloons (99)

————————— Deadly Sins (7)

————————— Steps to Heaven (3)

—— Trombones (76)

———————— Way Stretch (2)

The ———————— o'Clock Club (9)

Pebble Mill at ———————(1)

————————— Days a Week (8)

Space ————— (1999)

82

———————— And All That (1066)

———————————— Love Songs and You (1,000,000)

ALPHA

Players: Any number

Players are given 10 minutes to list as many words as they can which begin and end with the same letter of the alphabet. The winner is the player who comes up with the longest list. Examples include: Amnesia, Dressed, Endive, Fluff, Gyrating, Hitch, Kayak, Maximum, Success, Tournament and Xerox. An alternative version is to go through the alphabet trying to think up the longest possible words beginning and ending with the same letter. A point is scored for each letter. Thus 'Partnership' scores 11 points, 'Deteriorated' 12 and 'Yellowy' 7. Problems arise when it comes to I, J, Q, U, V and Z.

THE LADY'S HANDBAG

Players: Any number

This rather quaint game invites players to enter the secret world of a lady's hand-bag, the contents of which have hitherto remained something of a mystery to most men. Draw up a list of items likely to be found in a lady's handbag and jumble them up into anagrams. Writing each anagram on a slip of paper, scatter the slips around the house and ask the players to unravel as many objects as they can in the space of 10 minutes. The player who has unscrambled the most answers wins the eye-shadow of his or her choice. In case you have no knowledge whatsoever of a lady's handbag, here are a few items which you might encounter within its walls: lipstick, mascara, cheque-book, comb, nail file, scissors, aspirin, door keys, purse, handker-chief, diary, perfume and, for American guests, a revolver.

REWRITING HISTORY

Players: 6 or more

Don't be put off by the title. This isn't a game solely for eminent historians – indeed they would probably frown at the frivolity of it all. Players are divided into teams, each containing three or four players, and take it in turns to suggest eight historical characters. The teams are then given 15 minutes to think up a story – the more ludicrous the better – in which all eight characters feature. At the end, the efforts are read out and the most inventive tale is named the winner. Obviously the more diverse the characters the greater scope there is for imagination. These two lists feature a good assortment through the ages:

Vlad the Impaler	Queen Victoria
Margaret Thatcher	Nell Gwynn
Edward the Confessor	Ivan the Terrible
Hitler	Boadiccea
Guy Fawkes	Ronald Reagan
Marie Antoinette	Richard III
Richard Nixon	King Canute
Elizabeth I	Alfred the Great

LIMERICKS

Players: Any number

This ever-popular pastime can be played in two ways as a party game. Either each player selects a town from an atlas and composes the entire limerick, or it becomes a group effort. In the second instance, the first player writes the first two lines and then folds the paper over concealing what he or she has written. The last word – the rhyming word – is then written in a visible place on the paper. The second player writes the next two lines before handing over to the third player who composes the last line, making sure that it rhymes with the word at the top of the sheet. A prize goes to the wittiest offering. In the unlikely event that you are unsure of the style of limericks, here is an example which has the added advantage of promoting dental hygiene:

'There was a young lady from Neath

Who had the most God-awful teeth

Those that weren't blacked

Were decidedly cracked

With lorry-loads of plaque underneath.'

Clearly anyone who has the misfortune to pluck
Llanfairpwllgwyngyllgogerychwyrndrobwllllantysiliogogogoch
from the atlas is in for a tough time.

PICTURE PUZZLE

Players: 5-10

You will need:

Magazines or travel brochures

Look through some old magazines or travel brochures and find a series of large photographs (one per player) with plenty of detail. Then choose a letter from the alphabet – something easy like S, C or T – and ask each player to write down as many things as they can see beginning with that letter in their photograph. At the end of two minutes, get them to read out their answers. To ensure fair play, players should draw on their picture a circle around each item they list. That way the judge can determine whether that white spot is really a distant seagull or just a print mark.

FIRST NAME TERMS

Players: Any number

The host dictates to the players a list of 20 surnames of famous people, dead or alive, true or fictional, and gives them two minutes in which to write down the appropriate first name. In order to make the game more competitive, it is a good idea to include a few surnames which could have more than one first name – for instance 'Rutherford' could refer to Ernest or Margaret. Here, players get one point for a correct name which is also on other people's lists of answers, but two points for a name which nobody else has thought of. This list might help to get you started:

1. Hemingway
2. Gardner
3. Rameau
4. Edison
5. Doggie
6. Copernicus
7. Becker
8. Joyce
9. Marples
10. Fox
11. Hobbs
12. Madgwick
13. Schumacher
14. Watts
15. Tyler
16. Rendell
17. Poulsen
18. Crompton
19. Fontana
20. Wainthropp

Answers: 1. Ernest 2. Ava, Erle Stanley or John 3. Jean-Philippe 4. Thomas Alva 5. Auggie 6. Nicolaus 7. Boris or Lydia 8. James or William 9. Ernest 10. Edward, James, Samantha, Noosha, Charles or George 11. Thomas or Jack 12. Abel 13. Michael or Ralf 14. Alan, George, Charlie, David or Curly 15. Wat, John or Bonnie 16. Ruth 17. Valdemar 18. Richmal or Samuel 19. Domenico, Lucio or Wayne 20. Hetty

CRAZY DEFINITIONS

Players: Any number

The art of punning has never received the credit it deserves. It is always looked down upon by supposedly superior wits – indeed the punmaster is treated with the sort of disdain usually reserved for double-glazing salesmen. But here is a game where such wordsmiths can come into their own, concocting preposterous definitions for everyday words. Each player is assigned a letter of the alphabet and has 10 minutes to come up with as many daft definitions as possible for words beginning with that letter. The one with most answers is the winner. These excruciating examples will help set the tone:

> Festival – in the beginning
> Fungi – man who likes to party
> Parasite – army camp
> Disgruntled – a pig that has lost its voice
> Nickname – steal someone else's identity
> Battery – place where bats live
> Minimum – a small parent

AUTHOR, AUTHOR!

Players: Any number

Another punning game. Players are given 10 minutes to think up as many authors as possible with punning names to fit book titles, such as the old schoolboy favourite My Life of Crime by Robin Banks. Here are a few more:

The Medical Guide by Arthur Itis

A Life of Prosecution by Bill Stickers

Word Games by Anna Gram

Lewis Carroll: a Biography by Alison Wonderland

An Introduction to Gay Sex by William Fitzpatrick

The Works of Rossini by Barbara Seville

Depression for Beginners by Mona Lott

Oh Yes He Did! by Betty Never

ACROSTICS

Players: Any number

Choose a word of six or seven letters from a newspaper and get the players to write the word down in a column on the left side of their paper and then to write the same word in reverse, i.e. upwards, on the right-hand side. If the chosen word is MENTHOL, the sheet would look like this:

```
M                          L
E                          O
N                          H
T                          T
H                          N
O                          E
L                          M
```

The players then have five minutes to write the longest words they can think of beginning and ending with the letters marked out by the columns. A point is scored for each letter. Here is how it works:

```
MinstreL                    = 8
EgO                         = 3
NintH                       = 5
TransparenT                 = 11
HistoriaN                   = 9
OperatE                     = 7
LogarithM                   = 9
```

Total: 52

YOUNG AT HEART

Players: Any number

If you're a fan of old children's TV programmes like Trumpton, The Clangers and Thunderbirds, then this is the game for you. Kids' favourites have habitually operated in twos — all you have to do is think up a list of characters and their sidekicks, jumble them around and get the players to pair them up again correctly. Be prepared for plenty of angst as the local building society manager desperately tries to think of the name of Yogi Bear's partner. To put him out of his misery, tell him it was Boo Boo. Here are some other suitable pairs:

The Lone Ranger and Tonto

Batman and Robin

Hawkeye and Chingachgook

The Range Rider and Dick West

Secret Squirrel and Morocco Mole

Quick Draw McGraw and Baba Looie

Ivanhoe and Gurth

Hector Heathcote and Winston

Twizzle and Footso the cat

Mike Mercury and Jimmy Gibson

Dick Dastardly and Muttley

SELF-PORTRAITS

Players: 5-10

The players are seated around a table and told to draw a self-portrait. But just as they are about to begin, the host points out that it must be done with the hand they don't normally write with. So a right-handed person will have to draw left-handed. Unless a number of the guests are ambidextrous, the end results will look like an exhibition of abstract art. A prize should go to the most gallant attempt. The least inspiring artist could be told to paint himself in oils… as long as you show him where you keep the Duckham's.

ROAD SIGNS

Players: Any number

Compile a list of around 10 road signs, but only write the first letter of each word of the command, showing the remaining letters as asterisks. Thus 'No Parking' would appear as N*P******. Hand copies of the list to the players and allow them five minutes to fill in the answers. The winner receives a free copy of the Highway Code. Here are some other suggestions:

1.   K***L***
2.   R*****S****N**
3.   N*O*********
4.   B**S***
5.   H****P****C*******
6.   A****O***
7.   O**W**S*****
8.   N*R****T***
9.   G***W**
10.   D***C**********A****

Answers: 1. Keep Left 2. Reduce Speed Now 3. No Overtaking 4. Bus Stop 5. Heavy Plant Crossing 6. Ahead Only 7. One Way Street 8. No Right Turn 9. Give Way 10. Dual Carriageway Ahead

BRAND NAMES

Players: Any number

Are names like Adidas and Nike all foreign to you? Do you struggle to tell the difference between Oxo and Paxo? Well you can test your knowledge – or lack of it – with this quick-fire game in which players have a minute to write down as many product brand names as they can think of beginning with a certain letter. The host starts the ball rolling by calling out a letter. If it is C, players may scribble down Coca-Cola, Caramac, Clark's Shoes, Crunchie, Curly-Wurly, Cadbury's Cream Eggs, Chanel No. 5 etc. At the end of the minute, the host calls out another letter and the players must write down as many brand names as they can think of starting with that letter. The game continues in this way until five letters have been covered and everybody's arm is about to drop off. The player with most brand names wins a bottle of Martini; the loser gets a bottle of Harpic.

HUMAN ACRONYMS

Players: Any number

Each player is given the name of a famous person and told to think of an appropriate sentence in which each word begins with the letters of the celebrity's surname and in that order. Thus a sentence based on Tony Blair could read: 'Boyish Looks Accrue Instant Rewards.' The game can also be played using the names of friends although this has been known to cause offence. For instance Colin may be a friend no longer if described as 'Clumsy Oaf Lives In Norwood' while Shaun may not be too thrilled to hear himself labelled 'Surly Hypocrite And Uncouth Neighbour'.

FAMOUS LAST WORDS

Players: Any number

Each player is given 15 minutes to think up appropriate last words for five famous living people or, if it is not thought to be tempting fate, for five friends at the party. Maybe Bruce Forsyth's final words would be, 'It was nice to see you, to see you nice.' Or Steve Davis might gasp, 'I should never have missed that pink in 1983.' Or Arnold Schwarzenegger might vow with his dying breath, 'I'll be back.' Give your imagination full rein.

OKAPI

Players: Any number

The players are given 10 minutes to think up as many five-letter words as they can in which the first letter is a vowel, the second a consonant, the third a vowel, the fourth a consonant and the last letter another vowel. An example of a word with this combination of letters is Okapi – hence the name of the game. Other words which fit into the category include: Irate, Alive, Arena, Unite, Opera, Awake, Aroma, Elope, Evade, Image, Abide and Urine. The player with the longest list wins.

LUCKY NUMBERS

Players: Any number

Prepare a list of some 20 facts connected with numbers and write them out in abbreviated form. For instance 24 hours in a day would be written 24 = H in a D and seven days in a week would be 7 = D in a W. Give a copy of the list to each player and allow them 10 minutes to fill in the answers. These may prove useful:

1.   360 = D in a C
2.   18 = F-C C C
3.   9 = I in the C I
4.   57 = H V
5.   6 = S to a H
6.   51 = S in A
7.   7 = W of the A W
8.   12 = P in a W L T
9.   16 = O in a P
10. 49 = N in the L
11. 8 = F in a M
12. 77 = S S
13. 52 = P C in a P
14. 5 = G L
15. 29 = D in F in a L Y
16. 64 = Y in the R of Q V
17. 18 = H on a G C
18. 4 = O in the W
19. 32 = D F at which W F
20. 13 = a B D

Answers: 1. Degrees in a Circle 2. First-Class Cricket Counties 3. Islands in the Channel Islands 4. Heinz Varieties 5. Sides to a Hexagon 6. States in America 7. Wonders of the Ancient World 8. Players in a Women's Lacrosse Team 9. Ounces in a Pound 10. Numbers in the Lottery 11. Furlongs in a Mile 12. Sunset Strip 13. Playing Cards in a Pack 14. Great Lakes 15. Days in February in a Leap Year 16. Years in the Reign of Queen Victoria 17. Holes on a Golf Course 18. Oceans in the World 19. Degrees Fahrenheit at which Water Freezes 20. A Baker's Dozen

LINKWORDS

Players: Any number

More work for the long-suffering host! Think up a series of a dozen or so linkwords – words which can be linked to a word before or after. An example is Sheep (Dog) Biscuit. Here the linkword is Dog because it can connect to the word either side – Sheepdog and Dog biscuit. Having compiled your list, copy it out on sheets of paper and give the players five minutes to come up with the answers. These should help to give you the general idea:

1. Danger (Mouse) Trap
2. Greg (Norman) Tebbit
3. Nigel (Short) Bread
4. Down (Fall) Out
5. John (Major) Tom
6. Baseball (Bat) Mobile
7. Bus (Station) Wagon
8. Boy (George) Bush
9. Old (Spice) Girls
10. Rocking (Horse) Box
11. Sand (Paper) Chain
12. Clive (James) Last

POWDERS

Players: 5-10

You will need:

Various edible powders or granules, saucers

This is another tasting game but here, instead of liquids, players have to identify a succession of powders – no illegal substances please! The powders are arranged in a row of saucers and the players move along the line tasting each one in turn by dipping in the end of a finger. They then have to write down what they think it is. Salt, flour, sugar, gravy granules and bicarbonate of soda are staple ingredients of this game.

LITERARY LIONS

Players: Any number

In this game players write, in a variety of literary styles, on a topic which would appear eminently unsuitable. Each player writes on a slip of paper the name of a celebrated author, a newspaper or a magazine. While the slips are being collected, the host announces the topic. The slips are then mixed up and the players each draw one. Listen for the gasps of horror as players realise that they have to write an article on The Virtues of Ready-Mix Concrete in the style of Charles Dickens; or The Sun; or Barbara Cartland; or Shakespeare; or Cosmopolitan. Other suggested subjects are:

A Weekend in Cleethorpes

Flared Trousers: A Fashion Statement

Home Electrical Maintenance

An Alien Landing

The Music of Roger Whittaker

BLURBS

Players: 4-8

You will need:

Some paperback novels, a hat or bowl

This game is extremely popular amongst budding authors. The host chooses a novel from the shelves and writes down the first line on a slip of paper. It is best not to choose a book with a classic opening line, such as Rebecca, because it will rather defeat the object of the game. With the players assembled, he or she then reads out the blurb on the back cover of the book, making sure that the players don't see the title, the author or any other identifying features. Having gathered that this is a tale of 'smouldering passion, insatiable greed and homicidal envy', they then have five minutes in which to compose what they think could be the first line of the novel. Their endeavours are then collected and put into a hat or bowl with the slip of paper bearing the authentic first line. The host then reads out all of the slips and the players have to guess which is the genuine article. The first person to do so wins the round and the game continues with the host reading out the blurb from another pre-selected novel. Given participants with literary leanings, it is surprising how often some of the made-up first lines sound better than the real thing.

THE END ZONE

Players: Any number

Think up a list of around 20 words which finish in the letters END. Then write out a clue for each one. Give a copy of the list to each player and allow them 10 minutes to come up with the answers. To save you exercising the grey matter unduly, here's one I made earlier:

1. Correct
2. Climb
3. Protect
4. Salary
5. Clergyman
6. Mix
7. Companion
8. Sell
9. Have in mind
10. Swell out
11. Hang up
12. Profess falsely
13. Go down
14. Repair
15. Dispatch
16. Make crooked
17. Take care of
18. Give warning of
19. Bestow
20. Pay out

Answers: 1. Amend 2. Ascend 3. Defend 4. Stipend 5. Reverend 6. Blend 7. Friend 8. Vend 9. Intend 10. Distend 11. Suspend 12. Pretend 13. Descend 14. Mend 15. Send 16. Bend 17. Tend 18. Portend 19. Lend 20. Spend

THE AGEING PROCESS

Players: Any number

Scour the newspapers for the 'Whose birthday today' section and prepare a list of diverse celebrities or famous people together with their ages. Having supplied the players with paper and pencil, call out your list of names and ask them to fill in what they think each celebrity's current age is. Handy hint: Most actresses are 29. After collecting up their estimates, read out the correct answers and wait for comments like: 'He was old when Methuselah was a lad!' or 'She's had more face lifts than Covent Garden!' Add up the discrepancies on each answer sheet between the proper ages and the guesses and the winner will be the player with the smallest overall difference. These ages are current at 1 November 2000:

Meryl Streep 51
Martina Navratilova 44
Nadia Comaneci 38
Prince Philip 79
Bob Dylan 59
Prince Charles 51
Vanessa Redgrave 63
Alan Bennett 66
Joanna Lumley 54
Muhammad Ali 58
Des O'Connor 68
Barbara Streisand 58
Sophia Loren 66
Pele 60
Bob Monkhouse 72

SILHOUETTES

Players: 5-10

You will need:

Old magazines, some plain card

Sift through a pile of old magazines and find some nice glossy photographs. Then carefully cut out certain objects from the photos – maybe a table, a knife, a bunch of flowers, a sofa – so that, when set against plain card, they leave a series of silhouettes. The players have to study the pictures and write down what they think the missing objects are. The one with the most correct answers claims the spoils.

STUD BOOK

Players: Any number

This is a game of intelligence and imagination which will appeal to students of the horse-racing form book. Compile a list of 20 imaginary sires and dams, the names of which are loosely connected in some way. The players then have 15 minutes to think up suitable names for the various foals. Although you will have prepared your answers in advance, there is no hard and fast rule about right or wrong. One of the players may come up with an equally good – if not better – suggestion than your own so points have to be awarded for ingenious answers as well as the ones you had thought of. The following should help you get out of the starting stalls:

1.   By Ajuga out of Last Post
2.   By Ian Botham out of Tar Baby
3.   By Plug Away out of The Feather
4.   By Spaniel out of The Artist
5.   By Oak Tree out of Sirocco
6.   By Lyons Maid out of Day of Rest
7.   By San Francisco out of Sweet Slumbers
8.   By Hawkeye out of King Edward
9.   By Eros out of Trapeze Artist
10.   By Cadbury's Flake out of Cinderella
11.   By Pigtail out of Union
12.   By Julius Caesar out of Proboscis

13.   By Wentworth out of Society Dance
14.   By Eiffel Tower out of First Class Mail
15.   By The Pied Piper out of Grand National
16.   By Cornflake out of Dr. Crippen
17.   By Homburg out of Paul Daniels
18.   By Yorkshire Cricketer out of Victor Kiam
19.   By Mandarin out of Sir Robert
20.   By Providence out of Communist

Answers: 1. Bugle 2. Cricket Pitch 3. Electric Light 4. Prince Charles 5. Woodwind 6. Ice Cream Sundae 7. California Dreaming 8. Mashed Potato 9. Piccadilly Circus 10. Chocolate Buttons 11. Ayr United 12. Roman Nose 13. Golf Ball 14. French Letter 15. Rat Race 16. Cereal Killer 17. Hat Trick 18. Close Shave 19. Orange Peel 20. Rhode Island Red

The game is open to abuse. Manchester United fans might argue that By Badly out of Contention must be Newcastle United. The game can also be played in reverse whereby players are given the names of the foals and have to think of appropriate names for the sires and dams.

KEYWORDS

Players: Any number

A slightly easier game involving word combinations is 'Keywords'. Here the host calls out a proper three-letter word such as 'rid', and gives the players three minutes to write down as many words as possible which contain that keyword. Examples could be: arid, pride, ride, grid, griddle, riddle, bride, bridle, acrid, lurid, meridian, pride, stride and torrid.

BLOCKBUSTERS

Players: 5-10

Pluck a letter from the alphabet and think up 12 questions, the answers to which are all words beginning with that letter. Read out your questions and after each one give the players 30 seconds to jot down the answer. At the end of all 12 questions, see who has managed the highest score. If the game proves popular, you can move on to another letter... or two... or three... or four... until everyone is intellectually exhausted. If your chosen letter is F, your questions could be:

1.   Which F was an English comedian famed for his ukulele?
2.   On what F might you find a stamen, a corolla and a calyx?
3.   What F has a capital of Helsinki?
4.   Which F starred in The Prisoner of Zenda?
5.   Which F is a port in Western Australia?
6.   Which F succeeded Richard Nixon as U.S. President?
7.   Which F is a short raised deck at the bow of a ship?
8.   Which F is equivalent to 220 yards?
9.   Which F was a style of painting inspired by van Gogh?
10.   Which F is a member of the thrush family?
11.   Which F was an Italian mathematician who had a series of numbers named after him?
12.   Which F is a Scottish football team playing at Brockville?

Answers: 1. Formby (George) 2. Flower 3. Finland 4. Fairbanks (Douglas Jr) 5. Fremantle 6. Ford (Gerald) 7. Fo'c'sle 8. Furlong 9. Fauvism 10. Fieldfare 11. Fibonacci 12. Falkirk

TWISTED TUNES

Players: Any number

Prepare a list of 15 song titles and convert the words into anagrams. Give the players 15 minutes to unravel the letters. The one with the most correct titles could win a prize like a Crowded House CD, the loser getting a Nana Mouskouri CD. These may save you some time:

(To make things a little easier, the years of the songs are in brackets)

1.   Llawdrowne (1995)
2.   Homebani Shayprod (1975)
3.   Noxeran (1979)
4.   Spottyresee (1995)
5.   Pungjim Ajkc Shalf (1968)
6.   Gyabg Storesur (1980)
7.   Tubestuist (1966)
8.   Pushdad Oyu Café (1981)
9.   Ttamschalk Enm dan Ttamschalk Stac dan Gods (1978)
10.   Gonkwin Em Gonkwin Uoy (1977)
11.   Scaleser Wipersh (1984)
12.   Ramka Loncheema (1983)
13.   Threes a Yug Skrow Wond Eht Hiphopsc Wrasse She Slive (1981)
14.   Gribed Rove Droublet Trawe (1970)
15.   Ni Het Arey 5252 (1969)

Answers 1. Wonderwall 2. Bohemian Rhapsody 3. Roxanne 4. Stereotypes 5. Jumping Jack Flash 6. Baggy Trousers 7. Substitute 8. Shaddup You Face 9. Matchstalk Men and Matchstalk Cats and Dogs 10. Knowing Me Knowing You 11. Careless Whisper 12. Karma Chameleon 13. There's a Guy Works Down The Chipshop Swears He's Elvis 14. Bridge Over Troubled Water 15. In The Year 2525

102

AWKWARD LETTERS

Players: Any number

This game is for people whose idea of a good read is a dictionary. Some English words boast letter combinations which are so unusual, it's difficult to envisage them occurring in any known word. An example is the WKW in awkward. So give your dictionary buffs the thrill of a lifetime by drawing up a list of a dozen or so tricky three-letter combinations and allow them 10 minutes to find English words into which the sequences fit. If anybody comes up with a word different from the one you'd thought of, award them an extra point. Here are some good examples: vacUUM, harDSHip, baZAAr, duMBFound, quaRTZ, autUMNal, laWYEr, haphAZArd, witHHOld and preSBYtery.

WHO SAID THAT?

Players: Any number

From time to time, everyone wishes they had come up with a witty riposte or a bon mot, especially at parties. Perhaps you and your guests can draw inspiration from the words of others as you play this game based on quotations. Search through a book of quotations (there are plenty in the library if you don't have any at home). Pick out 20 of the best, jumble up the speakers' names and give players five minutes to attribute the quotes to the correct people. This list of verbal gems may prove helpful:

1. 'There is only one thing in the world worse than being talked about, and that is not being talked about.'
2. 'He who can, does; he who cannot, teaches...'
3. 'What you said hurt me very much. I cried all the way to the bank.'
4. 'I never hated a man enough to give him his diamonds back.'
5. 'A successful man is one who makes more money than his wife can spend. A successful woman is one who can find such a man.'
6. 'Anyone who goes to a psychiatrist should have his head examined.'
7. 'I used to be Snow White, but I drifted.'
8. 'Asking a working writer what he thinks about critics is like asking a lamp-post what it thinks about dogs.'

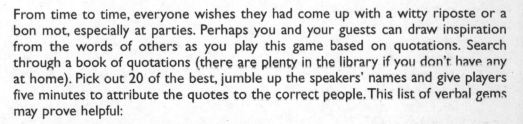

9.   'I don't want to achieve immortality through my work. I want to achieve it through not dying.'

10.   'The reports of my death are greatly exaggerated.'

11.   'When a man fell into his anecdotage it was a sign for him to retire from the world.'

12.   'Too bad all the people who know how to run the country are busy driving taxi cabs and cutting hair.'

13.   'A woman's place is in the wrong.'

14.   'You never realise how short a month is until you pay alimony.'

15.   'A bank is a place that will lend you money if you can prove that you don't need it.'

16.   'Life is rather like a tin of sardines – we're all of us looking for the key.'

17.   'Moral indignation is jealousy with a halo.'

18.   'A bore is a man who, when you ask him how he is, tells you.'

19.   'Gossip is the art of saying nothing in a way that leaves practically nothing unsaid.'

20.   'A cannibal is a guy who goes into a restaurant and orders the waiter.'

A.   George Burns
B.   Mae West
C.   Bert Leston Taylor
D.   James Thurber
E.   Oscar Wilde
F.   Mark Twain
G.   Liberace
H.   Walter Winchell
I.   John Barrymore
J.   Alan Bennett
K.   Zsa Zsa Gabor
L.   Sam Goldwyn
M.   Bob Hope
N.   John Osborne
O.   George Bernard Shaw
P.   Lana Turner
Q.   Woody Allen
R.   Jack Benny
S.   Benjamin Disraeli
T.   H.G. Wells

Answers: 1E 2O 3G 4K 5P 6L 7B 8N 9Q 10F 11S 12A 13D 14I 15M 16J 17T 18C 19H 20R

HOLLYWOOD PUT DOWNS

Players: Any number

Hollywood can be a playground of bitchiness with the movie industry's cruellest jibes being reserved for the inflated egos and wage packets of its stars. With so much wit at their disposal the comments of executives, critics and fellow performers make wonderful reading, as long as you're not on the receiving end. For this quotation game, select 10 Hollywood barbs and ask the players to write down whom they think was the object of ridicule. You can either call out the quotes or have them printed on sheets of paper. In the latter event, allow the players five minutes to come up with the answers. Here are a few to fire your imagination:

1. 'Well, at least he has finally found his true love – what a pity he can't marry himself' – Frank Sinatra
2. 'Wet she's a star, dry she ain't' – Joe Pasternak
3. 'Working with her is like being hit over the head with a Valentine card' – Christopher Plummer
4. 'To tell the honest truth, he isn't such a helluva good lay' – Carole Lombard
5. 'A professional amateur' – Laurence Olivier
6. 'She is not even an actress... only a trollop' – Gloria Swanson
7. 'I love to play bitches, and she certainly helped me in this part' – Joan Crawford
8. 'As wholesome as a bowl of cornflakes and at least as sexy' – Dwight MacDonald
9. 'She ran the gamut of emotions from A to B' – Dorothy Parker
10. 'Silicone from the knees up' – George Masters

Answers: 1. Robert Redford 2. Esther Williams 3. Julie Andrews 4. Clark Gable 5. Marilyn Monroe 6. Lana Turner 7. Norma Shearer 8. Doris Day 9. Katharine Hepburn 10. Raquel Welch

PERSONAL COLUMN

Players: 4-8

You will need:

Newspapers

Players are asked to construct a short advertisement for inclusion in the personal columns of a newspaper or magazine. You know the sort of thing: 'Sincere boy, 20, seeks girl with own house, yacht, sports car and annual income of over £150,000. No photo necessary.' But the catch to the game is that the players' choice of words is strictly limited. When you supply the pencils and paper needed to write out the advertisements, also give each player a strip from a newspaper. In size this should amount to one column from a broadsheet like The Daily Telegraph or The Times or two columns from a tabloid such as the Daily Mail or Daily Express. Apart from two 'free' words of their own choice, all of the words for each player's advertisement must be taken from their cutting. And to ensure fair play, the words selected from the newsprint must be circled. However, there are no restrictions as to the order in which the words can be used. When everybody has finished their composition – 20 minutes should be sufficient – ask the players to read out their efforts and marvel at how a tender plea for artistic companionship has emerged from a cutting about waste-disposal methods in Mongolia.

ODD ONE OUT

Players: Any number

This is always a popular game at parties and one that is not necessarily too intellectually demanding. However, as with all quiz games, if you have a highbrow guest list, you can make the questions much harder. Prepare 10 groups of four names, covering people, places etc. In each case, three of the names will have something in common – the players' task is to find the odd one out. The winner is the one with most correct answers in 10 minutes but, unless you want to have a mutiny on your hands, do remember to be flexible. Someone may come up with an answer which, although it is not the one on your list, may still be perfectly acceptable. In such cases, it is diplomatic not to act as sole judge but to listen to the wishes of the majority. Here are a few sample 'Odd Ones Out':

1.   Copperhead, taipan, agama and fer de lance.
2.   I'm All Right, Jack, Dr. Strangelove, The Wrong Box and Those Magnificent Men in Their Flying Machines.
3.   Unst, Hoy, Yell and Fetlar.
4.   George Swindin, Billy Wright, Peter Shreeves and Don Howe.
5.   The Hollies, The Searchers, Herman's Hermits and Freddie and the Dreamers.
6.   Earl of Roseberry, Marquess of Salisbury, Earl of Derby and Earl of Liverpool.
7.   17, 13, 14 and 19
8.   Pink, Chrysanthemum, Sweet William and Carnation.
9.   Madam, sonic, radar and noon
10. Athabasca, Saskatchewan, Peace and Green.

Answers: 1, Agama – it's a lizard, the rest are snakes 2, Those Magnificent Men in Their Flying Machines – the other films all featured Peter Sellers. 3, Hoy. It is one of the Orkney Islands – the other three are part of the Shetlands. 4, Peter Shreeves. He managed Tottenham Hotspur Football Club – the others managed Arsenal. 5, The Searchers. They came from Liverpool – the others hailed from Manchester. 6, Earl of Roseberry. He was a Liberal Prime Minister – the others were all Conservatives. 7, 14 – the only one which is not a prime number. 8, Chrysanthemum – the other three are members of the Dianthus family. 9, Sonic. The remainder are palindromes – they read the same backwards as forwards. 10, Green. It is a river in the United States. The other three are in Canada.

ROYAL ACADEMY

Players: 6-10

Divide the players into two teams. On the command 'Go!', one member of each team trots over to the host who gives them both the same scene to draw. They scuttle back to their groups and set to work drawing without uttering a single word, while the other team members have to guess what the illustration is supposed to be. The game can be played over a number of rounds with the host supplying a different subject and the teams a different artist for each round. The team that achieves most correct solutions is declared the winner. The more unusual the subject for illustration, the more enjoyable the game will be. Suggestions include Pope John Paul II shopping in *Tesco*, *Batman* taking a bath and Queen Victoria appearing on *Blind Date*.

GUESS THE SLOGAN

Players: Any number

Write out 20 well-known advertising slogans and give players 10 minutes to fill in the names of the products concerned. If your mind has gone blank, here are a few suitable examples:

'The Listening Bank' (Midland Bank)
'The Sweet You Can Eat Between Meals' (Milky Way)
'The Amber Nectar' (Fosters Lager)
'Pure Genius' (Guinness)
'The Drive of Your Life' (Peugeot)

COLLECTIVE NOUNS

Players: Any number

We are blessed with some curious collective nouns, particularly in the world of ornithology. So let's hear it for a murmuration of starlings, a parliament of owls and an ostentation of peacocks, not to mention an exaltation of larks. A challenging game is for players to try and invent their own highly appropriate collective nouns. For instance, the collective noun for probate solicitors could be a clash of wills or a gathering of sperm donors might be a packet of seeds. Give everyone 10 minutes to indulge in this pastime while you're replenishing the drinks and then read out their creations. After such mental exertion, the least you can do is award a prize to the wittiest submission.

TALENT SPOTTER

Players: Any number

See how good your guests are at spotting celebrities by cutting a dozen or so photographs from magazines or colour supplements, sticking them on paper and giving the players five minutes to name as many as they can. Don't choose people who are too well-known or too obscure (the Queen is a bit of a giveaway while virtually any member of the Conservative shadow cabinet is impossible) but opt for B-list celebrities like Patsy Kensit, Caron Keating or Eamonn Holmes. An alternative version is to collect magazine photographs of famous faces and cut out a nose here, the eyes there, one of the chins and so on and then ask the players to make their identifications from what's left.

ATHLETIC
PURSUITS

ARE YOU THERE, MORIARTY?

Players: Two plus onlookers

You will need:

Rolled-up newspapers, blindfolds

This is definitely not a game for those of a nervous disposition. It takes its name from Sherlock Holmes' notorious adversary, Professor Moriarty, and purports to re-enact their life and death struggle at the Reichenbach Falls. However, there is one major difference: Holmes and Moriarty did not set about each other with rolled up copies of the Daily Star. The contest takes place between two players, but there are sure to be plenty of enthusiastic spectators egging them on from the sidelines. Both participants are blindfolded and told to lie face-down on the floor, each grasping the other's left wrist with their left hand and clutching a rolled-up newspaper in their right hand. One then asks, 'Are you there, Moriarty?' to which the other replies, 'Yes', before quickly slithering away to another spot as the rolled-up newspaper comes crashing down from on high. If the newspaper scores a clean blow on the opponent's head, the game is won; if the strike misses, it is the other player's turn to ask the question and take aim. As each battle ends, there should be no shortage of spectators only too willing to fill the breach. After all, a lightly-throbbing head is a small price to pay for such enjoyment.

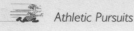
THE JAFFA RELAY

Players: Any even number

You will need:

Oranges

What better way of running off that fourth sausage roll, than by waddling up and down the lounge as fast as you can with an orange wedged between the head of you and your partner? Although yet to acquire Olympic status (surely this is just an oversight by the IOC), 'The Jaffa Relay' is a long-standing party favourite. Players are split into two teams and then sub-divided into pairs. Bearing in mind that the orange has to be held between the foreheads, it is advisable that those paired off are of similar height. Pairing off a six-foot lad with a girl barely five-foot in her heels is a recipe for disaster… and sore necks in the morning! The game starts with the first pairs from each team poised behind the starting line, facing each other with the orange held between their foreheads. When the starter shouts 'Go!', they set off for a line five yards away, then turn for home where their places are taken by the next pair in the team. If the orange is dropped at any time, the players must stop and replace it between their foreheads before carrying on with the race. They must not use their hands to hold the fruit in place although they can put it in position manually when handing over to their team mates. The relay continues until one team finishes. In case of accidents with exceptionally squashy oranges, it's a good idea to have a couple of spares on standby.

TREASURE HUNT

Players: Any number

You will need:

An assortment of small items, pencils and paper

'Treasure Hunt' is the classic party game for enabling guests to stretch their legs in a few minutes' gentle exercise. Before the party you need to scour cupboards, the larder, even, if you are particularly brave, your teenage son's bedroom, and produce a dozen or more small items that can be secreted somewhere about the house. These could include a shoe lace, a bus ticket, a clothes peg, a pencil sharpener, a sock, a small screwdriver, a comb, a nail file, a stamp, a cork, a milk bottle top and a key. Once you have your items, it is time to hide them in suitable places. Whilst you don't want the players to find them immediately, each object must be visible – it is unreasonable to expect even Poirot to find a paper clip which has been stuffed beneath a pile of magazines. Underneath shelves or mantelpieces are always good locations, in which case you will probably need some sticky tape to make sure the item doesn't drop off. And don't hide objects in places which are too inaccessible, especially if your guests are elderly or somewhat on the rotund side. There is nothing more embarrassing than having to call out the fire brigade because one of your guests has become wedged between the fireplace and the wall while searching for that elusive milk bottle top in 'Treasure Hunt'. As you find a home for each item, don't forget to make a note of where it is – it is really frustrating if at the end of the game nobody, not even the host, has a clue where the bus ticket is. At the start of the game, call out the list of items and, having given the players pencils and paper, tell them that they have to write down each location alongside the relevant item. A tip for players is not to get too excited when discovering an object. Frantic jumping up and down, punching the air in celebration and cries of 'Eureka!' merely tend to alert your fellow competitors – far better to move away from the object and then note its location down quietly. The first player to find every item on the list wins the game or, alternatively, a limit of 20 minutes can be imposed – the one with the most correct answers in that time being declared the victor. Of course, if all of your guests happen to be myopic, you may need larger objects – a gas cooker for example. Better still, you could try playing a different game.

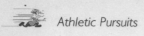
APPLE DUCKING

Players: Any number

You will need:

Tubs of water, apples (one per player)

This is another old favourite – the sort of revelry which one can imagine being played at the court of Henry VIII. The rules are simple. One or more tubs of water are placed on the floor and floating on the surface are several nice, juicy apples. Unless you are playing this game in the kitchen, it is wise to protect your carpet with some form of plastic covering. The players then have to kneel down and, without using their hands to steady the fruit, sink their heads into the water, bite into one of the bobbing apples and lift it clear. If two players are competing at the same time (this is only possible if you have a large tub), the first to emerge with an apple in his or her mouth is the winner. If players are competing individually, the contest could be decided on the basis of the fastest time. Anybody with loose dentures is advised to give this game a miss. To make the contest even more challenging, try blindfolding the players. Or you could try filling the tub with beer instead of water, the only problem being that certain guests will spend an inordinately long time below the surface and end up forgetting about the apples altogether.

FOX AND GEESE

Players: Any number

This game is energetic to the point of rowdiness and is therefore much loved by rugby players. It can be played either in a large room or out in the garden. One person is selected to be the mother goose and another, usually a man, to be the fox. The remainder of the players parade behind the mother goose and pretend to be little fluffy goslings, putting their arms around each other's waists to form a line. Obeying his instincts, the fox sets out to snatch as many goslings as possible but this act of carnage can only be done from the back of the line. In order to get to the back, the fox must use speed and cunning to evade the mother goose – he is not allowed to use physical force to push her out of the way. Once captured, each gosling is taken to one side (probably in preparation for the Paxo) and the ever-hungry fox tries to snatch another offspring. The more successful he gets, the harder his task becomes for it is much more difficult to avoid the mother's beak when the line behind her is short. This game is not suitable for vegans.

KANGAROO RACING

Players: Any number

You will need:

Balloons

Not a game for the faint hearted, 'Kangaroo Racing' is just one of a 101 silly things to do with balloons. Players line up at the start, each with a balloon between the knees, and on the command 'Go!', bound off down the course like kangaroos. Any racer who drops their balloon must reclaim it, replace it between their knees and start again from the spot where balloon and 'Skippy' parted company. A burst balloon results in instant disqualification. The winner is the first player to reach the finish with their balloon intact.

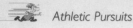

PASS THE CLIP

Players: Any even number

You will need:

A supply of paper clips

Players are divided into two teams which stand facing each other, about a yard apart. The members of each team stand with their wrists crossed in front of them so that they're clasping the opposite hands of the people on either side. At one end of each line is a small table on which are scattered a number of paper clips (one per team member). At the other end is another small table, this time empty. The game begins with the first player in line taking the hand of the player next to him or her and using it to pick up a paper clip. The second player passes it to the third player in similar fashion and it continues down the line until the last player, who has one hand free, deposits it on the table at the other end. Meanwhile, more paper clips have begun their journey from the top table. Players must keep their hands clasped to their team mates at all times and are not allowed to move their feet – although they may twist, bend and squirm their arms, legs and bodies where necessary. If a clip is dropped at any stage, the umpire picks it up and puts it back on the top table. The first team to transfer all its clips to the bottom table wins the game. Similar games can be played with oranges, apples or tennis balls.

PING-PONG PUFF

Players: 6-12

You will need:

Table tennis balls

This game is guaranteed to take your breath away. Played on a long table with a table tennis ball, it's just like the real thing except there's no net and instead of using bats, the players rely on sheer lung power. Players are divided into two teams who position themselves on opposite sides of the table. A table tennis ball is dropped into the middle of the table and the players have to try to blow the ball over the opposite edge which their opponents are defending. Each time they do so they score a point, the first team to reach 21 points being the winner. After each point, the ball is replaced in the centre of the table. Players must keep their hands behind their backs at all times. In a more refined version of the game, the players blow through straws to propel the ball.

ANKLE RACE

Players: 5-10

Excruciating embarrassment is never far away in an event which becomes increasingly unpredictable with each pint consumed. The competitors have to race bent over with a hand on each ankle. As they set off along the course as quickly as possible, they must keep hold of their ankles at all times. Any runner who lets go, albeit momentarily, or who trips and falls, must suffer the added indignity of having to return to the start and begin all over again. The first player to reach the finishing line in one piece is the winner. As even the most accomplished ankle racer can end up flat on his face at a moment's notice, it's essential to ensure that the course is cleared of all furniture…

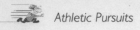

THE PENNY DROPS

Players: Any number

You will need:

A bucket of water, 50p and a supply of two-pence coins

This familiar activity, a favourite at summer fêtes, can serve as a welcome interlude during some of the more exhausting party games. A 50-pence piece is dropped into the bottom of a bucket of water and, from a standing position, each player attempts to drop a two-pence coin so that it comes to rest on top of the 50 pence. Whoever manages to do so experiences the additional satisfaction of winning the money.

THE GREAT GREY-GREEN GREASY LIMPOPO

Players: Any number

As if proof were ever needed that many adults are really just big kids, just watch them enjoy playing this long-standing children's favourite. The game can either be played inside in a large room or outside in the garden. The Limpopo River is marked with string across the centre of the room, or lawn, from one side to the other, its imaginary banks being about eight feet apart. One player is then chosen for the coveted role of the crocodile, while the other players are explorers who try to run back and forth across the river without being caught. If the crocodile manages to touch any of them, they are automatically tagged and obliged to join the crocodile in the river with a view to catching passers-by. All the parts of the crocodile must be linked physically at all times, usually with hands around the waist, and at least one part of the reptile's body must remain in the water. The winner is the last person to remain uncaptured, by which time everybody will be ready for another drink… but not from the waters of the great grey-green greasy Limpopo!

FLEET STREET

Players: Any number

You will need:

Old newspapers, pieces of card

Cut a dozen or so headlines from old newspapers. Each headline should be between six and nine words long and, most importantly, should be in a different typeface. If your choice is so restricted that you have to include two headlines with the same typeface, at least ensure that one is in block capitals while the other is in upper and lower case. Now cut each headline into four or five parts, leaving minor words such as 'the' or 'an' attached to the more significant ones. For example: 'CITY MAGISTRATES TO ACT ON INDECENT SHOWS' would be divided up thus: CITY/MAGISTRATES/TO ACT ON/INDECENT/SHOWS. These sections should then be pasted on to separate pieces of card. Words from more than one headline can be fixed to the same card, but be careful not to put two words from the same headline on the same card. In front of the first word in each headline, write an identifying letter (A, B, C etc) together with the total number of words in the headline so that the players know the extent of their search. Then distribute the various pieces of card around the house. By remembering the type faces and the subject matter, players have to reassemble the headlines in full and with the words in the correct order. The one with the most correct solutions in 20 minutes wins the game.

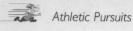
BROOM HOCKEY

Players: 8-12

You will need:

Two brooms, a rag, four chairs

Bring all the excitement of Olympic ice hockey into your own home with this robust team game. Although shoulder padding is not essential, matters can get out of hand and happily there is every potential for the sort of mass brawl which epitomises the sport. As will be gathered from the title, the sticks in this game are brooms and the puck is an old rag. The goals are marked by two pairs of chairs at either end of the room. Players divide into two teams and stand between their goalposts, the width of the goals thus dependent on the number of players. Before the match begins, each player is given a number. If there are 10 players, they'll be numbered one to five on each team. Play starts with the host placing the rag and the two brooms in the middle of the 'rink' and then calling out number one. At that point, the two number one players rush forward, seize their brooms and begin frantically sweeping the rag towards their opponent's goal. There, the other defending team members use their feet to try to prevent the rag from being forced between the chairs, and this is where things can get a shade physical as bare ankles come into contact with solid broom handles. It has been known for defenders to stand on the broom head in a bid to immobilise the attacker. Whenever a goal is scored, the rag and brooms are returned to the centre and the next player numbers are called out. Fifteen minutes is probably quite long enough for this game, by which time a couple of your guests might already have been taken to casualty.

CUT THE TAPE

Players: 3-6

You will need:

Lengths of ribbon, pairs of scissors, drawing pins

Cut a roll of ribbon into roughly identical lengths, one length per player, and then pin one end of each length firmly to the wall. Arm each player with a pair of scissors and position them at the other ends of the ribbon. Their task is simply to cut their piece of ribbon into two lengths all the way along. The first to reach the end wins. Anyone who veers from a true line and accidentally cuts a piece off is disqualified. This may sound easy but it is quite a challenge, especially after a few drinks, and you have to face the very real prospect that there will be no winner, in which case you can either bestow victory upon the player who made the furthest progress or save yourself having to give anybody a prize.

TOSSING THE EGG

Players: 12 or over

You will need:

A supply of eggs

Unless you are either in the throes of moving or redecorating, this is definitely a game best played in the garden and preferably in old clothes. Two marker lines are laid out with string, about 10 feet apart, and the players are divided into teams of six or more people. Half the members of each team station themselves on one side of one marker line with the other half on the other side of the second marker line. The members of both halves of each team stand in single file, facing each other. Then comes the messy part. The respective team leaders are each given an egg and, on the shout of 'Go!', have to toss their egg to their waiting team mate opposite who has to catch it one-handed. Two-handed catches are strictly illegal and a broken egg results in elimination. As soon as a player tosses an egg, he or she steps out of the line to make way for his or her next team mate. The game continues in this manner until every team member has had a turn. When the team leader steps up to the marker line once more and successfully catches the egg, the game is over and that team is the winner. For a less-hazardous encounter, you could always use hard-boiled eggs.

SARDINES

Players: Any number

If you need to recharge your batteries at any point in the party, what better than a quiet lie-down somewhere private, particularly when it can be played within the framework of a game such as 'Sardines'? Apparently, this was once played by Queen Victoria, who may or not have been amused by the prospect of a dozen subjects secreting themselves beneath her voluminous dress. 'Sardines' is a proven favourite with all age groups. The rules are straightforward enough. One person is allowed three minutes to hide somewhere in the house, after which all of the lights are switched off and the others grope around in the dark in search of the missing player. Whenever someone finds him (or her), they have to join him in that place – be it under a bed (or in it), in the larder or even the coal cellar (the oven is not recommended, especially if it's on at the time) – whilst doing their utmost to make sure that they're not seen by any of the others. As each person discovers the hiding place, they too join the fugitives. The game continues until there's only one searcher left. Besides being an enjoyable way of filling half an hour (all the more so depending on who you're pressed up against), 'Sardines' is also an excellent way of getting rid of the party bore for a while. All you have to do is send him off to hide and then forget about him for an hour or three.

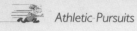

FAN THE KIPPER

Players: 4-8

You will need:

Newspapers and magazines, string

This deceptively violent game is another where the decks have to be cleared to allow for an obstacle-free course. Cut a page from a newspaper or magazine into the rough shape of a large kipper (you need one kipper per player) and drape lengths of string across opposite ends of the room, one acting as the start line, the other as the finish. Then give each player their kipper and a magazine, the aim being to propel one's kipper along the course by wafting the magazine behind it. Be warned, some players resort to thrashing the magazine at the floor, creating more of a hurricane than a gentle breeze giving the neighbours the distinct impression that the Horse of the Year Show is taking place in your lounge. There are rules governing the amount of force which can be used to speed up the kipper's progress. Kicking or molesting the aforementioned fish or prodding it with the magazine are all strictly forbidden and will result in instant disqualification, as will deliberately obstructing a fellow competitor. The winner is the first player to coerce their kipper across the finish line without cheating.

PEANUT PICK-UP

Players: 5-10

You will need:

Peanuts, cocktail sticks, paper bags

This game requires concentration, composure and unerring accuracy and is therefore much more entertaining when played by people who are in the early stages of inebriation. Each player is handed two cocktail sticks and a small paper bag and is told to use the sticks to pick up the collection of peanuts which have been strewn across the floor. At some parties the host will find it necessary to scatter the peanuts on the carpet personally, at others he or she can just let events take their natural course and rely on the general untidiness of the guests. Using the cocktail sticks like chopsticks, the players crawl about the floor lifting the peanuts into the paper bag. Naturally, you are not allowed to use your hands to pick up the nuts directly. When all of the peanuts have been gathered, the player with the most bulging bag is declared the winner.

BACK AND FORTH

Players: Any even number

You will need:

Large bowls or casserole dishes, a quantity of objects

Two teams, each with the same number of members, stand sideways in parallel lines. On the floor at one end of each team line are two large containers, such as a glass bowl, casserole dish or bucket. One of each pair of vessels is empty but the other contains a number of diverse objects – ideally there should be at least three times as many objects in each container as there are members in each team. On the command 'Go!', the first player picks an object from the vessel and passes it to the next person and so on down the line. When it reaches the far end, it begins the return journey but this time instead of players handing it to one another in front of them, it is passed behind their backs. Meanwhile, other objects will be making the outward journey, thus forcing players to switch their hands hastily from front to back. The game is over when all of one team's objects have completed both the outward and return journeys and have been deposited in the second container. The degree of difficulty can be compounded by the objects chosen. The best items are those which are tricky or particularly slippery to handle. Although the pet goldfish meets these criteria perfectly, he'll doubtless prefer it if you leave him in his bowl and use, say, a bar of wet soap instead. Other suitable objects include a hot potato, a peeled banana, a drawing pin and, depending on your circle of friends, a condom.

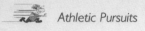
IDENTIKIT

Players: Any number

You will need:

Magazines or colour supplements, pieces of card, sticky tape, pencils and paper

Cut out large portrait-sized photographs of the faces of 10 famous people from magazines or colour supplements. If possible, use cover shots from the same magazine so that the paper will be of uniform texture and therefore offer fewer clues. Next, cut each photo into four sections – hair, eyes, nose and mouth – and paste or stick each one on to a separate piece of numbered card. So with 10 subjects, there will be 40 cards. Finally, place the cards in strategic positions around the house, supply the players with pencils and paper and tell them that they have 15 minutes in which to piece the faces together by writing down the correct four card numbers that bear the features of each individual celebrity. If somebody produces an identikit which turns out to have Michelle Pfeiffer's hair, Sean Bean's eyes, Anthea Turner's nose and Jimmy Hill's chin, suggest they see an optician immediately.

NAME THE FACE

Players: Any number

You will need:

Newspapers or magazines, sticky tape, pieces of card, pencils and paper

This game also involves cutting out photographs of people from newspapers or magazines, but here it works better if the subjects aren't famous. Therefore a local paper may be your best source of material. Select around 20 photos and stick each one onto a separate piece of numbered card. Below each picture attach a slip of paper bearing a first name. This does not have to be the real name of the person in the photo – it can be any name you fancy. It's a good idea to choose a few similar names – Ralph and Rolf, Graham and Graeme, Anne, Anna and Annabel – just to confuse the players. Distribute the cards around the house and then give the players seven or eight minutes to try and memorise which name goes with which face. At the end of the time limit, collect the cards, remove the name slips and give each player a pencil and paper. Then hold up each card in turn and ask the players to write down the name that goes with it.

BASH THE BALLOON

Players: Any number

You will need:

A balloon, a blindfold, a newspaper

In this vigorous pastime, blindfolded players take it in turns to wield a rolled-up newspaper and vent their frustrations on a balloon. All of the players stand in a circle with the exception of the one whose turn it is to be blindfolded. He or she stands in the centre of the circle with rolled-up newspaper in hand. A balloon is then lobbed into the circle and, amidst cries of 'Bash the Balloon!', the player has three attempts to deliver a blow. If the balloon is hit on the first strike, three points are scored; a second-strike hit earns two points and a third-strike success one point. Bursting the balloon with any blow earns a five-point bonus – a rule which can lead to scenes of excessive violence and complaints from half the street. Failure to hit the balloon at all means no points are scored. When everyone has competed, the points are added up and the player with the highest score is the winner. In the event of a tie, there is a play-off.

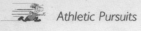

MATCHBOX

Players: Any even number

You will need:

Matchboxes

Those who somehow manage to cram every conceivable item into their case when going on holiday – including three hairdryers, a dozen paperback novels and the microwave oven just in case the food isn't up to much – will surely relish the opportunity to take part in a packing contest on a considerably smaller scale. Players pair-off for this game, each duo being given a matchbox and orders to fill it with as many different articles as they can. They are permitted to search the house and garden but must not include more than one specimen of the same object – in other words 48 blades of grass. The winning pair are the ones who have managed to squeeze the most items into the box… as long as they've not made off with the host's jewellery.

AEROPLANES

Players: Teams of 3

You will need:

Plastic or paper cups, lengths of twine

Each team of three players is issued with a 15-foot length of twine and a plastic or paper cup in the bottom of which has been cut a hole just large enough for the twine to pass through unhindered. Each team threads their length of twine through their cup. Two team members hold the ends of the twine, keeping it taut, while the third acts as blower. Before the race begins, the cup is moved along to the end of the twine which faces the open top of the cup. With all of the cups in position, the starter gets the race underway and the team blowers immediately start puffing into the open ends so as to advance their cup along the twine course as rapidly as possible. The winner is the first to reach the other end. Anyone caught smearing lubricant on his or her twine to achieve a faster passage is liable to be excluded from the next game.

SOCK FISHING

Players: 6 or more

You will need:

Long socks, a variety of small objects

The object of this team game is straightforward enough – to be the first to remove a series of small items in the correct order from a man's sock, preferably one that has been washed within the last six months. Having sought out one sock per team, fill it with small objects, about a dozen in all. The range could include buttons, pebbles, beans (not baked in tomato sauce), hairpins, paper clips and coins of different sizes. To confuse the players, try and find items which feel similar. Play begins with each team leader holding a filled sock. The host calls out the first object to be found and the first players on each team rummage in the sock. They are only allowed to pull out one item at a time. If it's the right one, they take it to the host; if they are wrong they must try again. When the first object has been handed in, the host calls out the second article and the next player goes for a lucky dip. The game continues like this until the last item has been successfully located.

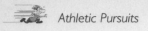

KICK THE CAN

Players: 6 or more

You will need:

A biscuit tin or can

This hectic game is best played in the garden, although a large room cleared of furniture would also suffice. A biscuit tin or a can is placed in the middle of the lawn (or room) and one player is elected to guard it. Given the physical nature of this game, it is best if that person is muscular, fearless and rugged. Or you could choose a man. It is the guard's job to prevent any of the other players from kicking the tin by touching them in a tag-like fashion. Anyone tagged is temporarily eliminated and must stand by the tin. But when another player manages to force his or her way past the guard to kick the tin, all captured players are immediately released. The game continues in this vein until either everyone has been captured or sheer exhaustion has set in. If there are more than eight players, two guards are chosen to protect the tin.

POTATO RACE

Players: 5-10

You will need:

Potatoes, bowls, table knives, chairs

Place up to five chairs facing inwards at either end of the room. On each of the chairs at one end, put three large potatoes and on each of the opposite chairs place a bowl. Each player is assigned a chair with the potatoes and a table knife and, on the command 'Go!', must pick up a potato on the flat end of the knife and carry it across to the bowl on the other side of the room. If a potato falls to the floor en route, it must be picked up with the knife. No hands are allowed to touch the potatoes once the race is under way. The first player to deposit all three potatoes in the bowl is the winner. To accommodate more players, potato racing can be staged over two heats and a final, the fastest two from each heat going through to the eliminator. If you're contemplating buying a new carpet, you can play this game with eggs.

SCAVENGER HUNT

Players: 10 or more

You will need:

Pencils and paper

Short of calling a fire drill, there is no easier way of getting your guests out of the house for half an hour than by staging a 'Scavenger Hunt'. Before the party, you need to come up with a list of 20 or so articles – the more unusual the better – which can be found in your house, garden or immediate environs. You must be specific in your descriptions so that there is no room for misconception. It is not enough to say a leaf, for example, you must say an oak leaf. The players are divided into teams and each is given a list of the items to be found. They are then given 30 minutes to bring back as many things on the list as possible, the usual tactic being for the teams to split up and search for individual items. The sort of things you could include are: a blonde hair, a photograph of your family, a Boyzone poster, a book about Genghis Khan, a garden gnome, a bra, a Peter Rabbit alarm clock, a table mat depicting Ye Olde Fighting Cocks Inn at St. Albans and a cuddly hippo. If you're conducting a running feud with your neighbour, you may of course be tempted to include his prize-winning chrysanthemums on the list of items to be retrieved.

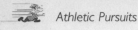

WASTEPAPER BASKETBALL

Players: Any number

You will need:

A wastepaper basket, a rubber ball

This innocuous diversion keeps your guests occupied while you prepare the next big game. All you do is place a wastepaper basket next to a wall and see how many people can bounce a spongy ball once on the floor and then into the basket from a distance of around three yards. Each player is allowed three attempts, anyone who fails to score a single basket being eliminated from the competition. Those who succeed move on to the next round where the distance increases to four yards. The distance between player and basket continues to increase with each round until there is either just one person left, or your guests are stopping traffic in order to take aim from the middle of the street.

NOSE BALL

Players: 5-10

You will need:

Table tennis balls, pieces of string

If you've suffered all your life from having a big nose, this is where you finally come into your own. In this game a sizeable snout is definitely an advantage over a cute little snub nose. Lengths of string are stretched across either end of the room to denote the start and finish lines and each player places a table tennis ball on the start line. Kneeling behind their ball, they then have to nuzzle it along the course, the winner being the first to cross the finish line. If competitors are caught using any part of their anatomy other than their nose they will have to return to the start. Sneezing is also forbidden.

OBSTACLE COURSE

Players: Any number

You will need:

Blindfolds

A great favourite with practical jokers, this game can only be played once with the same group of people because it's an experience they're unlikely ever to forget. An obstacle course is laid out in the lounge, complete with tipped-up chairs, glassware, the best china tea service, marbles and drawing pins. Volunteers are enlisted and are led around the course once before being taken away to another room and blindfolded. In their absence, all of the obstacles are cleared away. Blissfully unaware of the subterfuge, the first blindfolded volunteer is brought in and taken gingerly around the non-existent course by one of the devious party goers. After stepping delicately over thin air and ducking under imaginary dangers, the poor victim is finally told that the ordeal is over. Only when the blindfold is removed does acute embarrassment sink in. When composure has been regained, the victim derives enormous pleasure from leading in the next unsuspecting performer. The game continues until the novelty wears off.

WHAT'S THE TIME, MR WOLF?

Players: 6 or more

This extremely silly game can be played either indoors or out. One player is chosen to be Mr Wolf and stands at one end of the room or lawn whilst the others, who are all rabbits, stand at the other end behind a marker line. The confrontation begins with the rabbits all calling out: 'What's the time, Mr Wolf?' (Now you know why you need a few drinks to play this game). Mr Wolf replies: 'Two o'clock' or 'six o'clock' or any number up to 12. Whichever number the wolf calls out, the rabbits take the corresponding number of bunny hops forward. After a few goes, the rabbits will be quite close to Mr Wolf and it is then that his reply to the standard question might suddenly change to 'dinner time'. Hearing those dreaded words, the rabbits turn tail and scurry back towards the safety of their line. Any caught by Mr Wolf before reaching sanctuary are enlisted as trainee wolves and thereafter may also devour rabbits on the call of 'dinner time'. The winner is the last rabbit left alive.

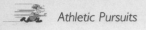

THE BELL GAME

Players: Any number

You will need:

Blindfolds, rolled-up newspapers, string of bells

Another faintly ridiculous game, this sees sensible adults, pillars of the community perhaps, trying to swat someone with rolled-up newspapers while wearing blindfolds. To add to the sense of folly, their victim has bells on. The game begins with all players but one being blindfolded and given a rolled-up newspaper. The player who is not blindfolded has a string of small bells hanging around his or her neck. As the action gets under way, the blindfolded players listen carefully to ascertain the precise whereabouts of the bells and endeavour to bash the jingling one with their newspapers while the latter attempts to dodge their blows. In the event of a direct hit, the successful assailant takes over the bells and the victim joins the blindfolded attackers. Note: any morris dancers present may take offence at this game.

CONUNDRUMS

Players: Any number

You will need:

Pieces of card, pencils and paper

Write out a selection of a dozen or more riddles, such as: 'When is a door not a door? – when it's ajar' or 'Why don't elephants like penguins? – because they can't get the wrappers off'. Give each question a number and each answer a letter and then scatter them on separate pieces of card around the house. Next, give the players 20 minutes to pair off the correct combinations by writing down the relevant number and letter. There are no short cuts, for even if they know the answer to the riddle, they still have to find the letter of the card on which it is written.

CITRUS CHALLENGE

Players: 5-10

You will need:

Lemons, tablespoons, two lengths of string

The two pieces of string are placed at opposite ends of the room, one acting as the start line, the other as a turning line. Each player is given a lemon and a tablespoon and, touching the lemon only with their spoon, must roll the fruit from the start to the turning line and back again, the first to do so being the winner. As an alternative to an individual race, this noble sport can be staged as a team relay.

CRUMMOCK

Players: 10 or more

You will need:

A supply of hats, umbrellas and children's spades, tennis ball or cabbage

The list of requirements suggests immediately that 'Crummock' is no ordinary game. Played in a garden or large room, it is a cross between hockey, lacrosse, hurling and The Clothes Show. The basic premise is conventional enough. There are two teams, a goal at either end of the pitch and the object is to put the ball into the opposing goal. However, the implement for hitting the ball is decidedly unorthodox and is basically anything that comes to hand. Devices have included umbrellas, children's spades and cricket stumps. Garden spades should be avoided for safety reasons. And whilst the game is usually played with a ball, the more avant-garde may prefer to use a cabbage or firm rounded lettuce. There is one more rule – players must wear a hat at all times. If you lose your headgear at any stage of the match, you are not allowed to continue until you have somehow managed to acquire a replacement. Consequently some players spend the whole game knocking off opponent's hats rather than pursuing the ball. It can surely only be a matter of time before Sky acquire the TV rights to 'Crummock'.

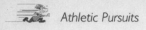

BLIND MAN'S BUFF

Players: Any number

You will need:

A blindfold

Arguably the oldest party game of all, 'Blind Man's Buff' remains a firm favourite with players of all ages. One player is blindfolded and staggers around the room trying to lay hands on any of the other participants. If someone is caught, the blindfolded person has to guess who it is. A correct guess results in the two exchanging places.

ADAM AND EVE

Players: Any number

You will need:

A blindfold

Of all the variations of Blind Man's Buff, this is one of the most entertaining. All but two of the players stand in a large circle holding hands. Inside the circle are a boy and a girl representing Adam and Eve, although fig leaves are optional. The boy, alias Adam, is blindfolded. The game starts with him calling out: 'Eve!' – to which she must reply: 'Over here, Adam!' He then gropes around in the dark trying to catch her. Whenever he calls for her, she must answer and she must remain within the circle. There is a time limit of two minutes and if Adam fails to catch Eve within that period, he keeps his blindfold and she changes places with another girl. If, on the other hand, Adam apprehends Eve in time, he hands his blindfold to her and swaps places with another boy. Eve then has to try to catch the new Adam. With the right people, this game has been known to lead to deep and meaningful relationships.

FOOTLOOSE

Players: Any number

After removing their shoes and putting them in the middle of the room, players plunge into the pile in an unseemly mêlée and mix up the footwear. Then everyone retreats to the corners of the room to wait for the lights to be switched off. Once the room is in total darkness, the scrum begins again as the players have just two minutes in which to find their shoes and put them on the correct feet. This game can get a little rough and is therefore not ideal for spinsters of the parish and maiden aunts, unless they happen to be black belts in karate.

MY MOTHER'S CAKE

Players: Any even number

Two teams sit in rows facing each other with their legs outstretched so that their feet are touching (this game can be played barefoot if desired). Each player is given the name of an ingredient in a cake recipe. The host then tells a story about how the cake was made, in the course of which the various ingredients are referred to. Whenever players hear the name of their ingredient, they must run up between the two lines, vaulting over the outstretched legs, before running back down behind their team to return to their original place. The fun starts when there are two or three ingredients mentioned in quick succession, all racing around at the same time, and when a player sits down breathlessly, only to be forced into action again straight away.

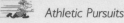

HOP, STEP, JUMP AND CRAWL

Players: 6 or more

This game is an admirable test of players' ingenuity... as well as making them look remarkably silly. The participants line up elbow to elbow and the first in the line moves forward a few yards in a distinctive manner – maybe a John Cleese silly walk, or by hopping, crawling, walking backwards, bottom shuffling or, for the particularly athletic, walking on their hands. Each of the other players in turn must then move forward the same distance but by a different method to any previous competitor. And so the game continues in rotation with every player trying to think of some new form of motion. Anyone who fails to come up with something new is eliminated. The last player left in is the winner.

BIRDS OF A FEATHER

Players: 5-10

You will need:

Feathers, plates

Each player is given a plate with a feather on it and on the command 'Go!' they have to race to the finish line while taking care not to lose their feather. The plate must be held at the side so that the hands have no contact with the feather. The use of glue to stick the feather to the plate is also forbidden. The game is definitely a case of more haste less speed because if the feather drifts away during the race, that player has to return to the start. The winner is the first person to cross the finish line with the feather still on the plate.

INCONGRUITIES

Players: Any number

You will need:

Pencils and paper

This game tests your guests' powers of observation. Prepare for the game by placing familiar objects in strange places around the house – such as a razor on the
mantelpiece or a mustard dish in the bathroom. All objects must be in full view.
Give each player pencil and paper and send them around the house in search of as
many incongruities as they can find in 10 minutes. The one to spot the most things
out of place is the winner. This game does not work well in a naturally
untidy house...

GRAND NATIONAL

Players: 6 or more

You will need:

Potatoes, brooms, paper plates, chairs, a length of string

This is a silly relay game in which teams have to ride a broomstick to a turning line
and back while balancing a potato on a plate on their head. Players are allowed to
grip the plate with one hand but must not hold down the potato. If the potato falls
off, they have to pick it up before they can continue. To make things even more
interesting for spectators, tie a length of string between two chairs, about a foot
off the ground, to form a fence halfway round the course. This obstacle has to be
jumped by the competitors. As they complete the course, the racers hand their
broomstick, potato and plate over to the next member of their team. The game
continues in this fashion until all the members of one team have fully negotiated
the course successfully. With three or more 'horses' racing round at the same time,
there are frequent fallers, refusals and even stewards' inquiries.

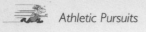
SOCKS APPEAL

Players: 5-10

You will need:

Pairs of socks, pairs of thick gloves, blindfolds

Before you play this game, you will need to provide an assortment of old socks and thick gloves, one pair of gloves per player. These should be unwieldy garments such as gardening gloves or oven gloves. The socks are piled up in the middle of the room and players are told to put a glove on each hand, but not a matching pair. The players are then blindfolded. On the command 'Go!', they must locate the pile of socks and, still gloved, put on as many pairs of socks as they can in a time limit of 10 minutes. The player wearing the most socks at the end of the 10 minutes wins the game. If any blindfolded competitor has difficulty finding the pile in the first place, he or she can be discreetly pointed in the right direction.

CROCODILE RACE

Players: 10 or more

Players divide into teams of equal numbers and form lines at one end of the room. They then squat on their heels and place their hands on the shoulders or waist of the person in front to form a stunningly realistic crocodile. When the signal is given to start the race, the crocodiles move forward in jumps and bounces until they reach the far end of the room. There they must turn and head back to the start/finish line. If at any time in the race a player loses contact with the person in front, that team must stop and re-group. To do this, the tail end of the crocodile must stay where it is while the front end goes back to join it. The reputation of the crocodile as a mean, efficient speed machine can be severely damaged by this game.

GUESS THE LEADER

Players: Any number

Depending on the personnel involved, 'Guess the Leader' can either be a gentle, sedate game or decidedly raucous and unruly. It begins with one player being sent out of the room – he or she becomes the guesser. Meanwhile, the others gather round and choose a leader who explains that, from then on, they must follow precisely whatever the leader does. When the guesser returns, he or she has to observe the various actions performed by the group and decide which of them is the leader. At first the leader's movements will probably be relatively simple – a spot of hand clapping and arm waving – but they may become increasingly curious, incorporating rolling around on the floor with legs in the air, impersonating Long John Silver or rubbing bottoms with the person next in line. Unless you all happen to be particularly close friends, anything stronger than nibbling ear lobes is inadvisable. The key to success is for the leader to switch actions when the guesser is studying the other players. When the leader is identified, he or she assumes the role of guessing.

BALLOON FIGHT

Players: Any number

You will need:

Balloons, newspapers, pieces of string

Even at the height of Culloden, Waterloo or Bosworth Field, the ferocity of combat did not match that of the average balloon fight. Each player ties a balloon to his or her ankle with a piece of string and, wielding a rolled-up newspaper, endeavours to defend the balloon against other players' attempts to burst it while simultaneously trying to burst theirs. No balloons may be burst by hand or by sharp implements. Any player who does suffer the ignominy of a burst balloon is eliminated, the last player left is declared the winner.

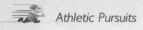

TV TITLES

Players: 4-15

You will need:

Pieces of card, pencils and paper

Compile a list of about 40 well-known television programmes (all with more than one-word titles) and split the titles in half as in LAST OF THE/SUMMER WINE. Write all of the second halves on separate pieces of card and distribute them in cunningly concealed places around the house. Give each player the first half of a title and send him or her away to find the slip bearing the second half. When the appropriate second section has been located, the player brings it back to you and is issued with a new title to find. The winner is the player who has tracked down most titles when you call time (a period of 20 minutes is reasonable).

MARBLE RACE

Players: 4-8

You will need:

Pencils, marbles, blindfolds

Blindfolded players have to carry a marble balanced on two pencils along an indoor course with at least one bend in it. The pencils must be held with arms out-stretched. Onlookers may assist in verbally steering the players in the right direction and can also replace any dropped marbles on to the pencils. This event works best as a knock-out competition with two players racing against each other, the winner progressing to the next round.

BANG

Players: Any even number

You will need:

Chairs, a cushion

The principal requirement to playing this game successfully is an ability not to betray your emotions through the expression on your face. Players are split into two teams who sit opposite each other. To one side of the room is a chair with a cushion on it. Each team writes the names of the opposing team members on separate slips of paper. Team A then places one of the slips beneath the cushion and invites any member of team B to go and sit on that chair. The aim of the game is to avoid sitting on your own name. If you do, the opposing team chorus loudly: 'Bang!' and you are effectively dead and therefore out of the game. If it is not your name however, you return to your team unscathed. It is then team B's turn to select a name to be put under the cushion and so the game continues until one team has been completely wiped out. The important thing is not to appear too excited when you know that any of your opponents are about to sit on their own name. For seasoned performers will be on the lookout for telltale signs even as they lower their bottom into position. If they suspect something is amiss, they can pull out at the last minute and return to their team, as long as buttocks and cushion have not actually come into contact.

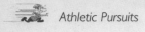

PEANUT HUNT

Players: Any number

You will need:

Peanuts, paper bags, blindfolds

This is a slight variation on the earlier game, Peanut Pick-Up. Pigs at feeding time pale in comparison to the undignified sight of adults scrambling about the floor hunting for peanuts. The players are blindfolded, given a paper bag and told to search for the peanuts which are scattered around the room. After five minutes of frantic activity, the blindfolds are removed and a count is made to see who has collected the most peanuts. The game works best with large numbers of people, particularly when five or six converge on the same stray peanut.

BACK-TO-BACK RACE

Players: Any even number

Players form pairs and line up at one end of the room back-to-back with their arms linked. At the off, they must race to the far end of the room and back again, keeping their arms linked at all times. Any couple who become untangled must return to the start. Where possible, it is always advisable for the front runner to be the heavier partner in each pair as he or she will have to do any pulling. A slim girl dragging along a burly hod carrier could result in a fairly slow lap time.

HOBBY HORSE

Players: Any even numbers

Few people of sound mind would attempt this game but, if sufficient alcohol has been consumed beforehand, that is unlikely to disqualify any of your company from taking part. It sounds simple enough – players have to carry their fellow team members across the room one by one – but the catch is that the same method of transportation cannot be employed twice by the same team. So whilst the first carriers will probably play reasonably safe with fireman's lifts and piggy backs, the last to go have to come up with something infinitely more imaginative. Styles such as piggy back front-to-front suggest that mating is imminent and could lead to disquiet in some quarters, as could the sight of collapsed couples writhing around on the floor. Those with hernias should opt to be baggage.

THE WARDROBE GAME

Players: Any number

You will need:

Two overnight bags, four night-caps, four large nightdresses, four pairs of slippers, four dressing-gowns

Players are split up into two teams which are then sub-divided into pairs. The first couple in each team are given an overnight bag containing two night-caps, two large nightdresses, two pairs of slippers and two dressing-gowns. Starting from one end of the room, they have to carry their bags to two chairs situated at the opposite end, take off their shoes, put on the night-caps, nightdresses, slippers and dressing-gowns, run round their chair once, take all the nightclothes off again, put their own shoes back on, repack their bags and race back to the start where they hand over to the next couple. The relay continues until the final couple in one team cross the finish line complete with repacked bag. The sight of grown men running around in nightdresses is more than enough justification for including this game in your party. The worrying time is when they appear to be enjoying it.

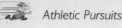

PASS THE BONNET

Players: Any even number

You will need:

Two large bonnets, two large pairs of bedsocks

This is another dressing-up game which can cause a certain amount of embarrassment to the more staid members of the male community. To ensure the maximum unease, you need to prepare two outrageous bonnets with ribbons, the sort of headgear that Mrs Shilling used to wear at Royal Ascot. Instead of the traditional fruit, why not go for a bonnet laden with vegetables? How about parsnips, beetroot and carrots with the odd cucumber thrown in for good effect, and topped by a huge model wheelbarrow? Whatever you come up with, divide the players into two teams and line them up in rows for an exciting contest. The first player in each team dons the bonnet, tying it beneath the chin and, after removing shoes, puts on an outsize pair of bedsocks. The second player then undoes the ribbons, puts on the bonnet, ties the ribbons, removes his or her shoes and player one's bedsocks and puts on the bedsocks. It carries on like this along the line until every team member has worn the bonnet and bedsocks, at which point that team is declared the winner.

IDENTICAL TWINS

Players: Any number

You will need:

Two packs of playing cards

This is a team game in which players have to search the house for hidden playing cards. Before the party, you should place all 52 cards from one pack in various places around the house. However, they should not be concealed to the extent that guests have to set about demolishing your home in order to reach the ace of spades. Instead have one card protruding slightly from the pages of a book or another resting beneath an ornament – but not a valuable family heirloom. The game starts with each player being given a playing card and told to find its identical twin. When a card is found and returned to you, make a note of that person's team and give him or her another card to locate. At the end of the time limit (around 20 minutes is ideal) tot up the points to find out which team is the winner. Players will soon learn to make a mental note of any other card they stumble across while searching for their own, just in case they have to look for that one later. And, of course, they can help their team mates by telling them where a certain card is hidden. It might be best to whisper such information lest the enemy be listening in.

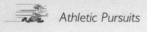

WAITER!

Players: Any number

You will need:

Table tennis balls, paper plates

In this team game, the members stand in lines with just enough space between each player to allow one of their number to weave in and out at speed. The first player carries a paper plate in the reverse palm of his or her hand – waiter-fashion. On the plate is a table tennis ball, denoting the breakfast egg. That player must run in and out of his or her team mates, announcing to each: 'Your breakfast is served, sir (or madam).' When he or she completes the slalom course and runs back to the starting point, the plate and table tennis ball are handed over to the second player who sets off on a new run with player one becoming the first person in the new line. If the ball is dropped at any stage (and no hands can be used to hold it down), the player has to go back to the start of that run. The first team to have every player complete the run wins the game.

RABBIT RACE

Players: 2-6

You will need:

Cardboard, chairs, lengths of string

There is nothing like a fast, all-action race to bring the party to fever pitch, even if the participants are nothing more than cardboard rabbits. The first thing you need to do to prepare for this game is to cut out the rabbits. There must be one rabbit per player and they should be identical in every respect – no sticking a fluffy cotton wool bobtail onto one because it will slow it down. Lastly pierce a hole in the centre of each bunny's head – it may sound cruel, but remember they are only cardboard. Once you have made your racing rabbits, line up a row of chairs – one for for each rabbit – and tie a length of string, about twelve feet long, to the back of each chair. Thread the strings through the holes in the rabbits' heads and place the animals at the start line. Now the players take over. At the off, they seize the loose end of the string and, by relaxing and tightening the string, the rabbit is inched forward towards the chair. For swifter progress, it is important that the rabbit should be inclined slightly towards the chair. Having reached the chair, the rabbits must turn for home. To make the rabbits change direction, the players need to waggle the string and tighten and relax it quickly. Again ensure that the rabbit is leaning towards the direction in which it is supposed to be heading. The first player to get his or her rabbit back to the start line wins a Fatal Attraction video.

NUTS AND APPLES

Players: Any number

You will need:

Nuts, apples, teaspoons, knives

Give each player a teaspoon and a blunt knife and ask them to stand at the opposite end of the room to a large table laden with assorted nuts and small apples. On the command 'Go!', they run over to the table with the spoon in their left hand and the knife in their right and attempt to scoop a nut onto the knife and an apple into the teaspoon. Obviously, with a mighty Granny Smith this is nigh on impossible, so smaller varieties should be provided. With both foodstuffs in place, the players must then dash back to the start/finish line, the first to cross it with nut and apple intact being the winner. Anyone who drops either item must get down on their hands and knees and try to recover it. This has been known to take some time. In fact, if you come downstairs the following morning and find any hapless guest still on all fours struggling to retrieve their nut and apple, it is kindest to put them out of their misery and allow them to go home.

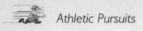

PEG-IN-THE-BOTTLE

Players: Any number

You will need:

Clothes pegs, empty milk bottles

A game of undoubted skill, this is eminently suitable for the less athletic among your guests. Divide the players into teams of four and supply each team with an empty milk bottle (a jam-jar will do) and 12 clothes pegs. Taking it in turns, each player stands with their feet together a couple of inches behind their team's bottle and tries to drop the clothes pegs into the bottle from the height of their nose. They must keep their feet together and hold their body up straight. Each player is allowed three attempts and any peg which misses may not be used again. When each of the players has had their go, the victorious team is calculated by adding up the total number of pegs in each bottle.

WHISTLE FOR YOUR SUPPER

Players: Any number

You will need:

A supply of water biscuits, chairs

Players line up in equal-numbered teams on the opposite side of the room to a row of chairs (one per team). The game starts with the first players in each team running over to the appropriate chair, sitting down on it and eating a water biscuit as quickly as possible. Having devoured the whole biscuit, they must then try to whistle. The sound doesn't have to be as clear as a Roger Whittaker solo, but it must be a definite whistle rather than just a blow. When the judge approves the whistling note, they race back to their line and hand over to the next player. And so it continues until one team has finished.

WITCH HUNT

Players: Any number

In truth this is nothing more than an excuse for adults to play hide and seek but what's wrong with that? One player is chosen to be the witch and, after turning off all of the lights, goes away to find a suitable place to hide. Five minutes later, the witch hunters set off in pursuit, still in total darkness. As they stumble around the furniture, they are allowed two cries of 'Where are you, Witchy?' to which the witch must reply with an eerie cackle. But there is nothing to prevent the witch moving somewhere else after each cackle. Whoever eventually succeeds in catching the witch dons the mantle for the next instalment. To add to the atmosphere, it is a nice touch to supply the witch with a pointed hat and a cloak. However, the authenticity should stop there and under no circumstances should any attempt be made to carry out Trial by Ordeal.

GENERAL POST

Players: Any number

You will need:

A blindfold, chairs

All of the players except one sit in a circle and call out the name of a town which is written down by you, the postmaster. The other person is placed in the middle of the circle and blindfolded. The postmaster then chooses two towns and announces: 'The post is going from Chipping Sodbury to Arbroath' or wherever. At that point, the two players whose towns are Chipping Sodbury and Arbroath must rush to change places without being caught by the person in the blindfold. Anyone who is caught takes a turn in the middle. But the greatest pandemonium occurs when the postmaster suddenly calls out: 'General Post!', for then every player must find a new seat without being caught and the country's post ends up in a bigger mess than it is anyway.

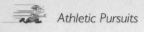
PANCAKE RACE

Players: 6-12

You will need:

Squares of newspaper, garden canes

For this ingenious re-enactment of Shrove Tuesday, you will need two pieces of newspaper, about a foot square, and four garden canes, each around three feet long. Each square of paper represents a pancake and two canes, held one in each hand, represent a frying pan. The players are divided into two teams and their aim is to pick up a 'pancake' from the floor at one end of the room with the 'frying pan' and carry it as quickly as they can to a table at the other end of the room. They then have to pick up the 'pancake' again, transfer it back to its original place on the floor and hand over to the next team member… and so on until one team has finished. Patience is definitely a virtue in this game as any hurried movement will result in your 'pancake' floating out of the 'pan'. So steady progress is the order of the day.

WOBBLY BOSOMS

Players: Any number

You will need:

Balloons filled with water

Unless you are prepared for a soaking, 'Wobbly Bosoms' calls for steady nerves and even steadier hands. Some homeowners would prefer to play this game outside, or at least on an easily mopped surface. Fill a number of balloons with water and carefully seal them up. Then gather all the players close together and start a nice gentle game of catch. Anyone who flinches at the crucial moment of catching the water-filled balloon risks either dropping it or, worse still, having it explode on them. In either case the penalty is elimination from the game. The winner of the game is the driest at the end.

STEPPING STONES

Players: 8 or more

You will need:

Shoeboxes

This is a team game where half of each team stand at one end of the room with the other half at the opposite end. The first player in each team is given two lidless shoeboxes and the race gets under way with him or her tossing one of the boxes on the floor a short distance in front. Stepping into the box with the left foot, he or she then raises the right foot off the ground and, balancing on the left, places the second box on the floor a little further forward. He or she then steps into that second box with the right foot and then balances on the right while turning to pick up the first box and lobbing that a little further up the course. And so it continues until he or she reaches the far end and hands over to the second member of the team. The game is over when all the members of one team have stepped gingerly from end to end. If any player loses balance and touches the floor with either hand or with the foot that is supposed to be off the floor, he or she must pick up both boxes and go back to start that leg of the race all over again. If you haven't got any shoeboxes, or if you're a secret hula-hoop champion, this game can be played equally well with cardboard squares or plastic hoops.

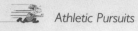

PAIRS

Players: 5-10

You will need:

Various matching items

Before the party, hide one item of a pair somewhere around the house. The pairs can either be identical ornaments or associated articles such as knife and fork, pepper and salt pots, pen and pencil. At the start, give each player one half of a pair and instruct him or her to find the other half. If, in the course of their travels, players stumble across someone else's quarry, they are advised to keep quiet. Nobody cares about the winner in this game (after all, it could be over in a matter of seconds) but the loser is the last person to find his or her pair and is consequently subjected to a forfeit.

ORANGE-HOPPING

Players: 5-10

You will need:

Spoons, oranges, two lengths of string, chairs

Construct a circular racecourse featuring two fences made from a length of string tied about 18 inches off the ground between two chairs. The runners line up at the start on one leg with each one carrying a spoon in their left hand. On the floor, in front of them, are a line of oranges. At a signal, they pick up their orange with the spoon without touching the ground with their hands or their non-standing foot. They then set off hopping around the course, orange and spoon in hand. If any oranges are dropped, they must be picked up with the spoon. The winner is the first to complete two circuits.

FOUR-LEGGED RACE

Players: Teams of 3

You will need:

Lengths of rope or strong twine

A step up from the traditional three-legged race, the 'four-legged race' features teams of three. This means that the right leg of the centre member of the team is strapped to the left leg of the team-mate on the right and the centre player's left leg is tied to the right leg of the team-mate on the left. The teams limp along the course (which should either be the length of a room or in the garden) and the first to cross the finishing line with their legs still strapped are the winners, regardless of whether they are standing, crawling on all fours or writhing along on their stomachs like demented snakes.

TRUE OR FALSE

Players: Any even number

You will need:

Plenty of chairs

Two teams sit on chairs facing each other. At either end of the room, between the two rows, is an empty chair. One is the 'true' chair, the other the 'false' chair. The host makes a statement to each pair of players in turn. If they think the statement is true, they run to the 'true' chair, if they think it's not, they run to the 'false' chair. Whoever sits on the correct seat wins a point for their team. When both players dash to the same chair, the first to be seated wins the point. The best statements to use are ones which are open to confusion, such as 'Harry H. Corbett operated Sooty.' (Harry Corbett operated Sooty, Harry H. Corbett starred in Steptoe and Son).

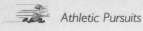
BALLOON RELAY

Players: Any even number

You will need:

Wire clothes-hangers, balloons, garden canes, chairs

Arrange two pairs of chairs in opposite corners of the room, one pair for each team. Over the back of each chair hook a coat-hanger and wedge a balloon onto the horizontal rung of the hanger. Using only a piece of garden cane (preferably without half the garden still attached to it), the players have to release the balloon from its resting place, guide it over to the opposite chair and force it onto the shelf of the coat hanger there. Then the next player takes over and so on until every member of one team has successfully transported the balloon from one chair to the other. For once, there is no penalty if the balloon hits the floor.

CAT AND MOUSE

Players: 2

You will need:

Blindfolds

Even though it is only for two players, this is the perfect way to round off a dinner party as the spectators will have as much fun as the participants. It is played round the table with a male guest chosen to be the cat and a girl to be the mouse. If any guests think that is sexist or rodentist, feel free to reverse the roles. Both players are blindfolded, spun around three times and steered towards the table, but neither is told where the other is. The game itself should be played in total silence with the cat listening intently for any hint of mouse and vice-versa. When the cat does finally catch his prey, another pair of Tom and Jerrys will be only too keen to take over.

PEA-SUCKING

Players: 4 or more

You will need:

Dried peas, straws, saucers

Three saucers are set out in the room, one at either end and one in the middle. One of the end ones contains a number of dried peas. On the command 'Go!', the first member of each team lifts a pea from the full saucer by sucking it through a straw. With the pea held like that, the team member runs over to the saucer in the middle of the room and drops the pea there. At the middle saucer a team-mate takes over and, in the same fashion, completes the transfer to the far end of the room. The team that switches most peas from one end of the room to the other in five minutes wins the game. Anyone caught blowing through the straw instead of sucking is liable to a stern reprimand and a bill for any damage.

UP FOR THE CUP

Players: 3-8

You will need:

Paper cups, paper plates

If you can excel at this game, it's a sure sign that you haven't had nearly enough to drink, for it is a contest which requires the lightest touch and perfect balance. Set out a small table at either end of the room. On one table stack a pile of paper plates; on the other a pile of paper cups. The object of the game is simple, but the execution is more difficult. Beginning with a plate, then a cup, then another plate, the players have to build the highest possible tower of alternate plates and cups, walking between the two tables to acquire fresh items. While on the move, their hands must only hold the bottom plate. If at any point their tower collapses, they have to go back to the plate table and start all over again. The player with the tallest tower at the end of five minutes wins the game.

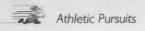
WORD SEARCH

Players: Any number

You will need:

Slips of paper

Before the party, think up a list of words of six letters, one word per player. Write the individual letters on separate slips of paper and scatter them around the house. Each word should have its own identifying number and this should be written on the pieces of paper. Thus if 'CASUAL' is word number one, the slips of paper bearing C, A, S, U, A and L should all carry the number one. Each player is handed a piece of paper giving details of the mystery word which he or she has to find. The information on the paper will also reveal the number of letters in the word and that word's identifying number. The players then go off to find their letters and work out their word. The first to do so wins the game.

MEDLEY RELAY

Players: Any even number

You will need:

Bananas, balloons, potatoes, chairs

In this crazy relay, couples compete against each other in a series of strange tasks. The race starts with the men and women lined up on opposite sides of the room. A row of chairs (one per couple) are arranged on the men's side. First, each man has to devour a banana, run to his female partner, kneel before her and hum a pre-designated tune. When the girl guesses the tune, she blows up a balloon, knots it, runs over to the chair and bursts the balloon by sitting on it. She then runs back to join her partner and, with a potato wedged between their foreheads, they shuffle across the floor together back to the chair. If the potato falls, they have to start that activity again. The race is over when the girl is seated in the chair with her man standing beside her.

BUTTER FINGERS

Players: 3-6

You will need:

Oven gloves (one pair per player), milk bottle tops, cardboard boxes with lids

Any man who has ever fumbled with a recalcitrant bra strap will know only too well the sensation of helplessness which can be experienced during this game. The competitors line up at one end of the room, all wearing oven gloves, ideally the sort which are joined together. They run to the other end and try to pick up a milk bottle top, which they then carry back to the start line where a row of cardboard boxes fitted with ballot-box style slots have been arranged. After posting the bottle top (no easy feat in oven gloves!), they go back for another one. The winner is the player with most successfully-posted bottle tops in three minutes. As a prize, he or she gets to keep the oven gloves.

STRIP TEASE

Players: Any number

You will need:

Streamers, sticky-backed paper

There's no need to worry about any of your guests' blood pressure – this game is by no means as risqué as it sounds, as becomes clear when you realise that the strips in question are strips of streamer. Prior to the party, cut the streamers into various lengths, from about two to eight inches, and hide them around the house in such a way that only the ends are visible. Next, cut some sticky-backed paper into small squares and put them in a dish. All the players have to do is scour the house for pieces of streamer and then stick them together with the adhesive paper. Whoever manages to assemble the longest streamer in 10 minutes is the winner.

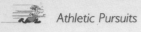

HUNT THE THIMBLE

Players: Any number

You will need:

A thimble

A classic party game in which all of the players except one leave the room while the remaining one hides a thimble. Whilst the thimble shouldn't stick out like a sore thumb, it musn't be too heavily concealed, either. The other players return to search for the thimble. When they locate it, they don't say anything but just sit down quietly. The last player to find the thimble is the loser and has to hide it for the next round. There are no winners in this game. If your household is a thimble-free zone, you can use any small object in its place… as long as you remember to tell your guests what they are looking for.

THAT SHALLOT

Players: Teams of 4

You will need:

Pickled onions, teaspoons

This hardly bears thinking about. Players are divided into equal teams, each member of which is given a teaspoon. The first player in each team holds a bowl replete with pickled onions and, on the signal to start, feeds two onions to the next player in line. When both onions have been eaten, and there is positively no sign of munching, player two takes the bowl and feeds player three with a pair of pickles. And so it continues, slowly and painfully, until player one has devoured the two offerings from player four. When deciding whether to include this game, it is important to take two matters into consideration – firstly, that none of the players have an inbuilt aversion to pickled onions and secondly, that there are no more close contact games planned for the rest of the evening.

THE GREAT FEATHER RACE

Players: 4 Teams of up to 6

You will need:

4 feathers, 4 small tables

Clear away the valuable furniture and choose four teams, each comprising of anything up to half a dozen members. They position themselves in the four corners of the room. Each team is issued with a small feather, the aim being to be the first to blow the feather across the room and land it on a table which is situated in the opposite corner. The four teams each start at the same time, so there is the prospect of 24 people converging on the centre of the room, all frantically trying to keep their team's feathers airborne. If a feather falls to the floor, it must be picked up and re-started from the same spot. If any player is seen transporting the feather illegally – by hand, head, shoulder, mouth or any other part of the anatomy – that team will automatically be disqualified. Any one player who inadvertently swallows a feather will be treated more leniently, probably in hospital.

FOR BUDDING OLIVIERS

CHARADES

Players: Any number

Championed on TV by the long-running Give Us A Clue, Charades has enjoyed a resurgence of popularity in recent years. And deservedly so – because with the right group of people, there are few more entertaining party games. The aim of the most common form of 'Charades' is to mime the title of a film, play, TV programme, song or book, but the rules can also be applied to ordinary words or phrases. Although the performance must be silent, a number of visual aids can be employed.

Film – The right hand cranks an imaginary movie camera
Play – Sweep each hand downward in an arc to represent stage curtains
TV programme – Draw a square in the air with both forefingers
Song – Put both hands to your mouth and release imaginary words. Born crooners may additionally choose to go down on one knee with a glazed look on their face, clasping their heart. This does not indicate an impending coronary but a tender ballad
Book – Two hands are placed together and opened palm up
Number of words – Hold up the appropriate number of fingers
The first word of the mime – Hold up one finger. If you are starting with the third word, hold up three fingers and so on
Number of syllables – Tap the relevant number of fingers on your forearm
The whole thing – If you are describing everything in one go, draw a large circle in the air with your arms
Sounds like – Tug gently at your earlobe
A short word – For words such as 'a', 'an', 'the', 'on', 'but', 'in' and 'of', hold an invisible space between your thumb and forefinger and wait until someone guesses the correct word
A correct guess – point vigorously at that person

When a mime is guessed correctly, the successful player performs the next mime, unless you're playing 'Team Charades', in which case your team scores a point and the next group has a go. If you're preparing a list of titles in advance, it's fun to tailor them to your guests' personalities. So the vicar gets to mime White Punks On Dope, or Fanny by Gaslight.

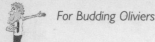
ANIMAL CHARADES

Players: Any number

In this version of 'Charades', players act out the names of animals or birds. This should be done by a combination of word miming and silent actions. Extroverts will relish the opportunity to bound around like a kangaroo; while quieter guests may prefer the three-toed sloth… although this can lead to an extremely long game. For a trick version of this, place slips of paper into a hat which all bear the same animal's name. Amid the utmost secrecy, each player picks out a slip, then one person is sent from the room to prepare the mime. When he or she returns, the other players – all of whom know what the animal is – deliberately avoid guessing the mime. It can be mildly amusing to watch a poor guest desperately trying to convey 'donkey', even to the point of eating a carrot, while all around are guessing goat, horse, cow, hippopotamus etc.

PROVERBIAL PANTO

Players: Any number

You will need:

Pencils and paper

Players are divided into two teams, each person writing down a proverb on a piece of paper. The teams then exchange the slips and players take it in turns to act out the proverbs they have been given. If their team mates guess the proverb correctly, that team gains a point. If the proverb isn't solved, it's passed across for the other team to guess.

SHADOW PLAY

Players: Any number

You will need:

A large white sheet, a lamp, two chairs

Two volunteers stand on chairs, holding the ends of a large white sheet. Positioned behind the sheet should be a bright light so that whoever is between the wall and sheet casts a clear, sharp shadow onto the sheet. The players act in pairs and, using the sheet as a screen, perform a short silent routine for everyone else to guess. This could take the form of a nursery rhyme, a proverb or a song title. Given the limitations of the medium, attempting to perform the whole of Act Two from King Lear by shadow acting is probably a trifle ambitious.

SUPERHEROES

Players: 4-8

Players take it in turns to assume the identity of various superheroes, either of their own creation or that of the host, and invite the other players to guess their name. The actors may speak but must not use the words contained in their name. Thus Television Repair Man may use every word in the English language with the exception of 'television' and 'repair'. Imagination is the key to the game. Avoid the likes of Batman, Spiderman and Superman and opt for less obvious heroes such as Coffee Percolator Man, Gravy Granule Man and Gerbil Woman.

ALIBI

Players: 5 or more

If you are a devotee of murder whodunnits and reckon you can crack the strongest alibi, this game will go down a storm at your party. Two players (the accused) are sent from the room and given 10 minutes to concoct an alibi for an imaginary crime. Their story should cover a specific time – say two hours – and they can refuse to answer any questions which do not relate to that period. Once they have agreed upon their version of events, one of the pair returns to the room to be subjected to five minutes' interrogation from the rest of the guests (the prosecution). The second defendant is then sent for and, over the next five minutes, is questioned intensely as the prosecution attempt to throw up discrepancies in the two defendants' alibis. If at any point the second defendant fails to corroborate the first's story, they lose the game and have to do a forfeit.

PROPOSALS

Players: 6-12

You will need:

Pencils and paper

Should you feel that your party is getting too cosy, a quick game of 'Proposals' might help to stir things up a bit. Ideally there should be an equal number of men and women playing this game although watching two heterosexual men declaring their undying love for one another can be amusing. Then again it is probably no more than they do after seven pints on a lads' night out. Everyone writes their name on a piece of paper and puts the slip in a pile (one for men, the other for women). The names are then paired off and one of each pair has to get down on bended knee and propose marriage to the other. This can be invigorating if you find yourself proposing to someone you've always lusted after... and downright dangerous if your partner is watching your every move.

166

DUMB CRAMBO

Players: Any even number

An old favourite in which two teams sit facing one another. One team selects a word to be mimed by the other but before they can mime it they must find out what the word is. This has to be done by trial and error, the only help they receive being when the captain of the first team gives them a word which rhymes with the mystery word. Then the members of the guessing team take it in turns to mime what they think the word might be. So if the chosen word is 'light' and the clue given is that it rhymes with 'kite', the guessing team could mime 'night', 'might', 'write', 'height', 'bite', 'fight', 'transvestite' and so on. If any player cannot think of a word to mime, a team-mate may whisper an idea, but no other words must be spoken by the guessing team, hence the name of the game. After each failed mime, the captain of the first team declares that the opponents have guessed incorrectly and the unsuccessful mime artist is roundly booed. However, a successful mime should be rewarded with a generous round of applause. Keep note of the number of mimes each team takes to guess the chosen word, each failure incurring a penalty point. At the end of the game, the team with fewest points are the winners.

MIND READERS

Players: Any even number

The players divide into two teams, one of which leaves the room. The remaining team thinks up a situation to be acted out – anything from hailing a taxi in Siberia to giving an enema – and calls in one member of the other team. Once that person has been told the situation, he or she mimes it to the next team member. This procedure continues through the team like a silent version of 'Chinese Whispers' until the action reaches the last member whose task it is to ascertain precisely what is being acted out. Obviously the more players there are, the greater the likelihood of departure from the original idea. The two teams then swap roles.

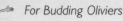

WORLD'S WORST

Players: 5-10

Before the party, think up a number of 'world's worst' categories. You then ask the players to perform suitable examples. For instance, if the subject is 'the world's worst kisser', the player may mime a horrendous tongue sandwich or simply point to her husband. Players are allowed to speak but must not use the key word, in this case 'kiss'. When everyone has exhausted a subject, move on to the next. The performer who gets the most laughs is the winner. In case you get stuck for inspiration, here are a few more subject ideas:

> World's worst contagious disease
> World's worst cook
> World's worst football team
> World's worst case of vertigo
> World's worst dress sense
> World's worst case of flatulence

THE RAILWAY CARRIAGE GAME

Players: 4-10

A popular exercise among wartime spy schools, 'The Railway Carriage Game' tests players' ability to detect a secret phrase. Players are divided into pairs, each member of which is given a secret phrase. They then climb into an imaginary railway carriage and talk to each other for five minutes, during which time they must slip the given phrase into the conversation as discreetly as possible. When the time is up, each must guess the other's mystery phrase. If the guess is unsuccessful, the puzzle can be thrown over to the fellow passengers. Here are a few likely phrases:

> I do so enjoy the taste of Pot Noodle
> My, what fascinating feet you have
> I feel one of my hot flushes coming on
> My pet stick insect is called Avril
> Who'd have thought the Pope was once a Bay City Rollers fan

SNEAKY SENTENCES

Players: 4-10

In this variation of 'The Railway Carriage Game', four players leave the room and think of four distinctive phrases to slip into their conversations, one per player. When the outsiders return, the other players must listen intently to their conversations and try to spot the chosen phrases.

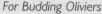

THE PLIMSOLL GAME

Players: 5-10

A letter of the alphabet is picked and everyone writes down the name of a famous person beginning with that letter. The names are then read out in turn and, via healthy debate, the players proceed to lay claim to their chosen person being the most eminent in his or her field. Thus, if the letter selected is D, players might argue that Ken Dodd is Liverpool's finest comedian, that Kenny Dalglish is Scotland's greatest ever footballer, that Sir Francis Drake was Britain's bravest seafarer, that Benjamin Disraeli was our most accomplished Prime Minister and that Deputy Dawg was the world's finest sheriff. The game gets its name from a session where someone cited Samuel Plimsoll as the finest man ever to have lent his name to the lines on the sides of ships.

PANTO

Players: 6 or more

You will need:

Assorted articles

Here is the chance to stage a pantomime in the comfort of your own home. Divide the players into teams and give each team three gloriously unconnected articles. The actors then have to perform a four-minute improvised pantomime incorporating all three articles. Try these combinations:

> a sink plunger, a tea bag and a tampon
> a sticking plaster, a cabbage and a golf ball
> a roll-on deodorant, a mouse trap and a set of false teeth

PANDORA'S BOX

Players: Any number

In a similar vein to Panto, 'Pandora's Box' requires individuals to weave a two-minute story around three random objects. The difference is that here they don't have to act the story, just tell it. Since the objects in question don't have to be produced, the choice is limitless but even so, some items are easier to connect than you might think. For example, a signed photograph of a top boy-band, a match and a waste-paper bin could be linked in one sentence easily. The following combinations, however, might prove more challenging:

Big Ben, a lobster and Burt Reynolds' toupee
A cardboard cut-out of Shirley Bassey, a combine harvester and a water bed
A suit of armour, a hot water bottle and an inflatable Spacehopper

FANCY UNDRESS

Players: Any number

This is a bit of fun at fancy dress parties. For half an hour, guests have to behave in the manner of a famous person other than the one they are dressed as. It can be quite disconcerting talking to a man dressed as Long John Silver but acting like Wayne Sleep or to a woman who is dressed like Queen Victoria but behaves like Mae West. At the end of the half-hour, everyone must work out who is pretending to be who. The best performance wins a prize, as do the best newcomer, best supporting artist, best acceptance speech etc.

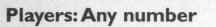

WHAT'S MY LINE?

Players: Any number

For the party version of this old TV favourite, prepare a list of occupations prior to playing. Make them as diverse as possible – brain surgeon, page three model, rat catcher, pizza chef. The first player is secretly given an occupation from the list and has to mime it to the others. Whoever guesses the nature of the job has the next turn. This can be also be played as a team game.

THE DESTINATION GAME

Players: Any even number

One team leaves the room and chooses the name of a town or city to which its members are supposedly travelling. On their return, the individual team members take it turns to mime a letter of their destination by performing an action which begins with the appropriate letter. For example, if the destination is Rochdale, the players could try Rowing, Ordering, Cutting, Heating, Diving, Agreeing, Lifting and, for a sting in the tail, Embalming. The mimes must be performed in the correct order. When all of the mimes are completed, the other team have five minutes to try to work out the destination, during which time they can ask for a mime to be repeated. If they guess the destination, it becomes their turn to think of a town or city. If not, the first team has another go.

DANCE CLASS

Players: 4-10

This is a 'must' for all those who sew their own sequins and are devotees of Come Dancing. Prepare a list of dances – tango, waltz, rumba, charleston, twist, bossa nova, military two-step etc – and ask each player in turn to mime a particular dance. This must be done solo with an imaginary partner. The other players must try to guess the name of the dance. Anyone who has only ever shuffled around a handbag should sit this one out.

AS THE WORD DECREES

Players: Any number

While one person leaves the room, the remainder think of an adverb to be discovered upon his or her return. The single player attempts to find the adverb by asking the others to perform mimes 'as the word decrees'. For example, he or she might say: 'Open a can of baked beans as the word decrees.' Depending upon the adverb, that player will then mime the opening of the tin passionately, slowly, breathlessly, dreamily, artistically, deviously, majestically, nervously, solemnly, ineptly, violently, athletically and so on. If the single player is unable to work out the adverb from that mime, he or she may ask someone else to do a different mime – say, hammering a nail – as the word decrees. A total of four mimes are permitted. If the adverb has not been deduced by then, a forfeit must be paid and another player is sent from the room.

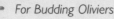
SPEECH PATTERNS

Players: 3 or more

This game is best played by groups of three who must conduct impromptu conversations in which the first letter of the first word of a sentence must be the same as the last letter of the last word of the previous speaker's sentence. Thus player one might begin: 'What shall we do today, Max?' And player two might reply: 'Xylophones! We'll get out the xylophones and play some jazz.' This puts player three in something of a predicament until he or she exclaims: 'Zounds! What a great idea.' And the game continues in strict rotation and alphabetical sequence with each player trying to drop the next one into the mire. Anyone who fails to think of an answer within 10 seconds, or whose answer is adjudged to bear no relation whatsoever to the conversation, is eliminated. When the first group are reduced to one, the next trio can have a go.

INQUISITION

Players: 3 or more

As with 'Speech Patterns', this game is best played in groups of three. Once again, the intention is for the players to hold a reasonably meaningful conversation but this time they can only speak in questions. Each question must be answered with another question. Anyone who gives a reply that is not a question is eliminated. The longer this game goes on, the more irritating it can become as every attempt to induce a statement is parried. In the circumstances it is advisable not to team up players of a volatile nature lest the proceedings degenerate into a brawl.

MIMICS

Players: Any number

Before the party, draw up a list of famous people (dead or alive, real or fictional) with distinctive voices. Assign a celebrity to each player and ask them, in turn, to read out a short newspaper cutting in the voice of their chosen character. The other players then have to guess who is being impersonated. There are no winners, but who cares?

TABLEAUX

Players: 6 or more

You will need:

A selection of old clothes

If you've got a pile of old clothes waiting to go out for jumble, use them first as the costumes for this entertaining still life game. With the players divided into teams, the first team dress up to depict a film, a book, a painting or even a scene from history such as Drake playing bowls while waiting for the Armada. The actors are not allowed to speak and must stand absolutely still either for a minute or until the other team guesses the subject matter correctly. If the title is not guessed within the time limit, the losing team must pay a forfeit. If it is guessed, the next team have a go. Unless you have a particularly large number of guests you should avoid attempting a scene from Ben Hur.

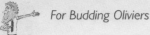

PAPER COSTUMES

Players: Any number

You will need:

A supply of newspapers, pins

Would-be Vivienne Westwoods can try their luck at designing something for the catwalk, using nothing more than the obituary column of The Daily Telegraph and the sports pages of The Sun. Each player is given 15 minutes to create a little number from a stack of newspapers which can be held in place by pins. Then they have to model it in front of their adoring audience who must to try to guess what on earth it's supposed to be – that is, provided the creator knows what it's meant to be themselves. Prizes can be awarded for the player who comes up with the most imaginative outfit as well as for the best model.

LATERAL THINKING

Players: 4-8

You will need:

Pencil and paper

One player thinks up a beginning, a middle and an end for a short play. This can be either dialogue or actions. The others then have 10 minutes to build a playlet around the set pieces, at the end of which they must perform it. A suitable framework might be:

> Beginning: 'Clive, it's the first time I've seen you since your
> sex-change operation went so horribly wrong.'
> Middle: The gun fell to the floor with a resounding thud.
> End: And she never ate anchovies again.

FIVE-MINUTE THEATRE

Players: 4-10

You will need:

Pencils and paper, pieces of card

In advance, write lines of dialogue (one per player) on separate pieces of card. Each player then picks a card and has five minutes to pen a script ending with the given line. The finished articles are then read out, the most ingenious story being declared the winner. Here are a few possible closing lines:

> 'Thank goodness Mrs Jenkins is a black belt in karate!'
> 'That's the last time I wear red nail varnish.'
> 'Phew! I thought that killer iguana was going to wipe us all out.'
> 'Who'd have thought trainspotting could be so exciting!'
> 'Anyone for porridge?'

MY NAME IS...

Players: 3-10

One player leaves the room and the rest think of a famous person. When the player returns, he or she is allowed to ask each of the others two questions in an effort to establish the identity. The questions can only be answered by 'yes' or 'no'. When the interrogation is complete, the player must do an impression of whoever he or she thinks it is. Poor questioning can lead to hapless individuals doing an impersonation of Boadiccea when they're supposed to be Fanny Craddock. But then again, it's an easy mistake to make.

WHAT'S THE USE?

Players: 5-10

You will need:

Various unusual objects

This is a quick-fire improvisation game whereby each player is given a strange-looking object (such as a sink plunger, a boomerang or a pair of cycle clips) and asked to think of as many amusing uses for it as possible. The one who comes up with the most ideas is the winner.

PARANOIA

Players: Any number

While one person is out of the room, the other players decide on a common factor which will dictate all their answers when he or she returns. By asking endless questions, the player has to work out what that factor is. They may choose to be cannibals, to end every sentence in a preposition or to treat the questioner as if he or she has an unpleasant social disease. Or, of course, they may drive the questioner to the brink of insanity by all pretending to be hard of hearing, in which case the game can go on and on indefinitely.

DRAMA SCHOOL

Players: 5-10

Impotence, frustration and anger. Besides being three emotions which occur on a daily basis among passengers on the London Underground, these are also prime examples of moods which players might be called upon to express in 'Drama School'. One player acts as judge and gives the others a range of emotions to convey, such as lust, panic, guilt, boredom and terror. A point is awarded to the player who gives the most convincing demonstration of each feeling, the winner being the one with the highest total at the end of the game. All of the actions should be silent and the game is even more rewarding if the players have to rely solely on facial expressions with no hand gestures allowed.

HAND SHADOWS

Players: 5-10

You will need:

A white sheet or a screen of white paper, a lamp, pieces of paper, a hat or bowl

Two guests hold a white sheet or screen of white paper at either end. A lamp is placed behind the screen. The names of various animals are written down on separate slips of paper and put into a hat or bowl. One by one, the players draw a slip and, using their hands only, must cast a shadow of the named creature onto the screen. The best results are achieved by standing at the side of the screen. While rabbit, dog and horse are fairly straightforward, the poor player who draws millipede may need to enlist a little help.

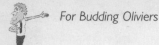

JUST A MINUTE

Players: 4-8

A popular Victorian parlour game, 'Just a Minute' has long been a mainstay of BBC Radio 4. Each player is given a topic by the referee and told to speak about it for a minute without hesitating, straying from the subject or being guilty of repetition. Any of the other players who spot one of the aforementioned sins may challenge the speaker, at which point the clock is stopped while the arguments rage. If the challenge is upheld by the umpire, the challenger earns a point and speaks on the same subject for what is left of the original minute. If the challenge is rejected, the first speaker gains a point and resumes from where he or she was so rudely interrupted. Whoever is speaking at the end of the minute scores a point or two points if it is still the original speaker. The following topics may prove suitable for earnest discussion:

> Mud
> The house fly
> The Battle of Cropredy Bridge (1643)
> Underarm hair
> Semolina
> The life and times of Arthur Mullard

FAIRY TALES

Players: Any number

Players are divided into two teams to act out improvised versions of well-known fairy tales, but as famous people rather than themselves. Thus, Little Red Riding Hood might feature Waynetta Slob as Red Riding Hood, Julian Clary as the Wolf and Tommy Cooper as the Woodcutter. At the end of each performance, the other team has to guess the fairy story and the double identity of all of the players. If you are blessed with a particularly artistic gathering, you may choose to have the play acted in the style of a famous film director. Quentin Tarantino's version of Cinderella where the Fairy Godmother turns out to be a serial killer and Buttons dies in a gangland shoot-out invariably proves popular.

SCENE AND HEARD

Players: 8 or more

You will need:

Pencils and paper

Each woman is supplied with a pencil, a paper and a man. Together they then compose the first scene of a film – it could be a farce, a murder mystery, a sci-fi extravaganza, a musical, anything. After five minutes, each of the men move round one so that the first man teams up with the second woman and works with her on the second scene of her scenario. After a further five minutes, he moves on to a third woman and helps with her third scene. The cycle continues until every woman has written one scene with every man. At the end, the screenplays are acted out and a vote is taken as to which is the most entertaining.

STRICTLY FOR POSERS

Players: Any number

You will need:

Pieces of paper, a hat or bowl

Write down a selection of adjectives – such as tragic, gobsmacked or amorous – on separate slips of paper and put them into a hat or some other container. Each player draws a slip from the container and has to strike a pose which captures the selected word. The others then have to guess the adjective.

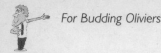
TELLY FAVOURITES

Players: 8 or more

Divide the players into two groups and ask three or four members of each group to act out a scenario from a TV series of their choice, anything from Casualty to Postman Pat. In doing so, they must not use any character names. At the end of the performance, which should not exceed two minutes, the other members of their team have to try to guess the name of the programme. If they fail to do so in three guesses, the second team are allowed a guess. Then the second team perform their scenario.

ROMEO AND JULIET

Players: Any even number

A man and a woman leave the room and the remainder think up identities for them to assume on their return. Each is told individually whom they are to be. They then have to woo each other intently for five minutes, at the end of which they must try to guess their suitor's identity. When thinking of pairs of names, try to come up with unlikely lovers such as Rambo and Bonnie Langford, Compo from Last of the Summer Wine and Joan Collins, Henry VIII and Mavis from Coronation Street, or Madonna and Rin Tin Tin.

PARTY GUESTS

Players: 4-8

One player acts as the host while the others are given secret identities, the more unusual the better. By studying what these 'guests' say and do when they arrive at the party, the host has to work out who or what each one is supposed to be. The only question the host is allowed to ask is the guess itself – for example: 'Are you a dyslexic signwriter?' If the answer is 'yes', the host moves on to the next guest. The game ends when the host has identified all of the guests. Here are some suggestions for your guest list:

Scrupulously honest second-hand car dealer
End of pier entertainer
Nun-turned-glamour-model
Gravedigger
Politically correct plumber
Tina Turner
Incontinent jockey

TAKING A BREATHER

PRINTER'S ERRORS

Players: Any number

You will need:

Newspapers or magazines

Cut out 10-line passages from newspapers or magazines, one passage per player. Then cut the passages into individual lines and rearrange them so that they make no sense whatsoever. (This stage can be skipped with The Guardian.) The players then have to repair their section of print so that the lines are in the correct order, the first to do so being the winner.

SUITCASES

Players: Any number

In this memory game, players have to recite an ever-lengthening list of strange items, supposedly the contents of a suitcase for a month abroad at an exotic destination. The players sit in a circle and the first may announce: 'I packed my suitcase and in it I put 36 back issues of Reader's Digest.' Then player two might say: 'I packed my suitcase and in it I put 36 back issues of Reader's Digest and a Tom and Jerry alarm clock with fluorescent numerals.' The burden then passes to the third player who may reveal: 'I packed my suitcase and in it I put 36 back issues of Reader's Digest, a Tom and Jerry alarm clock with fluorescent numerals and a size 10 black, frilly, lacy negligee from British Home Stores, Dagenham branch.' And so it continues, with anybody who forgets an item or gets it in the wrong order being obliged to drop out. The game ends when there is only one word-perfect suitcase packer left.

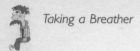

TABOO

Players: Any number

Pick a letter from the alphabet and declare that nobody is allowed to use a word containing that letter. Then ask each player in turn a question, cunningly designed to catch them out. If the forbidden letter is 'L', you may choose to ask: 'What is the capital of England?' Unable to say 'London' because it contains an 'L', a quick-thinking player may reply: 'The city on the River Thames'. As the questioning becomes more intense, any player who slips up and uses the taboo letter is eliminated. The last player left answering questions is the winner.

RHYMING TIME

Players: Any number

You will need:

Pencils and paper, a hat or bowl

Every player writes down his or her name and a simple word on a piece of paper and then puts the slip in a hat. One of the group acts as umpire and draws a slip, telling the person whose name it bears not to take part because that person knows the mystery word. The umpire then gives the other players a word which rhymes with the word on the piece of paper. If the word on the paper is 'night', the umpire may reveal that the word rhymes with 'tight'. Armed with this information, the remaining players try to guess the mystery word by asking a series of questions, whereupon the umpire must reply using the word being suggested. Thus 'Is it violent?' would be answered with 'No, it's not fight' and 'Is it the opposite to dark?' with 'No, it's not light'. The game ends when someone finally discovers the word.

SAUSAGES!

Players: Any number

Here, players bombard a chosen victim with two minutes of questions, to which the reply must always be 'sausages!' The interrogators tailor their questions in the hope of inducing the victim to crack up when answering 'sausages!' as the key rule of the game is that the respondent must keep a straight face at all times. If he or she fails to do so, the game is over and a new victim is selected. It may sound easy, but earnestly answering 'sausages!' is no mean feat with questions such as: 'What do you clean your ears with?' and 'What are baby pigs called?'

MYSTERY TOUR

Players: Any number

While one player leaves the room, the rest choose a country to where he or she is to pay an imaginary visit. On his return, the selected player asks the other players in turn: 'Where am I going?' Each player gives a different minor clue, such as Frida Boccara represented this country in the 1969 Eurovision Song Contest, the aim being to prevent the questioner from discovering the destination. When the country has been correctly identified, another player has a go – unless of course it took so long that everyone has gone home. In case you wondered, Frida Boccara represented France and was the joint winner with a catchy little ditty entitled Un Jour, Un Enfant.

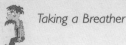

WORD ASSOCIATION

Players: Any number

Always a hit at psychiatrists' parties, 'Word Association' requires the players to sit in a circle. The first player says the first word that comes into his or her head. The second player immediately says the first word he or she can think of in response to the first player's word and so the quick-fire patter continues around the circle. Anyone who hesitates is eliminated. The game can, of course, reveal a number of secrets better left hidden so if the previous player says 'breasts', beware of blurting out the name of anyone other than your partner.

COMPOUNDS

Players: Any number

The first player calls out a two-word compound, such as 'washout', and succeeding players have to think up a corresponding compound in so far as the first half of the word is the same as that of the second part of the previous word. Thus 'washout' could be followed by 'outhouse', 'house mouse', 'mousetrap', 'trapdoor', 'doorstop', 'stopover', 'overarm', 'armrest' and so on. Anyone unable to find a continuation may claim that none is possible. If the claim is upheld, the previous player (the one who supplied the word) is eliminated and the challenger starts a new round. If, however, someone does think of a valid word, the challenger has to drop out.

PREDICAMENTS

Players: Any number

Life has a nasty habit of placing us in awkward predicaments, so this game may prove invaluable should you ever find yourself stuck in a lift with the world farting champion, attending a police identity parade in a heavily bloodstained shirt or turning up at a party dressed as King Canute when everyone else is in suit and tie. One player is sent from the room while the others choose an embarrassing situation in which to place him or her. When that person returns, he or she asks each of the other players in turn what they would do in certain circumstances, presenting different situations to each one. Totally disregarding the subject matter of the question, they instead have to give answers which relate to a completely different predicament which they have devised. From these answers, the person has to work out the precise nature of the chosen predicament. The game can create a succession of splendid non-sequiteurs. If the agreed predicament is that the questioner, a keen naturalist, accidentally enrolled in a naturists' weekend, the question: 'What would you do if you got your finger stuck in the teapot spout?' could prompt replies ranging from: 'Pray that the weather stayed nice' to 'Shake hands very carefully' or 'Just turn the other cheek'.

SPELLING BEE

Players: Any number

One player assumes the role of question master and asks the other players in turn to spell a series of words. Any player who gets a spelling wrong is eliminated. The winner is the last one left in. It is best to start with moderately easy words and then make the spellings progressively tougher as the rounds progress.

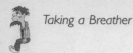

BACKWARD SPELLING

Players: Any number

The rules are the same as for 'Spelling Bee' except that here the players are presented with the additional problem that all of the words have to be spelt backwards.

INTRUDERS

Players: Any number

For this sophisticated version of 'Odd One Out', you need to prepare a list of at least 20 items which belong to the same category plus one which doesn't. If you read out Aire, Calder, Waveney, Esk, Cuckmere, Mole, Ouse, Trent, Rother, Fowey, Exe, Tees, Test, Taff, Nene, Itchen, Ribble, Eden, Thames, Avon and Don, the winner of that round will be the first person who calls out 'Taff'. That's because it is a Welsh river and the rest are English. Other likely categories could be FA Cup-winning teams (slipping in one club which has never won the Cup), Nobel prize winners (plus one who didn't) and number one hit songs (with one that wasn't).

COMMON FACTORS

Players: Any number

Prepare a series of lists, each comprising three seemingly unconnected people or objects but which do actually have something in common. The first person to call out the common factor wins absolutely nothing except the undying admiration of his peers. An example is 'Australian fast bowler, Gnasher and the London Fire Brigade', the connection being Dennis – Dennis Lillee, Dennis the Menace and fire engines made by Dennis. The more obscure you can make the link, the more fun you'll have as your guests flounder around aimlessly.

CALL MY BLUFF

Players: 5-10

The popular TV game can be equally successful at a party. Beforehand, sift through the pages of a dictionary and pick out a dozen or so obscure words. In addition to the correct definition, think of four additional bogus definitions for each word. Announce the first word, making sure to spell it out to the players and pronounce it correctly, and then read out the five definitions. Each player is then asked to say which he or she thinks is the correct meaning. A point is scored for each right answer.

191

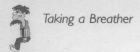

SONG TITLES

Players: Any number

Think of a word which occurs frequently in song titles – 'love', 'blue', 'you' etc. Going round the room, ask each player to think of a song title featuring the chosen word. Anyone who fails to come up with an answer has to drop out. And if you only want a very short game, try 'supercalifragilisticexpialidocious' as the keyword.

MINI WORDS

Players: Any number

For this game, you need to think of some eight-letter words which also contain anagrams of one three, one four and one five-letter word. For example, 'treasure' contains 'ear', 'rust' and 'erase'. It is important that these mini words use up all of the letters in the big word. First you give the players the three-letter word and invite them to guess the eight-letter word from that clue. Any correct deduction at this stage earns three points. If there are no takers, you give the four-letter clue, a successful guess at which earns two points. Finally you give them the five-letter clue which is worth one point. If the eight-letter word still remains unsolved, put them out of their misery and move on to the next word... or suggest something rather less intellectually demanding – like a nice easy game of musical chairs perhaps.

UP JENKINS!

Players: 6-10

You will need:

A coin, table and chairs

For this classic game of bluff, counter-bluff and counter-counter-bluff, the players sit as two teams on opposite sides of the table. The members of one team conceal their hands below the table and pass a coin along the row from hand to hand. When the leader of the other team shouts out 'Up Jenkins!' the players on the team with the coin must raise their hands, with fists clenched, well above the table. The opposing leader then commands 'Down Jenkins!' at which the raised hands must be slapped down onto the table, palms flat, as hard as possible to mask the sound of the coin hitting the table. The opposing team must now guess which hand the coin is under. This is where players with empty hands will deliberately mislead and behave is if they have the coin. After lengthy consultation, a verdict is reached and the leader taps the chosen hand. If it does contain the coin, the guessing team score a point; if not, the point goes to the team with the coin. After each round, the two teams swap roles.

THE SMELLING GAME

Players: Any number

You will need:

Various items with distinctive smells, saucers, cloths, blindfolds, pencils and paper

Place a selection of strong-smelling items in separate saucers and cover each one with a cloth. The blindfolded players pass along the row and endeavour to identify the assorted scents, writing down their answers on a piece of paper. A suitably pungent grouping might be: turpentine, lavender, crushed garlic, boot polish, sage, bleach, thyme, tobacco and raw egg. Players should be warned that they remove the cloth covering the saucer at their peril.

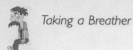

BALLOON ROLL

Players: Any even number

You will need:

Balloons

Since even the most sloth-like individual would be hard pushed to describe this balloon game as an athletic pursuit, it has made its way into these gentler offerings. The players are split into pairs and each pair is given a balloon. They stand facing each other with the balloon wedged between them at waist height. No hands may be used, the balloon being held in place solely by body pressure. Each pair have to turn three complete circles on the spot while keeping the balloon between them. If a balloon is dropped, it may be picked up by hand but it also negates one turn. Any couple who burst their balloon are automatically disqualified.

TRAVELLER'S ALPHABET

Players: Any number

With all participants seated in a circle, the first player turns to the person on his or her left and asks: 'Where are you going?' The second player must think of a destination beginning with an A. The first player then asks: 'And what will you do there?' whereupon the second player must reply using a verb, an adjective and a noun, all beginning with the letter A. If the destination is Argentina, the activity might be 'assessing Argentinian armadillos'. The second player then asks the same questions of the third player whose answers must all start with B. And so the game continues round the room with whoever is due to get Q breaking out in beads of perspiration. Any player who cannot come up with suitable answers is knocked out of the game, the winner being the last one left in.

ALPHABET SOUP

Players: Any number

For this alphabet game, the players should again sit in a circle. The first player announces: 'I went to a banquet' and thinks of a food beginning with A to eat – anchovies, apples etc. The second player has to do the same with B, so that he or she might say: 'I went to a banquet and ate anchovies and beetroot.' And so the game continues with a little sprinkling of custard, dates, eggs, fish fingers, gooseberries right up until the poor soul who faces a meal of zebra. It is probably best not to play Alphabet Soup on a full stomach.

HYPOCHONDRIAC

Players: Any number

The rules here are the same as for Alphabet Soup except that the subject matter is illness and disease instead of food. The first player might declare, 'I went into hospital because I had athlete's foot.' Soon one unfortunate will be revealing a medical history consisting of athlete's foot, boils, colic, dysentery, earache, foot and mouth disease, gangrene and hard pad.

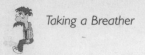

MATCHMAKER

Players: Any number

You will need:

An empty wine bottle, a supply of matches

This game requires the steadiest of hands and is therefore best played before too much alcohol has been consumed. Four matches are placed across the mouth of an empty wine bottle and players then take it turns to add a match at a time, the aim being to build up a mountain of sticks. There are no winners, but the player whose clumsiness causes the construction to collapse must pay a suitable forfeit.

CHINESE WHISPERS

Players: Any number

Usually played over a garden fence, this old favourite is the ultimate treat for local gossips. Everyone sits in a circle and the first player invents an item of gossip which is whispered once only to the person on his or her right. The morsel of information continues its journey around the room in this way until it arrives back with the originator who then reads out the first and last messages. Unless your guests are trained listeners, the end product invariably bears little relation to the original. An opening rumour of 'Ron's seeing Pam from the chip shop' will quickly be distorted to 'Don eats Spam in flip-flops' and may well end up as 'Last night I dreamt I went to Manderley again'.

LIKES AND DISLIKES

Players: Any number

Thought to be a favourite of Frances Hodgson-Burnett, author of *Little Lord Fauntleroy*, this game requires the utmost attention from participants. One player reads out a list of likes and dislikes, all of which have a common theme. The others have to listen intently and try to spot the link. The first person to do so wins the round. Here is an example:

> I like roses, but I don't like carnations
> I like wood, but I don't like timber
> I like fish, but I don't like chips
> I like biscuits, but I don't like cakes
> I like collars, but I don't like ties

The answer here is that all of the likes can be prefaced by 'dog' (dog roses, dogwood, dogfish, dog biscuits, dog collars) whereas the dislikes can't.

CONCENTRATION

Players: 4-8

You will need:

A pack of playing cards

An excellent test of memory, Concentration is played with a full pack of playing cards which are shuffled and placed face down on a table. Each player in turn selects two cards and turns them face upwards. The aim is to find two of a kind (threes, jacks, nines, aces etc) and when that happens, those two cards are removed from the table and placed next to the successful player who then has another turn. That player's turn continues until he or she fails to produce a match, at which point the cards are put back face down in the same positions. The winner is the player with most pairs when all 52 cards have been claimed.

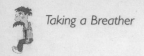

SHADOWS

Players: Any number

You will need:

A white sheet, a lamp, a variety of small objects

Hang a sheet in such a way that sufficient light is cast on it to produce a good shadow. From behind the sheet, hold a series of everyday items at such angles that their shadows make it difficult for the players in front to recognise. When doing this, you should try to keep your hand as much out of the way as possible for fear of confusing everyone still further. The first person to identify each object correctly earns a point. Items you could use include an alarm clock, a plug, a cotton reel, a corkscrew, nutcrackers, an eggcup and a light bulb.

BOTTICELLI

Players: Any number

Taking its name from the 15th-century Italian artist – even though it is highly doubtful whether he ever actually played it, at least not with a bowl of Twiglets in one hand – 'Botticelli' is a devious question and answer game. It starts with one player thinking of the name of a famous person (dead or alive, real or fictional) and announcing the first letter of the subject's surname to the assembled throng. They then have to bombard the player with a succession of indirect questions. If the mystery person is Samson and the letter is therefore S, they may ask: 'Are you a former leader of the Liberal party?' to which the player will reply: 'No I am not Sir David Steel.' They may try: 'Are you a cigar-smoking disc jockey?' to which the player will reply: 'No, I am not Sir Jimmy Savile OBE.' Trying to make each question more difficult, they may ask: 'Did you produce The Crystals?' in the hope that the player will be unable to come up with Phil Spector. If the player can't answer a question, the others are allowed to ask one direct question such as 'Are you alive?' or 'Are you male?' By engineering as many direct questions as possible, they should eventually arrive at Samson, but even then they can only seek confirmation of the fact once they have earned the right to ask a direct question.

INITIAL QUESTIONS

Players: Any number

Devise a series of questions which offer plenty of scope for the imagination, such as: 'What is your favourite food?', 'What is your pet hate?' or 'What turns you on?' Each player in turn has to come up with an answer, the words of which must begin with his or her initials. Thus Mildred Winona Beryl Edison might list as her favourite food 'Muesli With Boiled Elderberries', her pet hate as 'Men With Bushy Eyebrows' and confess that she gets turned on by 'Men Who Bruise Easily'.

TRAIN OF THOUGHT

Players: 4-8

This form of word association has an unexpected sting in the tail. The first player thinks of a word (perhaps 'kettle') and the rest in turn think of the first word that comes into their mind. When each player has had three turns (so that with eight players there would be 24 words in the chain), the next player has to rewind it, recalling each word in the correct reverse order right back to the start. If a player makes a mistake, it passes to the next in line. Whoever completes the rewinding process by announcing 'kettle' or whatever, wins the game.

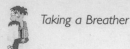

THE MINISTER'S CAT

Players: Any number

The first player thinks of an adjective beginning with 'A' such as 'aggressive' and declares: 'The Minister's Cat is aggressive'. The next player adds an appropriate adjective beginning with a B and subsequent players must repeat all the adjectives used after adding their own. Soon we learn that the Minister's Cat is 'zealous, youthful, xenophobic, wily, vengeful, uncouth, treacherous, spiteful, round, quixotic, promiscuous, odd, noisy, miserable, lethal, knowing, jumping, ignorant, healthy, ginger, fierce, erudite, devious, calculating, bombastic and aggressive.' When Z is reached, the players go back to A and start again.

CONVERSE IN VERSE

Players: Any number

This is a good game to play after a few drinks. All of the participants must talk in verse, anyone who slips up being obliged to pay a forfeit. It may take a while to warm up but once everyone has got the hang of it, they'll be chatting away in rhymes as if it was the most natural thing in the world to do… and probably long after the game has finished.

MISMATCHES

Players: Any even number

The players divide into two teams and study the lounge for 30 seconds. While one team leaves the room, the other has two minutes in which to make a number of minor alterations to the room – moving a vase, placing a different magazine at the top of the pile. Wholesale redecorating is not recommended, neither is emptying the water from the goldfish bowl. At the end of the two minutes, the absentees return and attempt to spot the changes. One point is scored for each correctly-spotted mismatch, the other team gaining a point for each one that goes unnoticed. Then the two teams swap roles.

THE ATLAS GAME

Players: 8-12

This game should not be attempted by anyone who scored lower than a grade D at GCSE geography. One player is sent from the room while the others decide upon the name of a town which the missing player must identify from a series of cunning clues. The town selected should have the same number of letters as there are players left in the room – say SCUNTHORPE for 10 players. Each letter of the town is assigned to a different player who must then think of another town beginning with that letter. It is this second town which will yield the clue. The questioner returns and says to the player with the first letter of the mystery town: 'Tell me something about your town.' The player with the S has thought of Sydney as the alternative and gives four clues relating to Sydney – famous cricket ground, heavy lager drinkers, big bridge, opera house. When the questioner has deduced that the town being described is Sydney, he or she will know that the first letter of the sought-after word is an S. The game continues in this way through the remainder of the letters. If the questioner is unable to detect any town being described, he or she is left with a blank space and must hope to solve the riddle from the other letters. You'll probably find that one round of this game is quite sufficient.

THE YES, NO INTERLUDE

Players: 5-10

Fans of the TV game show Take Your Pick (and there must be some) will revel in the opportunity to re-create the infamous 'Yes, No Interlude'. One person is appointed question master and the remaining players are then wheeled in individually and subjected to intense questioning, during which they must refrain from using the words 'Yes' or 'No'. The player who keeps going the longest is the winner. If this exceeds 10 minutes, give it up as a lost cause and move on to the next player.

INITIAL HELP

Players: Any number

The first player thinks of a letter in the alphabet, say H, and gives a clue to a three-letter word beginning with that letter, as in 'H plus two letters is what you make while the sun shines' (hay). Whoever guesses correctly then thinks up a clue for a four-letter word beginning with H and so it goes on with the words getting progressively longer. When you can't think of a 15-letter word starting with H, move on to another letter. Finish the game when terminal boredom has set in.

ANAGRAM ACTION

Players: 6 or more

Prepare a series of anagrams of seven letters or more and, with the players seated attentively, read out slowly and steadily the letters of the first anagram. The first player to call out the correct solution scores a point.

WHAT A CORKER!

Players: Any even number

You will need:

10 crown corks

The best thing about this game is that to obtain the equipment necessary to play it, you have to drink 10 bottles of champagne. Once you've sobered up, set the corks in two rows of five, serrated edges down, on opposite sides of a table. Divide the players into two teams and invite one player from each team to try to turn the corks over, using only one finger. This is done by placing the finger on top of the cork and pressing on its edge. When one player has turned over all five, the next team mate takes over in relay fashion. Note: digit dampening is prohibited.

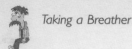
ALPHA AND OMEGA

Players: Any number

The players choose a fairly broad category – animals, rock bands, flowers, famous people etc – and the first person calls out any word belonging to the selected category. The second player then calls out another, beginning with the last letter of the first word, and the game continues in this fashion around the room. If the subject was rock bands, it could begin Genesis, Squeeze, Erasure, Eurythmics, Styx, XTC, Chicory Tip, Pulp, Prefab Sprout… Repetition or failure to think of a word results in elimination. The last player left in is the winner.

RAPID RESPONSE

Players: Any number

You will need:

Slips of paper, pencils, a hat or bowl

Give each player a pencil and two slips of paper and ask them to write the name of an unlikely object on each slip. All of the slips are shuffled around in a hat or bowl. The person chosen to act as question master draws out two slips at random and asks the first player a question – the dafter the better – the reply to which must mention both objects. For example, if the objects are a pair of Y-Fronts and an Eccles cake and the question is: 'Why do birds suddenly appear, every time you are near?', the reply could be: 'Because they come down for the Eccles cake which I hang up in a pair of your old Y-Fronts.' The person adjudged to have provided the best answer is declared the winner.

STINKETY PINKETY

Players: Any number

One player thinks up a definition, the answer to which is a rhyming adjective and noun. Thus 'a large sow' would be 'a big pig' and 'a metallic garden ornament' would be 'a chrome gnome'. The first player to call out the correct answer gains a point and supplies the next definition. As everyone becomes adept at this pastime, you can move on to rhyming words of more than one syllable such as 'a big cat on an Alpine mountain' (an 'Eiger tiger'), 'university intelligence' ('college knowledge') and 'a furry rodent from Merseyside' (a 'Wirral squirrel').

CROSS-EXAMINATION

Players: Any number

One player, the examiner, is sent from the room while the others decide upon an object or a person. When the examiner returns, he or she has to identify the object by asking four questions: 'Why do you like it?', 'When do you like it?', 'How do you like it?' and 'Where do you like it?' The answers to these questions must be truthful without revealing too much. For instance, if the respective answers were: 'Because it satisfies two people', 'First thing in the morning', 'Warm and moist', and 'Across the kitchen table', it would be an inspired guess to come up with the correct answer of tea bag. The examiner is allowed three guesses which can be made at any time during the questioning. Players take it in turns to act as examiner.

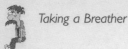

DISASSOCIATION

Players: Any number

Here is the opposite to 'Word Association' – a game where each word must bear absolutely no relation to the one before. Anyone who can spot a connection may issue a challenge and if the challenge is upheld by the other players, the challenged player loses a life. The first player to lose three lives brings the game to an end and must pay a forfeit. A sequence beginning 'orange, camel, cannon, lettuce, undertaker, golf ball, xylophone, chimney sweep' might seem totally unconnected but could bring about a challenge because Sooty, whose best friend is Sweep, used to play the xylophone, and might still do for all we know.

STRIP SEARCH

Players: 4-8

You will need:

A newspaper

Give each player one sheet from the same-sized newspaper. Starting at the top left-hand corner, they have to tear a continuous strip round and round until they have exhausted their sheet. The player with the longest unbroken strip wins.

TWENTY QUESTIONS

Players: Any number

Also known as 'Animal, Vegetable, Mineral', this is one of the most popular word games in the world, enjoyed by young and old alike. One person thinks of an object and tells the other players whether it is animal, vegetable, mineral or a combination of two. Humans count as animals, which will come as no surprise to anyone who's ever watched Arsenal play. The others then ask a series of questions, which can only be answered 'Yes' or 'No', in a bid to find the solution. If they succeed before 20 questions have been asked, they win. If not, the single player wins and as a reward is allowed to have another turn.

WEDDING GIFTS

Players: 5-10

You will need:

Pencils and paper, slips of paper and card

Each player assumes the role of someone who is soon to be married and who has just been presented with a wedding gift by work colleagues. He or she then has to make a thank-you speech, gushing over the joys of the present and how his or her future spouse will also derive enormous pleasure from it, but without ever mentioning it by name. To prepare their short speeches, the players are each given pencil and paper and a slip of paper bearing the name of the present. However, what they don't know is that the shop has accidentally sent an entirely different gift. As they read out their speeches behind a chair, the name of the replacement gift should be placed on a card in front of the chair so that the rest of the players can see it. Only when the speaker has finished does he or she discover the true identity of the gift. The prospective bride who has been eulogising about what she believes to be a sandwich-grill and how it 'cooks beautifully, quickly and evenly' may be rather disturbed to learn that she has been sent a budgie instead.

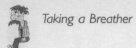
I LOVE MY LOVE

Players: Any number

'I love my love with an A', declares player one, 'because she is ambidextrous and acquiesces appealingly. I hate her when she is antagonistic and acts appallingly. I took her to Aberdeen and treated her to anchovies and apricots. Her name is Avril and she comes from Alexandria.' The game moves on to the next player who lists the same topics about his or her love, but with every word beginning with B, and so on through the alphabet. The little speeches should be announced without hesitation, anyone who falters or uses a word unknown to the English language is subjected to a forfeit.

WHAT'S THE BOOK?

Players: Any number

Here's a game for literary buffs. Lift a series of 10-line extracts from a wide range of books – from Jane Austen, to Noddy at the Seaside to the Volkswagen Polo User's Handbook – and read one at a time to your guests. Displaying their artistic acumen, they have to try to guess the title or at least the subject matter. Whoever is judged to be the closest earns a point.

TATE GALLERY

Players: Any number

You will need:

A large empty picture frame or rectangle of cardboard

In the centre of a circle of players, one person frames his or her face in an empty picture frame or similar-shaped object for two minutes without making any visible facial movement, other than the occasional blink. Anyone who fails to keep a straight face must hand over the frame to the next person and perform a suitable forfeit.

GHOST

Players: Any number

A game with more aliases than the average Crimewatch subject (it's also known as Donkey, Monkey, Wraiths and Chain Letters), this begins with all of the players sitting in a circle. The first player thinks of a word of four or more letters and calls out the first letter. The second player thinks of a word beginning with that letter and calls out the second letter of that word. The third player thinks of a word starting with the first two letters and calls out its third letter. The game progresses with each player trying to stretch the chain of letters and avoid calling out the last letter of a word. Any player who finishes a word loses a life. So if the first five letters are R, A, D, I, S, then the sixth player has no option but to add an H and thus complete a word. Players must always have a valid word in mind when adding a letter. They can be challenged if anyone suspects they have just plucked a letter at random without having any idea of a word. The challenged player must then reveal the word he or she was thinking of. If unable to come up with a valid word, he or she loses a life. But if he or she can declare a proper word, it is the challenger who loses a life. Any player who loses three lives is eliminated, the winner being the last player left in.

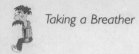

BACKWARDS GHOST

Players: Any number

For those whose intellectual capacity knows no limits, try playing 'Ghost' backwards, starting with the last letter of a word and working back towards the beginning. In this case, it is the player who announces the initial letter of the word who loses a life.

CARRY ON RHYMING

Players: Any number

The players sit in a circle and, in a clockwise direction, conduct a conversation so that the first word of their comment rhymes with the last word of the previous speaker's sentence. Anyone who fails in this task has to drop out. The last player left talking is the winner. A typical discussion might go along these lines:

> 'Now is the winter of our discontent'
> 'Bent – Richard III, his back was bent, I think.'
> 'Drink, don't mind if I do.'
> 'Sue, I'll fetch a glass in anticipation.'
> 'Asian Chardonnay, with a bit of luck.'

At this point, discretion is definitely the best part of valour.

ONE-MINUTE WONDERS

Players: 5-10

Each player has a minute to call out as many words as possible beginning with a pre-selected letter. Proper names are permissible but derivatives are not. So in the case of T, 'talk' is allowed, but not 'talked' or 'talking'. The highest score wins.

MOVIE QUIZ

Players: 6-10

This one's strictly for movie fans. Divide the players into two teams, flick through a film guide and announce the title of an old movie. Then ask the following questions: Who starred in the film? Name three co-stars. When was it released? Who was the director? What was it about? The questions should be open to both teams with a point awarded for each correct answer and at the end of, say, half-a-dozen films, the team with most points is the winner.

BO-OB

Players: Any number

In this game, players greet each other in the finest big business tradition of initials only. But the initials used are not those of the name of the player being greeted, but the first letters of a four or six-letter word. The reply must be in the form of the letters required to complete a word. For example, Mr Haddock might say to Mr C. Bass, 'Good morning, D.A.Z.', to which Mr Bass could reply, 'Nice to see you, Z.L.E.', making the word DAZZLE. The person doing the greeting must have a proper word in mind – if not, he or she faces elimination. And if the player being greeted does not complete the word within 10 seconds, he or she is also out of the game. The last player left in is the winner.

RING ON A STRING

Players: Any number

You will need:

A length of string, a ring

The players sit close together in a circle holding a piece of string which is long enough to stretch right around the circle. Threaded onto the string is a small ring. While one player stands in the centre, the ring is moved along the string from player to player, constantly switching direction. The player in the middle has to guess who has the ring at any given time. If he or she is right, the two players swap roles. After three incorrect guesses, another player takes over.

GALLOWS

Players: 4-6

You will need:

A length of string

The players sit in a circle with the tips of their raised forefingers meeting in the middle. Outside the circle lurks the executioner wielding a noose made of string. He slips the noose around the fingertips and holds up the end of the string. When he suddenly shouts 'Death!' and tugs at the string, the players have to try to whip their fingers away without becoming entrapped. Anyone who is too slow and whose finger gets caught in the noose is deemed executed. The winner is the last player left alive.

BACKWORDS

Players: Any number

Draw up a list of a dozen or so words which you can pronounce backwards, such as 'stink' (knits) or 'bulk' (klub). Call out the backward words and award a point to whoever deciphers each one first.

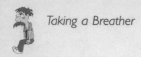

THE BIG MATCH

Players: Any number

You will need:

A large box of matches

Place the matches – 50 or more – in a pile on a table. Each player in turn takes up to six matches from the pile, the player who takes the very last match being the winner.

TEAPOT

Players: 3-8

'Alf wanted to teapot on the teapot pad, the one to the teapot of his typewriter.' It doesn't make a lot of sense until you realise that 'teapot' is the substitute for 'write' and 'right'. And that is the basis of this game – players have to substitute the word 'teapot' for a chosen word that has more than one meaning or for several words that are pronounced the same but have different meanings. One person leaves the room and the others choose their similar-sounding words. The single player then returns and asks a series of questions which must be answered by sentences featuring 'teapot'. When the questioner knows the word, he or she announces it and it is the turn of the player who provided the last answer to leave the room.

FORTUNATELY UNFORTUNATELY

Players: Any number

The players sit in a circle and the first player says a sentence beginning with 'Fortunately'. The next player must then say something beginning with 'Unfortunately' and this process of alternate 'Fortunately' and 'Unfortunately' sentences continues around the circle. Each sentence must make sense and anyone who hesitates unduly or who cannot think of a reply is ruled out. The last player left in is the winner. The key to victory is to try to catch the next person out with as ridiculous a statement as possible.

RINGS

Players: 4-8

You will need:

Wire coathangers, rubber rings

Almost an athletic pursuit, this gentle indoor version of quoits requires one coathanger and three rubber rings per pair of players. If you haven't got any proper rings, try sneaking the seals from preserving jars. The game is best played between two pairs at a time. The members of each pair should stand diagonally opposite each other, one with the rings, the other with the upturned hanger, so that the throwers have to lob the rings across each other's path to reach their respective targets – their partner's coathanger hook. Whichever pair gets most rings on the hook wins the game. The hanger holders are allowed to move their hangers to catch wayward shots.

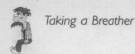

QUOTATION ROTATION

Players: Any number

This distinctly highbrow game begins with the players seated in a circle. In turn, they quote famous quotes at each other from memory, but each quote must contain at least one word of the previous player's quote. Anyone unable to think of a suitable quotation drops out. A similar fate meets any player found guilty of inventing a quotation (for these eventualities, it is best to keep a dictionary of quotations at hand). The last player still quoting is the winner.

CLUED UP

Players: 3-6

The quiz-master thinks of a word and reads out a one-word clue as to the identity of that word. If nobody guesses the word, another one-word clue is given, and so on until the puzzle is solved. The other players are each allowed one guess after each clue and whoever is the first to come up with the correct answer takes over as quiz-master for the next round. The initial clues should be difficult and open to all manner of interpretation, but the clues should become progressively easier. For example if the mystery word is 'horse', the clues could go: 'fly, clothes, hair, glue, box, radish, chestnut, foal, stallion, Dobbin.' If nobody has got the answer by then, it's really time they went home.

COLLECTIONS

Players: 5-10

You will need:

A collection of animal ornaments or cuddly toys, pieces of card

If you seem to have spent most of your life tripping over your children's cuddly bandicoot or fluffy Tasmanian Devil then here, at last, is an opportunity to put them to good use. Arrange a dozen soft animal toys on a table and place a name card beside each one. The imaginary names should be as similar as possible to maximise confusion – William, Willum, Wilhelmina, Wilma. The players are called in and have a minute to memorise the names. The toys and cards are then removed. Following a short interval (possibly while another game is being played), the toys are brought back in one at a time and the players are asked to name them. Whoever is first to call out the correct name gains a point. If your house is a cuddly-toy-free zone, you could always play the game with china animals.

I SPY

Players: Any number

Beloved by children, 'I Spy' is nevertheless a nice restful game for a party where everyone has already done too much rushing about. The rules are simple. One player thinks of an object that is visible in the room (say, a cobweb) and says: 'I spy with my little eye something beginning with C.' The other players then have to guess what the object is. The first to guess the word correctly takes over as spy... while the hostess swiftly fetches the dustpan and brush.

217

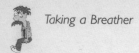

STEPPING STONES

Players: 3-8

You will need:

Pencils and paper

The degree of intelligence required for this game depends upon the attitude of the participants. The players have to give one of their number a journey from one subject to another via three stepping stones. Up to nine statements may be used to link the five subjects which must be covered in the order given. If a player is told to get from the Royal Family to Tennis via TV, America and Music, here is how the journey could be accomplished:

> The Queen lives at Windsor Castle. (Royal Family)
> Vic Windsor was a character in Emmerdale. (TV)
> Barbara Windsor has appeared in a number of Carry On films.
> The most recent Carry On film was Carry On Columbus. (America)
> It starred Bernard Cribbins who had a hit in the 1960s with
> Right Said Fred. (Music)
> Bernard Cribbins narrated The Wombles who live on
> Wimbledon Common. (Tennis)

If on the other hand the 'Stepping Stones' journey is from Nuclear Physics to Greek Literature via Latin Irregular Verbs, Wagnerian Works and the work of the Pre-Raphaelites, then you're probably at the wrong party.

DELIBERATE MISTAKES

Players: 4-8

Prepare a short story containing a number of factual errors, some obvious, others less so. For example, while most people will know that Nelson didn't fight at Waterloo, how many will remember, or perhaps care, which arm he lost? The story is then read aloud to the players who shout out 'Wrong!' whenever they suspect a mistake. If it is an error, that player gains a point. But an unsuccessful interruption loses a point.

MY OLD GRANNY

Players: 5-10

The object of this exercise is simply to make people laugh by uttering ridiculous statements – the sort of thing railway station announcers have been doing for years. The game leader goes to each player in turn and, looking them squarely in the eye, wails plaintively: 'Alas, alas, my old granny spontaneously combusted at bingo last night and I don't know what to do.' In reply, each player must make a reasonable suggestion while maintaining an inscrutably straight face. Anyone caught displaying the slightest hint of mirth will be disqualified. Those remaining take part in round two where the leader enlarges the problem. 'Alas, alas, my old granny spontaneously combusted at bingo last night and Mrs Jenkins next door has got a banana stuck in her ear and I don't know what to do.' After further helpful suggestions, any straight-faced survivors progress to the third and final round where the leader's dilemma reaches crisis point. 'Alas, alas, my old granny spontaneously combusted at bingo last night and Mrs. Jenkins next door has got a banana stuck in her ear and my boomerang won't come back and I don't know what to do.' Again suggestions are offered and any player who makes it through all three rounds should receive a prize.

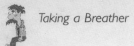
TWIN SPEAKERS

Players: Any even number

The players are divided into pairs, each of whom are secretly given connected identities – such as postmaster and postmistress, Pinky and Perky, snakes and ladders, cheese and onion, Sodom and Gomorrah. The first pair (maybe gin and tonic) step forward and the rest of the throng ask a series of questions of both partners. Each query is answerable only by a 'Yes' or 'No'. Whichever pair guesses the identities of the mystery couple will then take their place.

WHICH WORD?

Players: Any number

You will need:

Pencil and paper

Another variation of 'Taboo' but this time the forbidden fruit is a word rather than a letter. One person secretly writes the mystery word on a piece of paper and fires questions at each player in turn – the questions are cunningly designed to elicit a reply containing the banned word. For instance if the word is 'duck', questions might include:

> 'What would you do if a low-flying pigeon came towards you?'
> 'What's your favourite Chinese dish?'
> 'What do you see on the lake at the park?'
> 'What's the lowest score a batsman can get at cricket?'

All answers must be adequate, any player who is deliberately evasive, hesitant or who utters the forbidden word is eliminated. The last one left in is the winner.

SECRET LETTER

Players: 5-10

This is a bit like the game 'Taboo' except that here the players don't know the forbidden letter. The questioner picks a secret letter and asks each player in turn a question requiring a one-word answer. If the answer contains the letter, that player loses a life. The first to lose three lives has to pay a forfeit.

JACKANORY

Players: Any number

You will need:

A stop-watch

The players should sit in a circle with their legs intertwined. Those with an aversion to the person sitting next to them should either sit elsewhere or settle for touching knees. One player begins a story on any subject and must talk for 30 seconds without hesitation or repetition. The time is kept by a stopwatch-wielding judge who, at the end of the 30 seconds, calls 'Time up' and the story must then be continued from precisely where it left off (often in mid-sentence) by the next player. The 30-second stories continue round the circle with the judge watching for long pauses, repetition or anyone who makes the mistake of ending the story. Any player who is guilty of these deeds is promptly eliminated. The winner is the last player left talking.

MUSICAL INTERLUDES

MUSICAL STATUES

Players: Any number

You will need:

Music

This children's favourite can be equally entertaining with adults, particularly those blessed with no sense of rhythm or balance. The players dance away to the music and must be sure to move around rather than just jig on the spot. So even old Aunt Bertha must try a few steps to the sounds of Bon Jovi. When the music stops, everyone must 'freeze' and remain in that position. Any couple choosing to perform the literal version of 'Je t'aime…' could find this command quite pleasurable. Meanwhile, the host or hostess glides around the statues trying to make them move or giggle, but without actually touching them. Anyone who falls victim to their tactics is eliminated. After 20 seconds, the music re-starts and the next round begins. The game continues until only one dancer remains.

SOLDIERS

Players: Any number

You will need:

Two chairs

A chair is placed at either end of the room and when the music begins, all of the players must march around them like soldiers in single file. Whenever the music stops, they must perform the task set by their sergeant major. This could be anything from drill with a broom or marching and saluting on the spot to reciting the alphabet backwards. Any player who fails the inspection will be thrown in the guardhouse and will thus miss the remainder of the game. The sergeant major continues with the exercises until just one soldier remains.

FEELERS

Players: Any number

You will need:

Music, feather dusters

This saucy derivation of 'Musical Statues' sees players dancing around in a state of undress until the music stops. Then they must 'freeze' and, in the case of someone who is down to her bra and knickers, probably quite literally. Next, armed with a feather duster, the host or hostess strolls among the scantily-clad statues for 10 seconds and attempts to tickle their fancy before the music starts up again. Anyone moving so much as a muscle drops out and joins in the tickling for the next round, which is actually more fun than doing the dancing. The last player left in wins the game.

MUSICAL NUMBERS

Players: Any number

You will need:

Music

Watch your guests dance merrily around the room, but then suddenly stop the music and call out a number – 'threes', 'sixes', 'sevens' or whatever. The players immediately have to form groups of that number, anyone who fails to join a group being out. The last player left in emerges as the victor. If you want a short game, call out 'nines' when there are only eight players.

THE BLIND CONDUCTOR

Players: Any number

You will need:

Blindfold, pencil

All of the players stand in a circle except for one person in the middle who is blind-folded and holding a pencil. This is the conductor's baton. The conductor waves his baton merrily while the other players walk round in a circle singing or humming a well-known tune, but when he or she suddenly stops, the players in the circle also must stop immediately. The conductor then points to one of the players who has to sing the song alone, in a disguised voice if necessary. The conductor has to guess who is singing. If the guess is successful, the two players change places; if unsuccessful, the players in the circle all start singing a new song and the conductor has to try again.

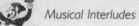

SIMON SINGS

Players: Any number

For this musical version of 'Simon Says', you sing out instructions to your players. It's similar to the well-known 'Simon Says' rules. If the command begins 'Simon sings do this', the players must follow suit, but if the order starts with: 'Do that', they must not copy. Any player who fails to obey an instruction is out. This game should be played at break-neck speed so that everyone becomes totally disorientated.

MUSICAL STICKS

Players: 5-10

You will need:

A garden cane or umbrella, music

The players sit in a circle and one of them is given a garden cane, an umbrella or some form of stick. When the music starts, the player with the stick taps one end on the floor three times and passes it to the player on his or her right. This person repeats the performance and the stick continues its journey until the music stops. Whoever is left holding the stick at that point is eliminated. As players fear the music is about to stop, the tapping will become increasingly frantic. The last player left wins.

I AM THE MUSIC MAN

Players: 5-10

The first music man sings out: 'I am the music man, I come from down your way and I can play.' At which the others query: 'What can you play?' Imitating perhaps the actions and noise of a trombone, the music man declares: 'I play the slide trombone.' The next in line assumes the mantle. 'I am the music man, I come from down your way and I can play.' 'What can you play?' Copying the first player's performance, he replies: 'I play the slide trombone', adding perhaps 'and the piano,' whereupon he does an impression of Elton John or Mrs Mills. The game continues with each player repeating the sequence and adding a new instrument. Anyone who fails to adhere to the correct order or who can't think of an instrument has to drop out. This game can last as long as a symphony, by which time if you hear that yet another music man comes from down your way, you'd probably want to move house.

GRAB

Players: Any uneven number

For this traditional game, all the players except one choose partners and parade around the room singing the following to the tune of your choice:

'There was a jolly miller who lived by himself

As the wheel went round he made his wealth.

One hand in the hopper, the other in the bag

As the wheel went round he made a grab.'

On the word 'grab', everyone must swap partners, including the singleton. After an unseemly scramble for a mate, reminiscent of the Top Rank on a Saturday night when the smoochy songs begin, whoever is left without a partner becomes the poor miller for the next round.

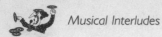

MUSICAL ISLANDS

Players: Any number

You will need:

Pieces of newspaper, music

Tear up some pieces of newspaper and scatter half a dozen or so (depending on the number of players) around the room to represent islands. When the music starts, the players dance around in a circle, but as soon as it stops, they must stand on an island. More than one player may stand on one island. Anyone who fails to find dry ground is considered to have been drowned – heartless, isn't it? After each round, an island is removed so that it becomes more difficult for the players to find sanctuary. The last player left in is the winner.

NEXT LINES

Players: Any number

Pre-record on to tape a number of well-known songs. Play them back to your audience but then press the pause button at a crucial moment and ask them to sing out the next line. The first player to sing the right words earns a point. The song should only be paused when most people would be able to identify it. In the case of a particularly distinctive intro, this could be before the first line, but usually it will be at the beginning of the chorus. Points should be deducted for singing like a cat on heat.

THE GRAND BALL

Players: Any even number of men and women

You will need:

Balloons, music

Guests are randomly given inflated balloons and must then seek out a member of the opposite sex with the same colour balloon. When everyone is paired off, the couples wedge their balloons between their knees and form a circular chain by holding hands. As the music starts, the whole chain shuffles around the room in time to the music, all those who drop or burst their balloon are disqualified along with their partner. The game continues until just one pair is left in the chain.

PASS THE PARCEL

Players: Any number

You will need:

An object, wrapping paper, music

Wrap a small object in layer upon layer of paper so that it assumes the guise of a sizeable parcel. The players sit in a circle and pass the parcel in a clockwise direction while the music is playing. Whoever is holding the parcel at the moment the music stops is eliminated. The last person left in unwraps the parcel and claims the prize.

PASS THE PARCEL – THE SEQUEL

Players: Any number

You will need:

An object, wrapping paper, music

In a more caring version of 'Pass the Parcel', whoever is holding the parcel when the music stops is permitted to remove one layer of wrapping. Nobody drops out and the person who removes the last layer of paper keeps the prize. Make sure that the parcel stays on the move while the music is playing to stop avaricious guests trying to hog it and thereby seize the mystery treasure.

SURPRISE PACKAGE

Players: Any number

You will need:

An object, wrapping paper, music

The preparation for this game is the same as for 'Pass the Parcel' except that in each layer of wrapping you should write a forfeit. When the music stops, the player holding the parcel undoes a layer and has to perform the forfeit contained within. If nobody is holding the parcel, the last person who touched it has to suffer the terrible ignominy of the forfeit. Suitable wheezes include:

Hopping around on one leg, shouting 'Pieces of eight, pieces of eight' (not to be given to anyone with an artificial leg)

Singing Orville's Song as Orville

Drinking a glass of water with a teaspoon

Reciting Little Bo Peep in a thick Birmingham accent (not for parties in the West Midlands)

Waltzing around the room with a lamp stand (don't forget to unplug it first)

ARCHES

Players: Any even number

You will need:

Music

Two pairs of players line up, one standing at each end of the room, and join hands and raise them above their heads to form an arch. The others players also pair off and, when the music begins, they dance through the arches. When the music stops, the arches lower their arms to ensnare any couples who happened to be passing through at the time. Any pair caught then forms another arch, with the game continuing until only one pair remains.

TV THEMES

Players: Any number

This is a job for the party's resident couch potato. He or she should hum, whistle or warble a succession of musical themes to well-known TV programmes – things like Bonanza, Only Fools and Horses and EastEnders. The first player to call out the correct answer gains a point.

CIRCLE LINE

Players: Any even number

You will need:

Music

This game can also serve as a useful ice-breaker at parties. The players form two circles, an inner and an outer. The women stand in the inner circle and the men in the outer. The two circles should be facing each other. When the music starts, the circles dance round in opposite directions. When it stops, the host calls out a subject and everyone must talk to the person opposite on that topic for a minute. It could be anything from a detailed analysis of the lyrics of Funky Moped to the virtues of clean underwear. As the music re-starts, the circles head off in opposite directions once more and a further one-minute conversation ensues, on a different topic. The game ends when everyone is fed up of dancing or talking, or when some couples have hit it off so well that they've disappeared into the bedroom.

RING ROUND

Players: Any even number

You will need:

Music

The set-up for this game is the same as for 'Circle Line' with women and men forming two circles, one circle inside the other, and dancing round to the music in opposite directions. But this time when the music stops, the players facing each other must perform a nominated forfeit. So if the host calls out: 'Bray like a donkey', the room will suddenly resemble Blackpool beach. The game continues until most players have performed a forfeit with each other or until everyone has had enough.

MUSICAL CHAIRS

Players: Any number

You will need:

Chairs, music

At some time in his life Oscar Wilde must have said: 'He who hasn't played Musical Chairs hasn't lived.' And the old favourite makes a splendid adult party game with the addition of a few forfeits. Place the chairs – one fewer than the number of players – in a circle with the seats facing outwards. The players dance around to the music in a carefree manner until the moment the music stops, when they make a dive for the nearest chair. Whoever fails to find a seat has to perform a forfeit and suffers the added pain of elimination. A chair is removed and the band strike up the music once more, the game continuing until there's just one player left.

LAP TOP

Players: Any uneven number

You will need:

Chairs, music

Arrange a circle of chairs, one chair for every two players. Sit half of the guests in the chairs and get the other half plus one to dance around to the music. When the music stops, the dancers leap on to the nearest lap, unless it's someone with whom they would rather avoid physical contact, in which case they seek an alternative lap at the risk of being eliminated, because the person who fails to find a lap is out. For the next round, one chair and lap are removed and play continues à la 'Musical Chairs' until there's just one dancer left. It's interesting to observe how some people will sit on absolutely anybody's lap rather than face losing the game.

ANTICIPATION

Players: Any number

You will need:

Music

One person is chosen to operate the music and stands with his or her back to the other players who are seated on the floor or on chairs. They have to anticipate whenever the operator is about to switch off the music, by watching for tell-tale signs. For when the music is turned off, they have to stand up immediately. Anyone rising while the music is still playing is eliminated, as is the last person to get up once the sounds have ceased. The game continues until one player remains.

MUSICAL SPOONS

Players: Any number

You will need:

Spoons, music, blindfolds (optional)

This is not a game for those who wish to emerge from the party with their dignity intact. Scatter a number of spoons on the floor, one fewer than there are players. At the sound of music, the players crawl about the floor, endeavouring to maintain as much rhythm as is possible on all-fours. When the music stops, everyone tries to grab a spoon. One unlucky individual is out. Before the music starts again, a spoon is removed and the game carries on until there are two players left fighting over a solitary spoon. The winner of that tussle is the overall victor. To make the game even more interesting, it can be played blindfolded which will probably lead to a lot of groping in the dark. And if it doesn't, play it again until everyone gets the message.

MUSICAL HATS

Players: Any number

You will need:

Hats, music

Seated in a circle, all the players except one are given hats of some shape or form. A good selection of headgear makes for a more entertaining game – such as a sou'wester, a floral bonnet and a crash helmet. When the music starts, the players pass round the hats and when it stops, anyone holding a hat puts it on their head. The player left hatless retires from the proceedings, taking away a hat for good measure. The game continues until only one player remains.

INSTRUMENTAL

Players: Any number

One player acts as the conductor with the rest as the orchestra. At random, the conductor points to a member of the orchestra and calls out the name of a musical instrument. The chosen person then has to imitate both the sound and the playing action of that instrument. If the rendition is judged hopelessly inaccurate, that player is sacked from the orchestra. The game ends when the full orchestra has been reduced to a soloist. Start with relatively easy instruments – trumpet, flute, violin – before graduating to the likes of cor anglais, flugelhorn and clavichord.

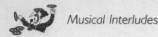

AVOID THE CUSHION

Players: Any number

You will need:

A cushion, music

A cushion is placed on its end in the centre of the room and the players form a circle around it. When the music starts, the players link arms and dance around the cushion. The aim of every player is to pull someone else over the cushion while at the same time trying to prevent themselves being subjected to the same fate. Anyone who knocks over the cushion is eliminated. The last player dancing round the cushion wins the game but looks a complete idiot.

MUSICAL HOTCH POTCH

Players: Any number

You will need:

Assorted small objects, music

A pile of small objects, one fewer than the number of players, is placed in the middle of the room. When the music starts, each player dives for an article from the pile and holds it up for the judge to see. The poor unfortunate who did not manage to claim an item is ruled out. Before the next round, one item is removed and the game continues in the traditional manner until only one player is left. Unless you've been desperate to get rid of that china anteater which the mother-in-law bought six Christmases ago, it's advisable to choose unbreakable objects as the 'Musical Hotch Potch' scrum can get quite physical.

MAESTRO!

Players: Any number

One player assumes the role of conductor and assigns each of the other players a specific musical instrument. When the conductor starts to clap, all the players must play their imaginary instruments, complete with actions and sounds. When the conductor stops clapping and indicates a particular instrument (maybe by drawing a pretend bow across an invisible cello), all the players except the cellist must stop playing immediately. Any musician who continues playing after the conductor has changed to another is eliminated, as is anyone who doesn't spot that the conductor has switched to his or her instrument. The best results will be achieved by a lightning conductor who swaps instruments with great frequency.

NOT
IN FRONT
OF THE VICAR

SPANKETY-SPANK

Players: 4-8

You will need:

A chair

Even if you don't know S & M from M & S, you'll be hard-pushed to play this game without deriving a modicum of pleasure. One person sits in a chair while another kneels in front with his or her head buried in the other's lap. For the sake of harmony, it is best if the two who at least start in these positions do not harbour a mutual loathing. The rest of the party skip delightfully around this little scenario, pausing en route to spank the bottom of the kneeler. Depending on whose posterior this is, the spank may take the form of a gentle caress or a full-blooded thwack (nothing too violent of course!) The kneeler's job is to guess the identity of any of the spankers, although if the kneeler is happy where his face is, he may not be in too much of a hurry to do so. When a spanker is recognised, it's that person's turn to kneel and to choose someone else to sit in the chair. There are no winners, but the kneeler invariably comes up with a smile.

DESIRE

Players: Any even number

You will need:

A pack of playing cards

Discard the picture cards and the aces from an ordinary pack of playing cards so that you're left with the numbers from two to 10. The game is played by pairs with the rest of the ensemble looking on, waiting anxiously for their turn. As host, you can exercise your power by nominating the pairs or you may prefer to allow them to choose for themselves. The first couple sit together and each pick a card without revealing the number. Without speaking (although sighing, moaning and grunting are permitted), they must proceed to act out the strength of their desire for each other, as determined by the numbers on their respective cards. The higher the card, the more intense the desire. At the end of the demonstration, the audience have to try to guess both numbers. If both participants draw a 10, it may be necessary to have a bucket of cold water at hand.

KISS, PIGGY, KISS

Players: Any number

You will need:

A blindfold

The players form a circle around one person who is blindfolded. They then prance around for a minute holding hands while the blindfolded one turns on the spot in the opposite direction. At the end of the minute, he or she fumbles around for the first available person in the circle and kisses them full on the mouth. From that fleeting moment of passion, he or she must try to recognise the owner of the mouth. In the event of a correct guess, the blindfold's removed and handed over to the kissee who then takes a turn in the middle. But if the blindfolded person fails to recognise the lips, or simply fancies another snog, he or she tries all over again. In the interests of safety, a time limit should be set on each kiss as it has been known for the fire brigade to be called out to prise lips apart.

CONTORTIONISTS

Players: Any even number of men and women

The players divide up into pairs – one man and one woman. Given the nature of this game, it's probably best if the couple are closely acquainted or, at the very least, not allergic to each other. The object of the exercise is for the pair to change into each other's clothes while still maintaining some form of physical contact – touching feet, holding hands or anything else they can manage. In the name of decency and, in some cases hygiene, all underwear should be kept on. The first couple to swap clothing without infringing the rules wins the game.

THE CROSS-DRESSING DERBY

Players: 4-8

You will need:

A supply of clothes (men's and women's)

Dig out an assortment of clothes – men's and women's – and place them in separate piles at one end of the room. Each pile should contain a complete outfit – shoes, stockings or socks, underwear, skirt or trousers, shirt or blouse and hat. The competitors line up at the other end of the room – the men opposite the women's clothes and vice versa. On the command 'Go!', each of the players run across to their respective pile and put on the first item of clothing, which could be a problem with burly men trying to squeeze into women's knickers. They then race back to the starting point, touch the wall and dash to put on another item. The first player to arrive back at the starting line, with every item of clothing somewhere about their body, is the winner and gets to change back into his or her own clothes.

PASS THE ORANGE

Players: Any number

You will need:

Oranges

Who would have thought that the humble orange could fulfil such an intimate role at a party? But thanks to this game, countless future partners first set eyes on each other across a juicy Jaffa. The players line up in teams of four or five. Each team is equipped with an orange. The first player places the orange under his or her chin and passes it to the next player's chin. Hands must not be used. The orange continues its journey in this fashion down the line and is then returned in the same way back to the first player. The first team to complete these two lengths is declared the winner. Any team which drops its orange en route must return to the start.

SCOOP!

Players: 3-8

You will need:

Pencil and paper

The first person thinks of a word to feature in a suitably lurid newspaper headline, the sort of thing you find in the News of the World. If the first player suggests 'NUNS', the second player has to think of a word to be added before or after, perhaps 'NAUGHTY'. And so it continues round the room with each player adding a word until the presses roll with something like NAUGHTY NUNS IN SEX ROMP WITH BAWDY BISHOP. It is best to limit the number of words to a maximum of 10, although you can always tag on a subsidiary heading such as '– Defrocked in the Vestry'.

SCOOP CONSEQUENCES

Players: Any number

You will need:

Pencils and paper

'Scoop' can also be played as a form of written consequences with five contributors for each headline. Either multiple or single words can be used. To make the game work, the first word should be an adjective, the second should be a noun, the third should be a verb, the fourth the object of the verb and the fifth a location. The first word is written at the top of the paper which is then handed to the next player. He or she adds another word, folds the paper to conceal the first word, and passes it on. Each time the paper is passed on, only the last-written word should be visible. The end product could be something along the lines of: GUN-TOTING POODLES ROB PET SHOP IN HIGH STREET – Police Looking For Leads.

FEEDING THE BABY

Players: Any even number

You will need:

Babies' bottles, bibs, drinks

Most men regress to childhood at least once a day, so what better than to take them back to the time when they were babies? 'Feeding the Baby' – and before you get too excited, this is bottle-feeding, not breast-feeding – begins with the women sitting on chairs at one end of the room, holding bibs and babies' bottles half-filled with something like lager or Lucozade, or even champagne for the well-heeled infant. Meanwhile, the men stand at the other end of the room. On the command 'Go!', they rush over to their partners and sit on their laps – for which they'll no doubt need minimum of encouragement – where the women tie bibs around their necks. The men then suck on the teat of the bottle as fast as they can. The men are allowed to grip onto their 'mother' but mustn't touch the bottle with their hands. Once the bottle is empty, the woman unties the bib and she and 'baby' run back to the starting line, the first pair home win. The situation can then be reversed with the men feeding the women.

ALL CHANGE

Players: Equal numbers of men and women

With the players pairing off into male/female couples, switch off the lights for two minutes. There then follows much groping in the dark and fumbling with bra straps as the couples attempt to swap as many clothes as possible. The pair who have put on the most of each other's clothes when the lights are turned back on are the winners.

BUTTOCKS

Players: 3-8

You will need:

Coins, a dish

Apparently a game much loved by royalty down the years, Buttocks certainly lives up to its name. It invites players to transport a coin between their clenched buttocks from one end of the room to the other and to deposit it in a dish. Hands may only be used for the initial loading process. The player who has deposited most coins at the end of five minutes wins the game. For fear of accidents, it's best if this activity is played fully clothed, but even then 5p pieces should be avoided because of their size and the hard edges of 50p coins can chafe... er, apparently.

SCRIMMAGE

Players: 10 or more

You will need:

A length of tape or string

If you've ever wondered what it would be like to host a full-blooded rugby scrum in your front room, here's your chance to find out. Two teams of roughly equal strength (not necessarily equal numbers) line up, heads down, in scrum style across a line of tape or string drawn down the centre of the room. By pushing, shoving and thrusting, each team tries to force itself over the line and prevent the other team from doing so. The team which gets every member across the line is the winner. The amount of dress worn for this game is optional, but bear in mind that the average scrum contains much mauling, tugging and groping of buttocks.

STRIP TABOO

Players: 4-8

The rules here are the same as for ordinary 'Taboo' except that whoever is guilty of uttering the forbidden letter has to remove an item of clothing as punishment. Extroverts may choose to wear practically nothing and then deliberately try to say the banned letter. Those who are more reserved, however, may either skip this pastime altogether or dress up in layer upon layer of clothing so that by the time there is any danger of an inch or two of bare flesh being revealed, everyone will have lost interest.

MALICIOUS RUMOURS

Players: Any number

You will need:

Pencil and paper

While one of your guests leaves the room, the other players huddle together and each tries to think up an item of gossip about the person outside. These rumours may contain an element of truth or they can be totally fictional, depending upon the sensitivities of the people involved. They could be anything from 'He only changes his socks once a week' to 'She even irons the face flannels'. Each item of gossip is written down next to the name of the rumour-monger and when the victim returns, the list of accusations is read out. The victim must attempt to match each rumour with the person responsible for spreading it, two points being awarded for a correct pairing. When the whole list has been discussed, the points are added up and the next player leaves the room while the first player finds out who really did say she slept with the milkman – and his horse. When everyone has had a turn, the player with the highest points total is declared the winner.

KEY CHAIN

Players: 3 or more

You will need:

A key, a length of string

The number of people able to play this game at any one time is governed by the answer to a simple question: How long is a piece of string? For the longer the string, the more players it can accommodate. The game is played with a key on a length of string. The players stand in a line – men and women alternating – and have to thread themselves onto the string. The first player threads the key down the inside of his clothes from the top of his shirt to the bottom of his trousers. The woman next to him then threads it up the inside of her clothes from her skirt to her neck, and so it continues along the line. There are no winners or losers but it can be a titillating experience, particularly if the dastardly host has placed the key in the freezer before the game…

SOUNDS SEXY

Players: Any number

The challenge here is to think of as many sexy words as possible, each beginning with the last letter of the previous player's word. The players sit in a circle and play proceeds in a clockwise direction. Any player unable to think of a word, or whose word is not deemed sufficiently sexy by the rest of the party, has to perform a suitable forfeit decided upon by the others. The degree of embarrassment of this game depends upon the nature of its forfeits. Players may defend the sexiness of their word vigorously in a bid to escape the forfeit. For example, if the 'Sounds Sexy' word sequence goes, 'sensual, lust, Thompson', the last player may argue that he finds Emma Thompson incredibly sexy. It is for the rest of the group to decide whether such feelings are likely.

TRICKY PREDICAMENTS

Players: Any number

You will need:

Pencils and paper

In advance of the party, you need to think up a number of bizarre predicaments, one per player. Each situation will form the climax of a story, hastily composed by the guest to whom it has been assigned. Deal out your endings to the most appropriate players and then allow each three minutes to produce a story which might plausibly lead up to the finale. Then get them to read out their efforts, a prize going to the most imaginative composition. Here are a few predicaments to give you an idea of what is required:

'The last thing I had expected was to have sex with a guardsman, especially in the middle of Trooping the Colour.'
'And that's how I came to be chained to a topless model on my stag night.'
'I never realised I could derive so much pleasure from a banana until I met Peter.'
'And the next thing I knew I was sucking strawberry ice cream off the toes of a High Court judge.'
'The plumber looked at me, ballcock in hand, and I instinctively knew that the ironing would have to wait.'

A TENDER BEHIND

Players: 6 or more

This is very much a game of surprise. One man starts chugging round the room like a train and invites a woman who takes his fancy to be his tender behind. She places her arms around his hips and they chug out of the room. When they are out of sight and earshot, he goes to kiss her but at the last moment gives her a playful slap instead. She is naturally aggrieved until he explains to her that it's all part of the game. So they rejoin the throng and pick another man to join the train. Once out of the room, the first man kisses the woman and she goes to kiss the second man, but slaps him gently instead. When a fourth person joins in, player one kisses player two, player two kisses player three, and player three feigns to kiss player four before changing it to a slap. With growing anticipation, further carriages are recruited, only to be rewarded initially with a slap in the face before the kissing begins. The game continues until everyone has joined the train, but spare a thought for the poor soul who is last to be picked and therefore misses out on all the kissing and just receives the slap in the face. To avoid occupying that unwanted position, go easy on the garlic dip.

LOUD AND LOW

Players: Any number

You will need:

A saucepan, a wooden spoon

This is a variation of the children's game 'Hot and Cold' where you used to say, 'getting warmer, very warm, hot, boiling hot' until the searcher found the hidden object. Here, the indication of proximity is made not in degrees Fahrenheit but by beating on a saucepan with a wooden spoon. The louder the tapping, the closer the hunter is to his or her goal, the final moments being greeted by a veritable wall of sound of which any steel band would be proud. The game begins with one player being sent from the room and everyone else thinking of something they would really like to see him or her do. Of course, the more risqué the suggestion, the more intruiging the consequences. If the best you can come up with is 'get him to make a nice cup of tea', then you'll probably find your guests leaving before the pubs have shut. Instead, get a man to kiss the woman you know he's fancied for ages or to nibble the earlobes of the local traffic warden. Then when the person returns, the pan-tapper sets to work, skillfully steering him or her towards the chosen target to the feverish anticipation of the onlookers. For this is one of those games where just as much pleasure can be derived from watching as from playing.

NAUGHTY NUMBERS

Players: Any number

Give each player a secret number – the men should have odd numbers, the women even numbers. Arrange your guests in a circle except for one man who is chosen to go in the middle. He then calls out two even numbers whereupon the women with those numbers rush forward to kiss him. The first to do so takes his place in the middle and then calls out two odd numbers, inviting the two men assigned those numbers to come forward for a peck on the cheek or something stronger depending on the level of attraction. Unless you are of a gay disposition, it's advisable to remember which sex has which numbers.

FOOD–TASTING RELAY

Players: 10 or more

You will need:

A quantity of whipped cream, spoons, chairs

Divide the players into teams of five and seat four members of each team in chairs. The fifth member is supplied with a tub of whipped cream (real or synthetic) and has to move along the line spooning a small portion of cream onto the bare flesh of each player. The key rule is that in each case it must be a different part of the anatomy – say a hand, a knee, a cheek or a bald head. Having done the smearing, the player races back to the start and goes down the line, licking off the cream from his or her four team-mates. When the run is completed, that player sits down in the first chair and the previous occupant is handed the tub of cream for a repeat performance. The first team in which all five members have smeared and licked one another is declared the winner. As the competitors race against the clock and the licking becomes more frantic, cream does tend to fly everywhere, so it's worth protecting your floors with plastic sheets.

WHOSE FEET?

Players: Any number

You will need:

A screen or sheet, pencils and paper

If you haven't washed your feet for a week or boast a distinctive set of verrucas, you'd best give this game a miss. For it requires two teams to try to identify each other from their bare feet. While the first team leave the room, the others remove shoes, socks, tights, corn plasters etc, and position themselves behind a large screen or sheet so that only their ankles and feet are visible. The first team then returns for close inspection. They may caress the feet but must not tickle in case the resultant giggle proves identifiable. The inspectors write down their answers and the player with most correct identifications wins the game. The two teams then reverse roles. This is generally a good-natured game although a bit of ill-feeling can creep in if Cindy Rogers, the model, finds her feet mistaken for those of Bert Blatherwick, the builder.

THE CATWALK GAME

Players: Any number

You will need:

Two volunteer models, clothing, pencils and paper

All of the guests are seated. They are then told that a female model will walk around the room, displaying the latest designer labels, and that they should make a mental note of what she is wearing. When she leaves, the players are handed pencils and paper and told to write down as much as they can remember about her outfit. Obviously the more accessories she can muster – gloves, jewellery, Zimmerframe etc – the better. Next the guests are informed that a male model will be parading on the catwalk and, sure enough, a man enters dressed only in boxer shorts or swimming trunks, whichever is readily accessible. The players are then told that they have two minutes to write down not what he is wearing, but what he will be wearing when he reappears fully dressed. On his return, the lists are checked and a point awarded for every correct prediction. The player with the highest combined total for both models wins the game.

WAGGING TONGUES

Players: 8 or more

You will need:

Peanuts

This game is best played by people who know each other fairly well, although if they don't at the start, there's a fair chance that they will by the end. The players are divided into teams of four who stand in lines. The aim of the game is to transport a peanut down the line, solely by the use of the players' tongues. No hands are allowed. In the event of swallowing or dropping one's nut, a substitute nut may be introduced but play must go back to the start. Any couple suspected of taking an undue length of time over transferring the nut from one tongue to the next may be hosed down with cold water. The first team to tongue-lift the peanut from one end of the line to the other wins the game.

FANTASIES

Players: Any number

You will need:

Pencils and cards

Players are asked to write down their secret fantasies, restricting their ideas to present company and surroundings. Their cards are collected, shuffled and re-distributed among the gathering. Where feasible, they must then undertake the prescribed task. Should the suggestion be too outrageous, they can refuse on the grounds that it may incriminate them. If they're really lucky, they'll be able to act out their own fantasy – although of course it will now become public knowledge – or conversely they may find themselves obliged to writhe around on the floor with Mrs Blenkinsop. Should the card fall to Mr Blenkinsop, he may choose to pass. When all of the suitable ideas have been performed, everyone must try to guess which fantasy belonged to whom. This is probably the most embarrassing part of the whole game.

DREAM DATE

Players: 5-10

You will need:

Pencils and paper

Choose two players (one man, one woman) who are to select partners for their blind date. Get each of them to write down a list of three questions which they would put to a potential suitor – such as 'Where would you take me on a dream date?'; 'Which celebrity do you think you most resemble, and why?'; 'Do you believe in sex before Match of the Day?' Then get each of the women to write down their answers to the man's questions and each of the men to compose their replies to the woman's. Beginning with the woman, and taking each question at a time, read out the men's answers without disclosing who wrote them. After listening to the replies, the woman must decide who she would choose to accompany her on their date. Only then is the author of the answers revealed. This can be a harrowing moment... The process is then repeated with the man listening to the women's responses.

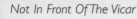
POSTMAN'S KNOCK

Players: Any number

No party is complete without this all-time favourite. One male guest is chosen to be the postman and as such has to leave the room. Meanwhile, the rest of the players are given numbers – even for the men, odd for the women. When they're ready, the postman knocks on the door and announces that he has something for a certain house number (odd) and adds 'Come and get it!' The woman with that number duly obliges and goes out to join the postman who tries to prove himself to be a first-class male by giving her a kiss. The pair return to the room and one of the women takes over the sorting bag in the guise of postmistress. The other players choose new numbers and the postmistress knocks to announce that she has something for a house with an even number. The occupant goes out to receive his kiss and the game continues until everyone in the street has a smile on their face.

CHOICES

Players: Any number

You will need:

Pencils and paper

The players sit in a circle and all compile lists of four people of the opposite sex. Each person's list is then passed on to the person immediately on their right. Faced with someone else's selection – the names can be celebrities or fellow party guests – the players have to explain their significance. For example, if a woman receives a list reading, 'Tom Cruise, John Cleese, Paul Daniels and Mr Watts, the local greengrocer', she may reveal that Tom Cruise is the person she'd most like to have an affair with, John Cleese is the person most likely to make her laugh, Paul Daniels is the person she would least like to employ as a librarian, and the local greengrocer is the person she is most likely to get her oats from. The most imaginative set of answers wins a prize.

THE FEATHER GAME

Players: 3-8

You will need:

A blanket, a feather

A large blanket is draped across the floor and all of the players sit beneath it, fully-clothed, pulling it up to their chin. Someone throws a feather into the air and everybody starts puffing furiously… and with good reason. For the penalty for allowing the feather to be blown over your shoulder is to remove an item of clothing which must then be raised above the blanket as proof. If one person is soon obliged to hoist a number of trophies aloft, there will be a discernible shift beneath the blanket as other players try to move closer to him or her. This is therefore one game where the loser can most definitely end up the winner.

BANANA TWIST

Players: Even numbers of men and women

You will need:

A supply of bananas

The players split up into male/female pairs and each pair is given a banana. The man stands with his legs apart, rather like the Sheriff of Nottingham's men used to do in The Adventures of Robin Hood and, on the command 'Go!', the woman has to use her hands to cajole the banana up the inside of the right leg of his trousers and down the left leg, the first banana to emerge from the bottom of the left leg earning victory. The push and squeeze is the favoured method and obviously the descent is much easier unless he happens to be wearing drainpipes. Inevitably, the tricky bit is across the top. Either route can be taken – fore or aft – but at no time may the man lend a hand. Nor may trousers be removed to free a trapped banana. If a banana does become lodged, you simply have to try to grin and bear it.

IN FULL
SWING

AS YOU LIKE IT

Players: Any number

You will need:

Pencils, name cards for each guest

Cards are prepared, each bearing the name of one of the guests, and are divided into two piles according to sex. Each woman is asked to draw a man's card and vice-versa. All of the guests are told to write some action or stunt – the more outrageous the better – on the card. It could be anything from singing Like a Virgin in just bra and knickers to downing a pint in one go or passionately kissing the hostess. Then comes the catch. Everyone assumes that the person named on the card has to perform the dubious deed but instead the host asks each player to read out what they have written and says: 'If that's what you want, let's see you do it!' Cue gross embarrassment...

SPANISH INQUISITION

Players: Any number

The players sit in a circle except for one person standing in the middle who acts as inquisitor and thinks up three categories – perhaps fish, American states and movie stars. Displaying the aggressive tactics which made Torquemada's reputation, the inquisitor points at a particular player, shouts out a category and demands an instant answer, such as 'halibut' if the category is fish. A split second later, he will be pointing at another unfortunate and yelling out a different category or maybe the same one. Again the reply must be immediate. Alternatively, he may even wish to persecute the same player on up to three successive occasions (the maximum allowed). The punishment for failing to give an answer straight away, or repeating an earlier answer, is elimination from the game... unless of course there happens to be a rack handy.

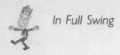
THE GRAPEFRUIT SHUFFLE

Players: 8 or more

You will need:

Two grapefruits

Two teams of equal numbers sit on the floor facing each other with their legs out-stretched. The game then begins with the host placing a grapefruit on the ankles of the first player in each team and they then have to pass the fruit down the line as quickly as possible without using any other part of their anatomy. Should the grape-fruit fall off or roll away, the offending team then has to start all over again. The winning team is the first one to finish the whole course. For those who like to throw all convention to the wind, this game can also be played with an orange.

SUPERLATIVES

Players: Any number

You will need:

Brown paper, string, sticky label, a small prize

This variation on 'Pass the Parcel' requires you to prepare a number of layers of brown paper, each layer tied with string and with a small prize (probably something useless like a broken zip) in the middle. Stuck to each layer is a written label and it is this which indicates to whom the parcel should next be passed. The labels will have written on them things like: 'To the woman with the most beautiful hair', 'To the man with the kindest eyes' or 'To the woman with the longest legs'. If you know all of your guests really well, you could alternatively try descriptions such as: 'To the man with the worst acne', 'To the woman with the biggest feet' or 'To the woman with the smallest boobs'. The rest can be left to your imagination. Suffice to say that the players are seated in a circle and the parcel is handed to one play-er at random. He or she reads the label on the outside before handing it to who-ever the description seems most applicable. The chosen one then unwraps the sec-ond layer and so the game continues until the prize is reached, by which time half of the party will be blushing and the rest will be livid.

MURDER IN THE DARK

Players: 6 or more

You will need:

Slips of paper, a hat

A number of slips of paper are dropped into a hat, one slip per player. All of the pieces of paper are blank except for one which bears a cross and another which bears a circle. The players then pull out the slips. Whoever draws the cross is the Murderer; whoever draws the circle is the Detective. The former remains silent but the latter announces the fact that he or she is now following in the footsteps of Morse or Miss Marple. All of the lights in the house are then switched off and the players move about stealthily. The Murderer locates a likely victim and whispers in their ear 'You're dead' at which the victim falls to the floor and screams loudly. As the Murderer hurries away from the scene, the Detective, hearing the screams, switches on the lights. From the moment the lights are switched on, nobody except the Detective is allowed to move. The Detective proceeds to question the various suspects, all of whom must answer truthfully except for the Murderer who can tell bare-faced lies unless asked directly, 'Are you the Murderer?' when he or she must confess. Naturally the corpse says nothing. If there are fewer than 10 players, the Detective is permitted only two guesses at unmasking the Murderer; if there are more than 10, the Detective has three guesses. This is not a game for those who are afraid of the dark or who have recently served a life sentence.

GRANDMA'S FOOTSTEPS

Players: Any number

By the time the party is in full swing and everyone has forgotten any inhibitions they may have had when they arrived, there is more and more scope for including the sort of silly games which are usually played at parties for five- and six-year-olds. You will often find that your guests will have more fun playing something like 'Grandma's Footsteps' than an exceedingly clever word game. And if their minds have become addled by alcohol, there is the added bonus of no complicated rules to remember. One person is chosen to be leader and, slowly but purposefully, walks from one end of the room to the other with the remaining players following dutifully behind in crocodile fashion. Suddenly, without warning, the leader will look round. This is the signal for everyone to stop dead in their tracks since anybody whom the leader catches moving is eliminated from the game. This ritual continues, with the leader's turns becoming increasingly frequent, until there is just one player left in the line.

THE LAST STRAW

Players: 8 or more

You will need:

Straws, two thimbles

The players are divided into two teams and are seated in rows facing each other. Each player places a straw in their mouth and a thimble is passed from one end of the team to the other by balancing it delicately on the end of the straws. No hands are allowed and if the thimble is dropped, it can only be picked up by using the straw. When the thimble has been successfully passed along the line, the last player races to the other end and everyone moves up a chair. The game continues as before until all of one team's members are back in their starting positions. With four team members, this will require four successful runs. Guests with a heavy cold or a nervous twitch are advised to sit this one out.

WATER LOT OF FUN

Players: 5-10

You will need:

Pen, paper, egg cup, jug of water, towel

You may want to play this sitting on a tropical beach – or, if there isn't one handy, an easily mopped surface will suffice. Granny's best Wilton carpet may not be ideal. Everyone sits in a circle with the props placed inside. One person is chosen at random and sits inside the circle. The chosen person then thinks of a list of items that roughly coincides with the number of people playing the game (not including themselves). So if there are five people, good lists would be all the members of The Beatles, English Sunday newspapers, numbers one to five, days of the week etc. The person in the centre then chooses one item from their list and secretly notes it down. Going round in a clockwise direction, those in the circle name items from the list, never repeating an item. The person who names the item that the water carrier has noted down has the egg cup of water thrown in their face.

MOUTH TO MOUTH

Players: 8 or more

You will need:

Spoons, two table tennis balls

The players are divided into two equal teams and each issued with a spoon. Standing in lines, they grip the spoons in their mouths by the handles and try to pass a table tennis ball down the line without using their hands. If at any stage of its journey the ball falls to the floor, the guilty team has to begin again. The winning team is the first to pass the ball from one end of the line to the other. To prolong the competition, it can be staged over the best of five games.

265

SPOT THE SQUEEZE

Players: Any number

Players stand in a circle with their hands by their sides while one player stands in the middle. The game starts with one of the circle squeezing the hand of the adjoining player who in turn squeezes the hand of the next person and so on. The player in the centre is trying to spot the squeeze and anyone caught in the act of squeezing has to take his or her place in the middle. To confuse the would-be spotter, the squeeze can suddenly change direction. The nature of the game means that few people are keen to stand next to the local sewage engineer.

EXPOSTULATE

Players: Any number

In this entertaining guessing game, one person goes out of the room while the others choose a verb such as 'mash', 'mince', 'kiss' or, if the party has degenerated to that level, 'fornicate'. The person outside returns and tries to guess the verb by asking a question of each player in turn, but in each question, the word 'expostulate' must be used instead of the word being guessed. So a question might be: 'Do I expostulate below the waist?' If the mystery word is 'gargle', the answer would almost certainly be 'No'. Players must only answer 'Yes' or 'No'. The game continues either until the word has been guessed or until the person doing the guessing surrenders. In the latter event, he or she has to pay a sizeable forfeit.

NEVER, NEVER, NEVER

Players: Any number

This one may take some explaining – so don't leave it until everyone has drunk too much. Going round the room, the players take it in turns to announce something that they've never done. It doesn't have to be true, the main criterion is that it is something which everyone else present is most likely to have done. So if you declare, 'I've never eaten a sherbert lemon,' you are on fairly safe ground as there are bound to be plenty of people who've tasted sherbert lemons. However, if you say, 'I've never ridden the winner of the Grand National', whilst it may be perfectly true, it's also unlikely anyone else in the room will have either. Should any of the other players have not done what you said you haven't done, you lose one of your three lives. It's complicated – but can be very revealing.

MY AUNT WENT TO TOWN

Players: Any number

This is another 'round game' where all of the players are seated in a circle. The first player chooses a letter (say, P) and reveals, 'My aunt went to town and bought a piano.' The next player takes up the theme. 'My aunt went to town and bought a piano and a pair of platform shoes.' Player three might continue, 'My aunt went to town and bought a piano, a pair of platform shoes and a platypus.' And on it goes with each succeeding player reciting the previous purchases in correct order and adding another. Anyone who slips up is knocked out of the game, the last person left in is the winner.

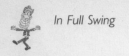

SIMON SAYS

Players: Any number

For this hardy perennial, one player assumes the role of Simon and issues orders to the remainder of the throng. If the leader declares: 'Simon says pat your bottom', then everyone must pat their bottom. But if he or she simply orders, 'Pat your bottom', they must not copy the action, anyone who does so being eliminated. Only instructions prefixed by the words 'Simon says' must be obeyed. The game is best played fast and furious with the last person left in emerging as the winner.

MAD HATTERS

Players: 2 plus an audience

You will need:

Two hats

A player enters the room carrying two hats. He or she puts one hat on his or her own head and hands the other hat to a second player. From then on, the second player must ensure that all his or her actions and words are as opposite as possible to those of the first player. So, if player one scratches the top of his or her head, player two should follow by scratching the sole of a foot. The rest of the party sit in judgement and anyone who is deemed to have slipped up makes way for another player. The winner is the one who can maintain the performance for the longest.

FARMYARD FROLIC

Players: 8 or more

You will need:

An assortment of sweets

The players split up into teams of four, one of whom is the leader. The team members have to adopt the identity of a different animal, complete with actions and noises, but no smells please. Even so, anyone masquerading as a skunk should be given a wide berth. This is all easy enough for those who collar dog, cat, cow or horse, but the likes of marmoset, gerbil, armadillo or iguana require greater imagination. Leaving the team leaders in the lounge, the animals set off in search of the sweets which have been scattered around the house by the host. When a player finds a sweet, he or she makes a noise like the chosen animal to alert the team leader who goes to collect it. It is therefore important that the leaders remember which animals are in their team. After 15 minutes, the team whose leader has collected the most sweets wins the game.

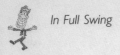

SHOPPING LIST

Players: Any even number

You will need:

Slips of paper, pencils

In this game, two teams go on an imaginary shopping trip without the hazards of having to steer a supermarket trolley with a mind of its own. On separate slips of paper, write 20 anagrams of items you could purchase at a typical supermarket and arrange the slips on a table. The two team leaders send one member of their shopping expedition at a time to the table to fetch an item. The happy shopper picks up a slip, takes it to the leader and – after it has been decoded – returns it to the table. Then it is the turn of the next team member. When the leader has deciphered all 20 items, the list goes through the checkout and if it is correct, victory is claimed. If you are not used to the rigours of the supermarket, here are 20 anagrams to save you some time:

Shif Grinsef (Fish Fingers)	Rwiserbreast (Strawberries)
Kenhicc (Chicken)	Ilteto Lorls (Toilet Rolls)
Shuntudog (Doughnuts)	Spircs (Crisps)
Rulof (Flour)	Suetsis (Tissues)
Membercat (Camembert)	Catpek Upso (Packet Soup)
Sumose (Mousse)	Moledean (Lemonade)
Scissortan (Croissants)	Seasgasu (Sausages)
Poshmoa (Shampoo)	Stibsuci (Biscuits)
Act Tritle (Cat Litter)	Nooni Grins (Onion Rings)
Slabi (Basil)	Stoatpetho (Toothpaste)

PASS THE BOTTLE

Players: 10 or more

You will need:

Two empty bottles

The players line up in two teams with an empty bottle standing on the floor at one end of each line. The first player picks up the bottle between his or her knees and then passes it to the knees of the next person in line. The bottle makes its way along the line in this fashion, the first team to get it to the other end being declared the winner. No hands are allowed and if the bottle is dropped at any stage, it must be picked up with the knees. Women in short, tight skirts may find this game a struggle but their efforts to bend will provide considerable pleasure for others.

NUDGE NUDGE

Players: Any number

The players are seated on the floor, close together, in a circle. One person is appointed leader. That person sets the ball rolling by nudging the player on his or her left. The nudge is passed around the circle until it arrives back at the leader who then starts a new discipline – perhaps the tweak of an earlobe. This action too is passed around the circle in clockwise fashion and when it reaches the leader once more, a fresh activity is initiated – maybe a peck on the cheek. The game can be played ad infinitum, the only rule being that the participants must keep a straight face at all times. Any sniggering or giggling will result in the guilty party being awarded a forfeit.

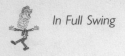

ADD ONE

Players: Any number

The players sit in a circle and the first person performs a simple action, such as stamping a foot, clapping hands or sticking out their tongue. The person on his or her left repeats the action but then adds another, maybe raising an eyebrow. The next person on the left repeats the first two moves and adds something else, perhaps the scratching of an armpit. The game continues around the circle in this manner with each player repeating the previous moves in the correct order before adding an invention of his or her own. Anyone unable to remember the sequence has to drop out. The last player left in is the winner.

BEADS IN THE JAR

Players: 3-6

You will need:

Jam-jars, beads, knitting needles

For each player, provide one jam-jar filled with tiny beads (or any similar-sized round objects) and two knitting needles. Using the knitting needles in one hand like chopsticks, the competitors have to lift as many beads as possible from their jar in three minutes, the highest total being the winner. This game calls for a steady hand and is therefore more entertaining, if less productive, when the guests have had a drink or two.

GOOD MORNING, MADAM

Players: Any number

You will need:

A pack of playing cards

This is a grown-ups' version of 'Snap', but here the excitement occurs when a particular card is turned up, rather than two of the same. Using a conventional pack of playing cards, each player in turn plays a card face up. In the event of the card being an ace, a king, a queen or a jack, all of the cards below are captured. But there's more. When an ace is laid, everyone slams down their hand on top of it. When it's a king, everyone stands to attention and salutes. When there's a jack, the players must get to their feet and curtsy. And when a queen is laid, they all shout out at the top of their voices: 'Good morning, Madam.' In each case, the first player to perform the prescribed action gains the booty. The game is over when one player has won all of the cards.

273

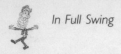

COLONEL BLOOD

Players: Any number

You will need:

A chair, a blindfold, a book

Historians will know Colonel Blood as the man who attempted to steal the Crown Jewels. Here is a chance to follow in his footsteps pursuing a rather more modest booty, a book, from under the nose of a supremely vigilant guard. At least, the guard would be vigilant were it not for the fact that he or she is blindfolded. The person chosen to be guard sits blindfolded on a chair in the middle of the room with the book on the floor next to the chair. The other players hover around and take it in turns to creep up to the book and try to steal it without being detected. If the guard hears a sound, he or she points in the direction from which it came. If that corresponds with the position of one of the would-be thieves, that particular mission is abandoned and the thief becomes the guard for the next round. This may seem harsh but is a more humane alternative to beheading, which was the usual punishment for jewel thieves. However, the guard must not accuse at random for fear of having to pay a forfeit. Should one of the players succeed in stealing the book undetected, the guard remains in the chair for the next round.

KILLER

Players: Any number

You will need:

A pack of playing cards

This fiendish game can spread terror among the most happy-go-lucky of party guests as everyone becomes terrified that they'll be the next to fall victim to the callous killer in their midst. Deal out part of a pack of playing cards – one card for each player – first making sure that the joker is among them. Whoever is dealt the joker becomes the killer but, for obvious reasons, keeps that fact a secret. The killer does his dirty work by winking at his victims, in the process ensuring that nobody else spots the dastardly deed. He does not rest until he has winked at every member of the company, thereby wiping out the whole lot. After being winked at, each victim must wait at least 30 seconds before dying, perhaps by slumping in an armchair or falling theatrically to the floor. Meanwhile, the other players, realising that a killer is on the loose, do their utmost to catch him in the very act of winking. Anyone who believes they have seen the killer at work must challenge the victim before he or she dies, rather than the killer. If the suspicion is confirmed, the killer is apprehended. However, if the accusation proves to be false, it results in the instant death of the accuser – another one for the killer to cross off his list. The silent but deadly goings-on are at their most effective when executed during a seemingly innocuous activity, such as clearing the table or passing round the salted peanuts. For that is the beauty of this game – nobody ever knows when the killer is about to strike. Don't have nightmares.

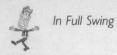
WHAT IS MY THOUGHT LIKE?

Players: 5-10

If you are a medium, or even an extra-large, this mind-reading game will be right up your street. One person is chosen to think of an object (animate or inanimate) and then asks each of the other players in turn: 'What is my thought like?' Mere mortals will presumably have no idea and will resort to making wild guesses. When everyone has made a suggestion, the first person names his or her object and then asks each player to say why their particular object was like the mystery item. Players should be given a few minutes to come up with their answers, a prize being awarded to the most imaginative. Let us assume that the chosen object was an aeroplane and that various players suggested a tube of glue, the Prime Minister, a tennis racket, a stripogram and a broken zip. The questioning could go:

> First player: 'Why is an aeroplane like a tube of glue?'
> Answer: 'Because you can get high on both.'
> First player: 'Why is an aeroplane like the Prime Minister?'
> Answer: 'Because both spend most of their time with their head in the clouds.'
> First player: 'Why is an aeroplane like a tennis racket?'
> Answer: 'Because both provide first-class service.'
> First player: 'Why is an aeroplane like a stripogram?'
> Answer: 'Because both take off throughout a day.'
> First player: 'Why is an aeroplane like a broken zip?'
> Answer: 'Because one flies through the air and the other lets air through the flies.'

DEAD ANTS

Players: Any number

Everybody stands around aimlessly, chatting about the price of washing-up liquid or the FT Index, until someone shouts: 'Dead Ants!' At the outbreak of mass insecticide, all of the players lie on the ground with their arms and legs in the air and must attempt to remain absolutely motionless. Any player who makes a movement is disqualified. All of the disqualified ants try to make the others move without physically touching them. Eventually just one dead ant remains and he or she, to mix insect metaphors, becomes the queen bee.

NOAH'S ARK

Players: 7 or more

You will need:

Pencils and paper

Oh calamity! Since the privatisation of Noah's Ark, Group 4 have been introduced to provide security, as a result of which all of the animals have escaped. In order to claim on the insurance, poor old Noah has got to make a list of the missing creatures. Each player takes on two roles – that of one of the animals and of Noah himself. The game begins with you assigning each player the name of a creature which makes a distinctive sound – pig, lion, lamb, frog, wolf, crow, seagull, duck, bee, donkey, goose, cow, horse, cockerel, snake, dog, cat, sea lion etc. Then all of the lights are turned out and everybody starts grunting, roaring, bleating, croaking, howling, cawing, squawking, quacking, buzzing, braying, honking, mooing, neighing, crowing, hissing, barking, miaowing and whatever noise sea lions make, all at the same time. While making the noise of their own animal, the players must also make mental notes of the other sounds they hear because, after five minutes of this mayhem, the lights are switched back on and, now wearing their Noah hats, they must write down the names of as many animals as they can remember hearing. Since you will have kept a check-list of the animals, you can mark the lists and work out who has got the highest total. He or she is the winner.

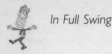

FIND YOUR MATE

Players: Any even number

Another disaster on Noah's Ark! All the animals have escaped on a stormy night and are desperately trying to find their mates. Players participate as pairs of a particular creature – two turkeys, two tigers, two hyenas and so on – and, in total darkness, seek out their partners by calling to each other in the manner of their allotted animal, in other words gobbling, roaring or laughing. The last couple to pair off must pay a forfeit.

RHYME AND REASON

Players: Any number

The idea of this game is to establish a chain of rhyming words. The first player thinks of a word which has plenty of possible rhymes, such as 'gate'. He or she then gives a short definition although the word that is being defined is not 'gate' but another word which rhymes with it. The next player has 30 seconds to work out that word and to give a definition for another rhyming word. Any player unable to solve the riddle or to think of a new rhyming word is eliminated. Here is an example of how the game works:

Player 1: A gate is something you go on with a girlfriend.
Player 2: No, you mean date, which you put on the end of a fishing rod.
Player 3: No, you mean bait, which determines your destiny.
Player 4: No, you mean fate, which is the opposite of early.
Player 5: No, you mean late, which means to dislike intensely.
Player 6: No, you mean hate, which the birds and bees do.
Player 7: No, you mean mate, which you eat dinner off.
Player 8: No, you mean plate, which you measure in kilograms.

And so the game continues until either there is just one player left or until everyone has run out of rhyming words.

MUMMIES

Players: Any even number

You will need:

Rolls of toilet paper

In Oedipus's favourite game, players pair off into couples, ideally one man and one woman. The woman is given a toilet roll and has three minutes in which to wrap her partner from head to foot in toilet paper so that he bares an uncanny resemblance to an Egyptian mummy. The winners are the couple adjudged to have created the most effective mummy.

PING-PONG ROLL

Players: Any number

You will need:

Table tennis balls, lengths of string

The players are divided into pairs and each pair is supplied with a table tennis ball and two pieces of string of equal length (about four feet). The team-mates stand at either end of the string and, with a piece in each hand, hold the lengths taut and fairly close together like railway lines. At the 'off', a non-competitor places the ball at one end of the lines and the player at the other end lowers his or her strings so that the ball can go downhill. When it reaches the far end, the players swap stances so that the ball will now slope back towards the start. Care should be taken not to go too fast as the ball can easily roll off a player's hands at the turning point. Any ball that falls to the floor must be returned to the start of that length. The first team to complete six lengths are the winners.

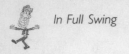
FAMILY SNAP

Players: 6-12

This is a game for the quick-witted. Prior to the party, prepare a list of imaginary names which are sufficiently alike to cause widespread confusion. Each player is given one of these names. For example, if there are 10 players, you could choose:

Mr James Lindsay
Mr Lindsay James
Ms Lindsey James
Sir Lindsley Jameson
Gemma Lindsay
Lynn James
Linda James
Lynn Jameson
Linda Jameson
Jem Lindsay

Inform the players of their names verbally, repeating the list so that it sinks in. Then explain that you are going out to call out a succession of quick-fire names – the ones you have allotted to the players, plus a number of 'ringers' such as James Lynn, Jeremy Lindsay, Gemma James and Jeremy Lynn. When a name is called out and its owner shouts out 'Snap', he or she scores three points. If it's one of the allotted names and another player calls out 'Snap', he or she scores one point. But if the name called out is one of the 'ringers' and anyone shouts 'Snap', that player loses two points. The secret of the game is to call out the names at short intervals, leaving the players little time for thought or to draw breath. Soon chaos will reign supreme, not least with the poor soul who has been given the job of keeping track of the scores.

HORROR STORY

Players: Any number

All of the players sit around the fire (even if it's not lit) to tell a horror story. The first player begins a spine-chilling tale, replete with blood-curdling images. As soon as he or she uses an onomatopoeic word (such as creaked or groaned), the next player must take over. The game continues until everyone is too terrified to carry on. Anyone who fails to spot an example of onomatopoeia (a word that sounds like what it describes) must pay a forfeit... like venturing outside alone in the dark.

FISH MARKET

Players: Any number

Even by the general standard of party games, this one is utterly meaningless and wonderfully silly. Everyone sits in a circle except for one person, the accuser, who is picked to stand in the middle. The others then each announce the name of a fish and the accuser in the middle must try to remember which person is which fish. To disorientate the accuser further, he or she must spin round twice before suddenly jabbing a finger at one of the players in the circle and screaming 'trout, trout, trout' or whatever. The aim is for the accuser to call out the name of the fish three times in quick succession before the player who is that fish can say it once. Should the accuser fail in this mission, as is highly probable, he or she must try again with another player and fish. Should the accuser succeed, he or she swaps places with the trout. There are very few rules to this pastime although any accuser who fails to point at a fish before speaking will have the challenge declared null and void.

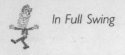
SOAP BUBBLES

Players: Any number

Can you remember which soap opera Alan Turner is associated with? Or what about Billy Kennedy? Or Simon Raymond? Or Judy Mallett? Here is a quick-fire game for telly addicts in which players are told that every name called out is or was a character in either Coronation Street, EastEnders, Brookside, Emmerdale or Neighbours. After the announcement of each name, the first person to call out the correct soap wins a point. In case you have better things to do than watch TV, here are some suitable characters:

> Coronation Street: Angie Freeman, Chris Collins, Fred Elliott, Martin Platt, Rita Sullivan, Judy Mallett, Ashley Peacock, Roy Cropper, Deirdre Rachid, Samantha Failsworth, Betty Williams.
> EastEnders: Nigel Bates, Lorraine Wicks, Pat Evans, Robbie Jackson, Sarah Hills, Bianca Butcher, Simon Raymond, Sanjay Kapoor, Clare Tyler, Wellard (Robbie Jackson's dog), Kathy Mitchell, Ruth Fowler.
> Brookside: Ron Dixon, Susannah Farnham, Elaine Johnson, Katie Rogers, Ollie Simpson, Sinbad, David Crosbie, Mike Dixon, Julia Brogan, Jackie Corkhill.
> Emmerdale: Linda Fowler, Kim Tate, Mandy Dingle, Betty Eagleton, Charlotte Cairns, Seth Armstrong, Alan Turner, Kelly Windsor, Ned Glover, Steve Marchant, Jack Sugden, Eric Pollard.
> Neighbours: Billy Kennedy, Lou Carpenter, Madge Bishop, Helen Daniels, Debbie Martin, Darren Starke, Susan Kennedy, Philip Martin, Marlene Kratz.

GET KNOTTED

Players: Any even number

You will need:

Lengths of string, several pairs of gloves

A team race which will appeal to Boy Scouts and retired Admirals alike. The leader of each team is given a piece of sturdy string, about three feet long. The race starts with the two leaders tying a loose knot in their string which is then passed along the line to their team-mates who also tie knots. The last player in each team takes the knotted string back to the leader who proceeds to untie one knot before passing it on. Each successive team mate unties a knot, the first team to have de-knotted their string completely being the winners. Sounds easy, doesn't it? There's just one thing I forgot to mention – all of the players must wear gloves.

FANCY THAT!

Players: 8 or more

You will need:

Pencil and paper

This game tests how well you know your fellow guests. One person is elected referee and leaves the room with pencil and paper. The other players in turn give the referee the name of the celebrity they most fancy. It doesn't have to be a particularly strong urge and it certainly doesn't have to have been consummated. Those who are reluctant to reveal their secret longings can always opt for a fictional character such as Desperate Dan or Homer Simpson. Anyway maybe your partner really does fancy Homer Simpson, in which case hide any blue hair dye. When everyone has given a name, the referee returns to the room and reads out the list twice. The players now have to try to work out who fancies who. One player is elected to start and may begin: 'Mildred, I think you fancy Brad Pitt.' Mildred (who has actually listed as her dreamboat John Selwyn Gummer) replies: 'No, but Reginald, I think you fancy Petula Clark.' Mildred has got it in one, at which point Reginald drops out and she moves on to another person. The game ends when everybody has been paired off with their romantic hero.

283

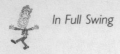
SPIN THE PLATE

Players: 6 or more

You will need:

Chairs, an old plate

The guests are seated in chairs arranged in a circle and one player is elected to start. He or she goes to the centre of the circle and is given an old plate, either china or tin, but certainly not the best crockery. The starter spins the plate as vigorously as possible and immediately calls out the name of another player who makes a beeline for the plate. Meanwhile, the starter rushes back to his or her own chair, hoping to sit down before the player whose name has been called out can catch the spinning plate. Should this be the case, the new player takes over as starter and spins the plate before calling out another name. If, however, the starter doesn't sit down in time, he or she must remain in that role, spin the plate again and call for another player. Each player who catches the spinning plate before the starter has sat down in his or her own chair scores five points. With a lot of dashing about and jumping up and down, this is a somewhat frenetic game, best limited to about 15 minutes before anyone keels over.

SILENT PARTNERS

Players: 11 or more

All of the players, except one, pair off with the person they know best – spouse, partner, bank manager etc. The singleton, who has probably been chosen for the role because he or she doesn't have any friends, acts as the Grand Inquisitor. When all of the players are seated, the Inquisitor goes over to one partner of a pair and asks a question. However, it is the other partner who must answer. If the player questioned answers or the partner doesn't, that pair are eliminated from the proceedings. The secret of being a wily Inquisitor is to move swiftly from pair to pair, leaving no time for a gathering of wits, and to think up questions which you know the person you're asking is desperate to answer, but which the partner is equally anxious to avoid. For example, faced with a wife who is an expert secretary and a husband who thinks Pitman's shorthand is a mining injury, you may choose to ask her about the merits of Tipp-Ex. Her natural reaction will be to blurt out the answer, but it is he who must respond. Or you may be confronted with a man with a huge spot on the end of his nose and a woman with a beautifully clear complexion. The obvious, if horribly embarrassing, question to the man would be: 'Does that spot on the end of your nose really hurt?' Yet it is she who is obliged to answer. A breakdown in communications between pairs, resulting in premature elimination, has been known to lead to acrimonious scenes in the car on the way home.

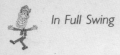
MOUTH-TO-MOUTH

Players: 8 or more

You will need:

Spoons, table tennis balls

This game is best played as a team contest. The players stand in lines and are each given a spoon which they hold between their teeth. The team leaders are each provided with a table tennis ball which is placed on their spoon. The ball is then passed down the line from spoon to spoon, the first team to transport the ball from end of the line to the other being the winner. At no time may hands be used. Even if the ball is dropped, it can only be picked up by a spoon in the mouth. If you don't have access to table tennis balls, you can use peanuts or grapes instead. But don't use anything too heavy – it might rattle your dentures.

PAPER MODELS

Players: Any even number

You will need:

Newspapers, pins

This is similar to the earlier game, Paper Costumes. Using sheets of newspaper, pairs of players each attempt to create a sensational new dress in five minutes, joining the different pages together with pins. Each pair are given the same number of sheets of paper and the same number of pins with one player serving as the model while the other acts as dressmaker. Holes can be made to accommodate arms and, if so desired, the designer may even run to a matching hat. The pair who create what is judged to be the best outfit win the game.

ANIMAL SNAP

Players: 3-6

You will need:

A pack of playing cards

Deal a pack of cards among all of the players who reveal that, henceforth, they will behave in the manner of a goat, pig, sheep or whichever animal takes their fancy. It's worth discouraging anyone from being a lemming as they tend to have a tendency to throw themselves out of the nearest window. The game then proceeds like 'Snap' except that whenever two cards are matched, instead of shouting 'Snap!', the players must make the animal noise of the player who lays the matching (second) card, regardless of whether or not it is their own. Thus, the air resounds to a chorus of moos or oinks in a manic free-for-all. The first player to make the correct noise wins the cards on offer. Any player able to make the sounds of both animals involved before anyone else is able to grunt or squeak automatically wins 10 cards. As with the more conventional version of 'Snap', the winner is the player who acquires the whole pack.

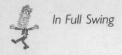

SLAVE AUCTION

Players: 10 or more

You will need:

Coins

This may not be the most politically correct of party games but with the right company, it can be one of the most entertaining. Half a dozen or so players are taken to one side and put up for auction. The rest are given an equal number of coins, say 20, and are instructed to buy as many slaves as possible. To keep any objections to a minimum, select both male and female slaves. The host acts as auctioneer and presents a colourful sales pitch to encourage bidding for the first slave. 'Slim, shapely legs, lovely silky hair, gorgeous figure, 'come-to-bed' eyes, so if anyone wants to buy Mr Pettigrew, the bidding starts at 2p.' The bidders meanwhile try to urge each other to pay over the odds, knowing that once their rivals have run out of coins, there'll be the opportunity to snap up bargains. The canny bidder watches others making panic buys while retaining his or her own coins for the later lots. At the end of the auction, the player who has purchased the greatest number of slaves wins. If it is a tie, whoever has most coins left wins. And then the players can do whatever they want with their slaves… at least, that's the theory.

CLIP TOGETHER

Players: Any even number

You will need:

Paper clips, chairs

Split the participants into two teams and seat them facing each other in rows. Give each player a paper clip to be held behind the back. At the off, the first player in each team passes his or her clip to the next person in line who hooks it onto his or her own and passes both clips to the third team member. The ever-growing chain continues in this way until it reaches the end of the line from where it is ferried back to the first person, this time in front of the players, and solely by means of the elbows. Once back with player one, he or she puts the chain behind his or her back, unhooks one clip and passes the rest on down the line, each successive player unhooking a clip. When all of the members of one team are each able to hold up a paper clip, that team is victorious.

MY LITTLE BIRD

Players: Any number

Everyone sits in a circle and one player is elected to be the leader. This individual begins by announcing: 'My little bird is lively' and then adds something followed by the word 'fly', maybe 'cuckoos fly'. If the object that is named can fly, the other players wave their arms around in the air and jump up and down making squawking sounds. If, however, the object named can't fly – like penguins, ostriches or gas cookers – the remaining players must remain absolutely still. Anyone who gets it wrong is eliminated, the last player left in wins the game. Apart from flightless birds, the trick is to put in things like lizards, squirrels and fish, all of which have species which can fly.

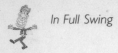

ALLITERATION

Players: 4-8

Another circular game where players have to remember and recite an ever-lengthening alliterative list. The first player thinks up a two-word alliteration beginning with 'O' and says something along the lines of: 'One organised okapi.' The next player might weigh in with: 'Two terrifying terrapins and one organised okapi.' By player three, the alliteration has extended by an additional word so the offering might be: 'Three thin, thoughtful thrushes, two terrifying terrapins and one organised okapi.' And so it goes on with each successive player adding a word to make an alliterative list matching the number at the start – such as 'four fat, fiendish, furry felines' – as well as reciting the previous offerings. Anyone who blunders is out, the last person left in being the winner.

DINNER PARTY

Players: 4-8

You will need:

Pencils and paper

It's every dinner party hostess's nightmare. In an effort to invite a representative cross-section of guests, she has merely succeeded in bringing together six people who have absolutely nothing in common and thus have nothing whatsoever to say to each other. For this game, each player must think up a list of six party guests who would be a disaster seated around the same table simply because they would have nothing in common. The guests can be dead or alive, real or fictional. Then, confronted with one list at a time, the other players must try to argue why some of the six would be able to engage in conversation. So while a list comprising William the Conqueror, Judith Chalmers, Bugs Bunny, Vincent Van Gogh, Sir Francis Drake and George Stephenson would appear, at first glance, to have no connections, it could be argued that Bugs Bunny would tell Van Gogh: 'That's not how you draw a carrot', George Stephenson would tell William the Conqueror how his invention has speeded up cross-Channel travel, and Sir Francis Drake would show Judith Chalmers his holiday snaps of Spain. And for good measure, Judith would point out to William that he and the Norman army would have found the journey more economical if they'd travelled Dieppe-Newhaven on a Weekday Return.

TISSUE TRAIL

Players: Any even number

You will need:

Drinking straws, paper tissues

Players split into two teams and place a drinking straw in their mouths. The team leaders put a paper tissue over the end of their straw and suck in, thereby ensuring that it is held in place. They then turn to the next players in line and pass the tissue on to them, the secret of success being for the first player to breathe out gently at the same time as the second player sucks in. Following this method, the tissue is passed along the entire team, the first team to finish winning the game. Other than at the very start, the only time the tissue may be handled is if it floats to the floor when it may be picked up and returned to its position at the end of the straw.

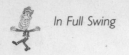
BEAN FEAST

Players: 3-6

You will need:

Bowls, baked beans, sweets, plastic sheets

This is a messy game, so much so that it is a good idea to cover your floor with plastic sheets. Each player is confronted with a deep bowl filled with baked beans, buried at the bottom of which is a sweet still in its wrapper. On the command 'Go!' and using only their teeth, contestants must burrow nose first into the morass of baked beans and pull out the sweet with their teeth, the first do so being the winner. Obviously, the deeper the bowl, the more fun the game. And if you don't want to use baked beans, you can always substitute mushy peas or, for a less mucky contest, cornflakes.

NAME CALLING

Players: Any number

This game tests players' ability to think against the background of a relentless jungle beat. Everyone sits around the table and sets up a continuous rhythm of clapping hands twice and banging on the table twice. On the second bang, the leader calls out the name of a category – say, jockeys – and on the next second bang, the first player shouts out a suitable example, maybe Frankie Dettori. The incessant rhythm must be maintained throughout and players must only answer on the second bang. Anyone who loses rhythm, answers at the wrong time or can't think of a reply, loses one of their three lives. The categories can be changed whenever a particular line has been exhausted. Interesting categories include: sex symbols, rock bands beginning with S, items of clothing and, if it really is getting late, swear words.

MYSTERY MAXIMS

Players: 4-8

One member of the group is sent from the room while the remainder decide upon a proverb. When the absentee returns, each of the other players in turn speaks a sentence which includes one of the words contained in the chosen proverb, and in the correct order. So the first sentence must contain the first word of the proverb, the second sentence the second word and so on. If the chosen proverb is 'Too many cooks spoil the broth', the statements could go:

1. Many gourmets are not too keen on custard.
2. To save time in the kitchen, many people use electrical gadgets instead of their hands.
3. I have seen cooks make excellent soufflés.
4. But they can spoil unless they are really light.
5. The work in a restaurant kitchen is extremely hard.
6. On a cold winter's day, you can't beat a good broth.

'Broth' is probably the giveaway, but until then there was also the possibility that the proverb could have been 'Many hands make light work'. If the player guesses the proverb following the first sentence (and only three guesses are allowed in total), six points are scored, after the second sentence five, and so on with decreasing value. When the answer has been revealed, it is the turn of someone else to leave the room. This game can be played equally well with song titles or film titles.

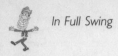

THE FORBIDDEN FRUIT

Players: Any number

You will need:

An envelope, a piece of paper

This game involves the entire party. At some stage in the proceedings, the host holds up a sealed envelope and says that it is a forbidden fruit and that whoever has possession of the envelope when it is time to go home is forced to perform the final forfeit of the evening which is written on a piece of paper inside. So from the moment of the host's announcement, everyone is on their guard in case someone slips them the forbidden fruit. Whenever this happens, the person offloading the envelope into a pocket, handbag or whatever, must whisper to the victim that somewhere about their person is the forbidden fruit. The victim in turn tries to pass it on but must take care not to be caught in the act, the punishment for such a crime being a forfeit. Alternatively, the game can be played using two envelopes – one containing a forfeit, the other a prize. So when the guests are told they've got the forbidden fruit, they are in a dilemma as to whether to keep it or pass it on.

WOOLLY TANGLE

Players: 3-6

You will need:

Chairs, balls of wool

Using one chair per player, wrap a ball of wool around the arms, legs and back of each chair so that it is in a total tangle. While remaining seated in their chairs at all times, the players must untangle the strands as quickly as possible and roll them back into a recognisable ball. The first player able to do so wins the game.

BLOW-OUT

Players: Any even number

You will need:

Candles, blindfolds

Two lit candles are placed on a table in the centre of the room, about eight inches apart. The players are divided into teams starting from diagonally opposite corners of the room with their backs to the candles. The first player in each team is blindfolded and they make their way towards the table with the intention of blowing out their candle only. The candle for each competitor is the one on their right. If a player happens to blow out the wrong candle, victory goes to the opposing team. In a bid to prevent this, the next in line on both teams can issue instructions, but only five words may be used – 'Left', 'Right', 'Up', 'Down' and 'Blow'. If matters get out of hand, a sixth word may be used – 'Fire!' After the candle has been blown out, the remaining team members have a go in turn, the eventual winners being the team with most successful blows and who still have all of their eyebrows. To minimise the chances of any singeing, one guest should be stationed at the table at all times.

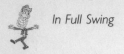

PICK-ME-UP

Players: 3-6

You will need:

Rice, gardening gloves, small bottles

This is a game requiring remarkable dexterity, a commodity which will almost certainly be at a premium at this stage of the evening. Each player puts on a gardening glove (or something similar) and, using only the gloved hand, has to transfer grains of rice from a table-top pile into a small, narrow-necked bottle. Furthermore, he or she must only transfer one grain at a time. Judges will be on hand to ensure fair play. Whoever has the most legally-acquired grains of rice in his or her bottle at the end of three minutes is the winner.

CATCH THE CANE

Players: Any number

You will need:

A stick or cane, chairs

Assign each player the name of a town and hand the list of towns to the person who has been elected cane master. While the players sit in a circle of chairs, the cane master stands in the middle, brandishing a stick or garden cane. Lifting his or her fingers from the stick, the cane master calls out the name of a town whose owner must somehow catch the stick before it hits the floor. Failure to do so results in elimination; success means that player takes over in the middle. The faster the game is played, the more fun it is.

HAPPY FAMILIES

Players: Groups of 3

You will need:

Pieces of paper

Before the game, write on separate slips of paper various animal families – mother, father and baby. The creatures should be chosen on the basis of being difficult to impersonate – like rhinoceros, hamster, stick insect. Gather the players around and distribute the pieces of paper among them at random. When play begins, each animal must try to find the rest of its family, solely by making the noise of that animal and by mimicking its movements. No human words may be spoken. So baby chipmunk will be scurrying around frantically, perhaps pausing for the occasional imaginary nut, in search of mother and father chipmunk. When all three have been reunited, the mother sits in a chair with the baby on her lap and the father behind her. This can create an interesting spectacle if the baby is played by a weightlifter and the mother by a hairdresser. The first group to line up like this wins the game although proceedings continue until the very last family – invariably the snails – are together. If you find yourself as a member of the mayfly family, don't take too long over this game.

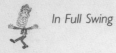

BAH HUMBUG!

Players: 4-8

This fast-moving word game is played like a tennis match around a table by two teams of up to four players on each side. One player on the serving team looks at a player on the opposite side and serves a word, at the same time beginning a tapping rhythm on the table which everybody else emulates. The word must be returned by the chosen player before the fourth tap and must either rhyme with or begin with the same letter as the served word. The only exception is any word starting with B which must be answered instead by 'Bah Humbug!' before play continues as previously. A player must always look at the opponent to whom he or she is hitting the ball. Failure to meet any of these requirements results in the loss of the rally, scoring being the same as in tennis. A typical rally might go: Jog, Dog, Dandruff, Dromedary, Dyke, Hike, Like, Limpet, Listen, Glisten, Grab, Gale, Hail, Bail, Bah Humbug! Mail, Mastodon, Medium, Tedium, Trip, Drip, Grip, Nip, Nothing, Never, Nuance, Nightingale, panic, panic, love-15.

APPLE ON A STRING

Players: 3-6

You will need:

Apples, lengths of string

For this old Halloween party favourite, you need to suspend from the ceiling a length of string for each player and to the end of each piece of string tie an apple. The apples should be above head height, but within mouth reach of the participants. At the off, the players must munch into their dangling apples without using their hands. The first player to get down to the core is the winner.

HAPPY TRAVELLERS

Players: Any even number

You will need:

Newspapers, chairs

This jolly little pastime recreates the perils of trying to read a broadsheet news-paper on the London Underground in rush hour, an activity which has been known to result in the loss of eyes, teeth and wallets. Two teams sit facing each other in rows, the team-mates so close together that their knees are touching. All are given copies of the same newspaper, the pages of which have been hopelessly muddled up. The first team to get all of their newspapers in the right order win. So that the flank players don't have the unfair advantage of extra elbow room, non-contestants should sit on the ends of the rows.

RUNNING FLUSH

Players: 12 or more

You will need:

A pack of playing cards

If you have 52 guests at a party – plus two jokers – this is the ideal game, reminis-cent of all those student attempts to cram as many people as possible into a phone box. But even with smaller numbers, it can still be great fun and none-too taxing on the brain cells. In the event of there being 20 players, you need to take a pack of cards and remove all of the aces, kings, queens, jacks and 10s. Shuffle those 20 cards and deal them out face down on the floor (the cards, not you). Each player races forward to grab a card and the four who end up with the aces call out the name of their suit and speed to the nearest chair. The other four players with cards of the same suit run over to their ace and sit down in formation. The ace sits on the chair, the king sits on the ace's lap, the queen sits on the king's lap, the jack sits on the queen's lap and the 10 perches, somewhat precariously by now, on the jack's lap. The first suit to get every player in position wins. At this point, it is worth estab-lishing whether any of the aces suffer from weak hearts.

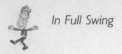

TALES OF THE RIVERBANK

Players: 3-6

You will need:

Paper clips, wire coathangers, a washing-up bowl

Fill a large washing-up bowl with water and empty a box of paper clips into the bottom. Each player kneels around the bowl wielding a length of wire which has been bent at one end to produce a hook. Wire coathangers can be straightened out to make acceptable fishing rods. On the command 'Go!', the anglers try to hook the paper clips amid a frenzy of activity which would scare off Jaws. When all the clips have been hooked, the player who has caught the most is declared the champion fisherman… while the rest get to talk about the paper clip that got away.

DICTATION

Players: Any even number

You will need:

Newspaper cuttings, pencils and paper

An equal number of bosses and secretaries line up on opposite sides of a table. Be sure that each secretary knows who is his or her boss and vice-versa but then arrange the seating so that no pair are opposite each other – in fact the further away they are, the better. Each boss is supplied with a different newspaper story of approximately the same length which she or he will endeavour to dictate to his trusty secretary, armed with pencil and notepad (or paper). All bosses begin dictating their different stories at the same time so it quickly becomes a nightmare for the poor secretary straining to hear her boss's words above all the others. To add to the confusion, arrange for the volume on the office radio to be turned up half-way through. At the end of the dictation, compare the secretaries' versions with the original newspaper stories. Any similarity will probably be purely coincidental.

TUNNEL BALL

Players: Any even number

You will need:

Balloons, blindfolds

Who would think that you could have so much fun with a balloon? Well, here's another simple game guaranteed to provide mirth and merriment for all but direct descendants of Oliver Cromwell. Two teams line up blindfolded with their heads down and their legs apart. This position may be familiar to those of you who have read back copies of Mayfair at the dentist. The first player in each team has a balloon and must pass it back between his or her legs to the next player. With everyone groping around in the dark, the balloon must continue its passage in this way until it reaches the end of the line. The first team to get the balloon through the last pair of legs wins the game.

CONVERSATION STOPPERS

Players: Any number

Two players agree privately on a word. Without mentioning the word itself, they strike up a conversation, dropping clues here and there. As other members of the ensemble decide that they know the word, they join in the conversation and try to prove to the pair, again without saying the actual word, that they know what it is. If it becomes clear that they don't, they have to turn their back on the company. There are no winners, but the last person to enter the conversation is judged to be thick and is given a forfeit. The best words to choose are ones with a double meaning such as 'back', 'crane' or 'ball'. That way, you can mislead the other players with a veritable shoal of red herrings.

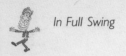

FEATHERS

Players: Any number

You will need:

A feather

With the players lying on their backs on the floor, throw a feather into the air. Everyone must do their utmost to prevent the feather landing on them, blowing frantically to force it in another direction. Players may move their head for the purposes of blowing, but no other part of their body. Whoever the feather lands on is out. The last person left in is the winner.

ARTIST, COMPOSER, WRITER

Players: Any number

Draw up a list of well-known artists, composers and writers and call them out one at a time. The first person who answers correctly 'artist', 'composer' or 'writer' to each name earns a point. To confuse matters, slip in a few miscellaneous historical figures who don't fit into any of the three categories. Players who shout out 'artist', 'composer' or 'writer' to any of these names lose a point. At the end of the game, the winner is the player with the highest total. Here are some suitable examples:

> Artists: Caravaggio, Chardin, Memling, Tintoretto, Angelico, Degas, Bellini, Fragonard, Botticelli, Correggio.
> Composers: Puccini, Rossini, Webern, Gluck, Berlioz, Delius, Sousa, Glinka, Mahler, Rameau.
> Writers: Boccaccio, Sheridan, Wieland, Baudelaire, France, Dostoevsky, Gautier, Pirandello, Rimbaud, Verlaine.
> Others: Fellini (film director), Artaud (theatre director), Bolivar (Venezuelan revolutionary leader), Daguerre (scientist), Galvani (doctor), Rasmussen (explorer).

GUZZLE GRAND PRIX

Players: 3-6

You will need:

Bowls, tea spoons

Here is the ideal sobering-up game after a surfeit of wine. Each player must drink a large bowl of water, using only a tea spoon, the first to scoop up every last drop feeling not only victorious but sufficiently invigorated to tackle another bottle of wine.

THE PRINCE OF WALES HAS LOST HIS HAT

Players: 6 or more

This game can seem positively baffling when everyone is sober, so if your guests have had a few to drink it is a recipe for total chaos. The players sit around a table and are numbered according to the amount of participants. Player one declares: 'The Prince of Wales has lost his hat' and adds that one of the others (say, number four) has found it. Number four immediately replies: 'No, sir. Not I, sir.' 'Then who, sir?' demands number one. 'Two, sir,' suggests number four. But player two counters: 'No, sir. Not I sir.' 'Then who, sir?' asks player four. 'Five, sir,' says player two. And so the round of questions and answers continues, gathering pace all the time. Anyone who gets the words wrong moves to the end chair (with eight players, this would be number eight) and the numbers change accordingly. Therefore, if number one made a mistake, he or she would then become number eight, eight would become seven, seven would become six, six would become five, five would become four, four would become three, three would become two and two would become one! So when you contemplate playing this game, don't say you weren't warned.

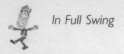
PASS THE POLO

Players: Any even number

You will need:

Cocktail sticks, Polo mints

The players line up as two teams with cocktail sticks between their teeth. The first player in each team has a Polo mint balanced near the end of his or her stick. The object of the game is to pass the Polo down the line from stick to stick without using hands, the first team to reach the other end being the winner. If a mint is dropped at any stage, the offending team has to go right back to the start. While calculating the right angle at the takeover point, players should refrain from stabbing their team mate with the stick.

THE BALLOON GAME

Players: 3-6

The Balloon Game represents the ultimate test of historical importance. Three famous people are flying in a balloon when the contraption springs a leak. The decision is: which of the three should be sacrificed by being jettisoned over the side so that the other two can be saved? The game begins with each player (or pair) choosing an occupant. The trio should be as diverse as possible to encourage lively debate. A good mixture might be Max Bygraves, Grace Darling and Judge Jeffreys. The latter might seem the obvious candidate for expulsion on the strength of mercilessly ordering the execution of 320 rebels in the 17th century, until you remember all those Singalong-a-Max albums. And there could be different grounds for throwing out someone like Henry VIII or Pavarotti, simply because the weight loss would enable the balloon to stay airborne a little longer. Any decision should be debated at length and then a vote taken to decide who goes. Of course, if the occupants were Michael Portillo, Tinky Winky and Gazza, the game would be simple. You'd just throw the lot of them out.

THE LAUGHING HANDKERCHIEF

Players: Any number

You will need:

A handkerchief

Party games don't come much dafter than this. One person stands in the middle of the room with a handkerchief (preferably clean) and the other players are positioned in a circle around the outside. When he or she lets go of the handkerchief, that is the signal for everyone else to start laughing like hyenas. But the moment it touches the floor, they must stop. Anyone who fails to laugh for the duration of the handkerchief's descent or who continues laughing after it has landed, is eliminated. The last player left in wins the prize — a jar of Michelle Pfeiffer's snot for the boys, and Charlie Sheen's for the girls.

I WISH...

Players: Any number

The players sit in a circle and think of the character, fact or fiction, dead or alive, that they would most like to be. Then the first player states: 'I wish I had been Sir Walter Raleigh' or whoever he chooses. Then he has to explain why — perhaps that when he threw down his coat, he would have got a good view of Queen Elizabeth's legs or that he would have been proud to have introduced the potato to Europe. The eventual winner is the person who gives the best reasons for his or her choice of alter-ego.

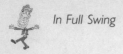
NEEDLE AND CORK

Players: 4-8

You will need:

Washing-up bowl, corks, darning needles

Float a number of corks in a washing-up bowl full of water (make sure there are at least three times as many corks as players) and supply each player with a darning needle. They then have to lift the corks out of the water by spiking them with their needles. The player who has recovered most corks in two minutes is the winner.

CHINESE PUZZLE

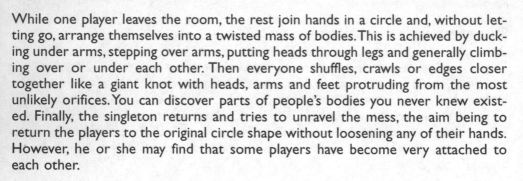

Players: 6 or more

While one player leaves the room, the rest join hands in a circle and, without letting go, arrange themselves into a twisted mass of bodies. This is achieved by ducking under arms, stepping over arms, putting heads through legs and generally climbing over or under each other. Then everyone shuffles, crawls or edges closer together like a giant knot with heads, arms and feet protruding from the most unlikely orifices. You can discover parts of people's bodies you never knew existed. Finally, the singleton returns and tries to unravel the mess, the aim being to return the players to the original circle shape without loosening any of their hands. However, he or she may find that some players have become very attached to each other.

QUICK CLUES

Players: Any even number

You will need:

Slips of paper, pencils, a hat or bowl

All of the players pair off and each person thinks of two similar items – rock stars, movie stars, TV stars, film titles, book titles, TV programmes, artists, authors, statesmen, sportsmen and so on. Each idea is written down on a separate slip of paper, folded over and placed in a hat, bowl or some other form of container. One partner then picks a slip of paper at random and has two minutes in which to describe to his or her partner what is written on the paper without using any of the actual words. If the partner guesses correctly, they move on to another slip, the pair who solve the most puzzles in their allotted two minutes emerging as the winners. The key to success is to deliver short, sharp clues which do everything but mention the words on the paper. For instance, if you had to describe 'Elton John', you might say, 'Rocket Man. Plays the piano. Big glasses. Colourful clothes. Silly haircut. Supports Watford, for God's sake…' If your partner suggests Reg Holdsworth, you might as well cut your losses and go home.

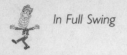

MAT FINISH

Players: Any even number

You will need:

Beer mats, chairs

Two teams line up sitting on chairs facing each other. At one end of each team, the respective captains sit with a pile of six beer mats on their knee. At the off, the captain picks up one of the mats and holds it at the top and bottom between the tips of his or her forefingers. The mat is moved towards the player on the captain's left. The captain removes his or her top finger, which is replaced by the second player's left finger. Together they turn the mat over and the captain removes his or her lower finger, to be replaced by the second player's right finger. This procedure is repeated along the line until the mat is perched on the last player's knee. That player then calls out 'Next!' and the second mat begins its journey. The first team to get six beer mats on the last player's knee wins the game. Any dropped mat has to go back to the captain who starts that 'leg' of the relay again.

SPOONS

Players: 6-12

You will need:

A pack of playing cards, spoons

The players sit on the floor in a circle in the middle of which is a pile of spoons, one less than the number of players. From the pack of cards, select four cards of a kind for each player. So if there are seven players, you need to use 28 cards – four aces, four kings, four queens, four jacks, four tens, four nines and four eights. The cards are shuffled and dealt to the players. If nobody has four of a kind (such as four aces), they all pass one card to their left simultaneously. They continue passing cards (always at the same time) until one player gets four of a kind. As soon as that happens, that player stops passing and grabs a spoon. This alerts the others who also dive into the middle to snatch a spoon. However, since there is one spoon short, one player is unlucky and is eliminated from the game. Before play resumes, another spoon is removed and the action continues, a bit like musical chairs, until there are just two card players competing for one spoon. As the tension reaches breaking point, whoever gets four of a kind snatches the final spoon in triumph… and probably embarks on a lap of honour around the sofa.

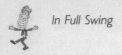

CONKED OUT

Players: Any even number

You will need:

Matchboxes

If you have a nose which puts Cyrano de Bergerac, and indeed large areas of the Cotswolds, in the shade, here at last is an activity at which your huge hooter may shine. For at 'Conked Out', a long nose has a distinct advantage over squat, flat, pug-noses. Players line up as two teams. The team leader pushes the cover of a matchbox on to his or her nose and tries to transfer it to the proboscis of the next player without using any hands. The matchbox proceeds in this manner down the line, with the first team to switch it right from one end to the other, solely via snouts, being the winner. If any player drops the matchbox or inadvertently touches it by hand, that team has to start all over again. It may seem a harsh penalty, but this isn't a game for wimps.

TELL THE TRUTH

Players: Any number

You will need:

Pencils and paper

Each player has to write down five supposed facts about himself or herself, of which only one is true. The other players then have to try to decide which is the true fact. Obviously if your life-long partner is among your fellow players, you'll need to dredge up something pretty obscure, but most people have some hidden secret, no matter how trivial. The important thing is not to make the genuine truth stand out like a sore thumb – your invented answers must be equally plausible. It won't take a genius to work out your true fact if your five suggestions are:

1. I once knocked out Mike Tyson, but nobody was watching
2. I once climbed Everest before lunch
3. I once stood in for President Clinton at a world summit
4. I once gave Demi Moore a tongue-sandwich
5. I once spotted 16 different makes of locomotive on Crewe station in 33 minutes

TIME FOR BED

THE PSYCHIATRIST'S COUCH

Players: Any number

You will need:

A sofa

After conversation and wine have been flowing in equal measures for several hours, why shouldn't you round off a memorable evening with a spot of psycho-analysis? The reason why not is because some of your answers may come back to haunt you. So be warned – don't volunteer to be a patient in this game if your tongue is loose. The chosen patient lies down on the sofa and is subjected to 10 minutes of intense questioning by the other players who act as psychiatrists. You'll get their bill later. The patient is told to answer all questions truthfully and at the end of the session, the psychiatrists analyse his or her problems, sometimes painfully. While the patient squirms at the diagnoses, he or she may even hear the odd grain of truth, however unwelcome. The psychiatrist whose evaluation turns out to be the most accurate wins the game. Then it is someone else's turn to lie on the couch – if anyone is mad enough or drunk enough.

ANALOGIES

Players: Any number

This is another game best played when everyone is plastered, simply in the hope that by the next day nobody will remember what was said. One person at a time is chosen from the gathering to be the subject of a series of analogies. The categories should be as wide-ranging as possible. For example in the case of someone called Tim, the questioning could go:

> If Tim was a breed of dog, what sort would he be?
> If Tim was a vegetable, would sort he be?
> If Tim was a means of transport, what sort would he be?
> If Tim was a film, what title would he be?
> If Tim was a drink, what sort would he be?
> And if Tim was a household item, what would he be?

If, after much debate, the general consensus of opinion is that Tim would be a toy poodle, a cabbage, a Sinclair C5, Bambi, Horlicks and a potato peeler, Tim would probably want the ground to open up and swallow him. However, if Tim were to emerge as a great dane, a fine sturdy carrot, a Harley Davidson, Terminator 2, Drambuie and the latest hi-fi, Tim would probably sleep contentedly that night. So it pays to be nice to your friends.

TONGUE-TWISTERS

Players: Any number

When everyone's too tired for a game requiring too much effort, slip in a few tongue-twisters. The beauty of this game as a late-night activity is that it can be played from wherever the participants happen to be at the time – flat out on the sofa, underneath the kitchen table or even hanging from the curtains. So test sobriety with 'The Leith police dismisseth us', 'Red lorry, yellow lorry', 'Sister Suzie sews silver shirts for soldiers' and 'The sixth sick sheik's sixth sheep's sick.' If there are ladies present, it might be best to avoid any reference to pheasant pluckers.

SLANDER!

Players: Any number

Here is an opportunity to get rid of all the bitterness and resentment which you may feel towards certain overrated, over-paid celebrities. Each player picks a famous person to slander and proceeds to tear him or her to shreds with a succession of vicious barbs, all the while avoiding any mention of the victim's name. The other players simply have to guess who is on the receiving end of such venom. On no account should any attempt be made to play this game using fellow guests as victims instead of celebrities... unless you're emigrating to South America the following day.

ALL TRUE

Players: Any number

This is not a game to enter into lightly. For all players must promise to speak the truth, the whole truth and nothing but the truth for its duration. That may sound innocuous enough for questions like: 'What's your favourite root vegetable?' But some guests will want to delve deeper and may ask: 'What's the worst lie you've ever told?' 'Have you ever been dishonest?' 'Have you ever had an affair?' And that is probably when you decide to forget about the rules and conclude that discretion is definitely the better part of valour.

PERSONALITY CHANGE

Players: Any even number

Another potentially dangerous game, this requires two partners to exchange personalities for five minutes at a time and behave in the manner in which they think their partner would behave. If this is a first date, it can bring a swift end to a relationship. Yet it can be even more devastating on a couple who've been together for years but who've kept silent until now about things their partner does which irritate them. So if you cruelly embarrass your wife by telling everyone present that she clips her toenails at the dinner table – usually during the soup course – expect an equally rough ride when it is her turn to lay into you.

ONE-MINUTE WALK

Players: Any number

You will need:

A watch

Cover all the clocks, confiscate all watches and egg-timers and tell the players they must walk from one end of the room in exactly a minute. They all start together and must maintain constant movement and adhere to an even pace. Anyone found guilty of stopping, even for a split second, or who reaches the finish too soon is eliminated. When 60 seconds are up, the host calls out 'Stop!' and whoever's nearest the finish line at that moment is declared the winner.

TODDLERS

Players: Any number

You will need:

Children's toys

For all the clever word games and inventive activities you come up with, don't be surprised if the most popular game at your party turns out to be one where grown-ups get the chance to revert to childhood. Tell your guests that, for 15 heavenly minutes, they are to go back to being three-year-olds and so there should be plenty of pushing and shoving, pulling and tugging and temper tantrums. It is essential to stipulate that the players behave as toddlers and not babies because then you won't have to change any nappies. If available, toys can be provided to be hurled around the room. You may even go as far as to dish out some jelly and ice cream, but this is only advisable if you intend re-decorating. And don't forget to hide the cat.

BEAUTY QUEEN

Players: Any number

You will need:

Pencils and paper

Don't worry, this isn't as tacky as it sounds. Instead it is a send-up of all those insincere beauty contest speeches where the contestants declare that they would like to 'travel, meet people, help little old ladies across the road and end world famine.' Each player is given a beauty queen title – 'Miss Nomer', 'Miss Place', 'Miss Chief' – and has to write down three things which he or she would like to do. These should be as ridiculous and pretentious as possible – such as 'rewrite Einstein's Theory of Relativity, discover a cure for hereditary flatulence and get my roots done.' The player who comes up with the wildest, wittiest or weirdest suggestions is crowned the overall Party Queen.

GURNING

Players: Any number

The ancient Cumbrian sport of gurning (where competitors have to pull the most hideous face imaginable) makes an admirable party game for that time of night when guests are no longer able to summon the power of speech. Simply imagine that someone has substituted vinegar for Coca-Cola and envisage the face you would pull as a result of drinking a glass. However, if it's been a good party the face you look at in the bathroom mirror the next morning may be only a marginal improvement.

MY BEST FRIEND

Players: Any number

At the end of a drunken evening, it's not uncommon for men to get exceedingly maudlin and grant whoever they happen to be with the accolade of being 'my best friend', even if they only met him an hour earlier. For this game, one male player sets the ball rolling by telling everyone else: 'You're my best friend.' In turn, the others (male and female) have to say why he is their best friend, too, but the answer they give must be a song title. Reasons for best mate-dom could therefore include:

> Player One: 'You Make Me Feel Brand New'
> Player Two: 'You Can Do Magic'
> Player Three: 'You Are The Sunshine Of My Life'
> Player Four: 'You Make Me Feel Like Dancing'
> Player Five: 'You To Me Are Everything'

After a couple of rounds, there won't be a dry eye in the house.

BUNNY RABBITS

Players: Any number

Announce to everyone that they're going to play 'Bunny Rabbits'. Get all the bunnies in line close together, stand at the end and tell them to copy whatever you do. First you use your hands to do the bunny's ears and everyone dutifully copies. Then you squat like a bunny and everyone squats with their hands between their legs. Then you hop like a bunny, and, as they hop up and down on the spot, you lean into the bunny next to you and send the whole line toppling like dominoes!

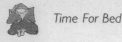
TRAUMAS

Players: Any number

One player leaves the room while the others think of a dreadful traumatic experience for him or her to have undergone at some time in life. It really shouldn't be anything half-hearted like the car breaking down on the way to an important meeting, but something which could leave deep emotional scarring such as discovering that your long-lost father is now known as Anita and lives with a Rugby League prop forward. On returning, the player has 20 questions in which to learn the nature of his or her trauma from the other participants. All questions, however, can only be answered with a 'yes' or a 'no'. When the precise suffering is revealed, someone else has a turn at being traumatised.

IF THE CAP FITS

Players: Any number

You will need:

Pencils, slips of paper

Each player writes down an adjective to describe someone else in the room. The chosen word should be truthful but not necessarily complimentary. On the top right-hand corner of their slips of paper, the players should write the name of the person to whom the adjective refers. The individual slips are then folded over and handed to the host who reads out the first word. The players then argue over which of them it describes best. Even the person who chose the word joins in, if only to avoid being identified as its author, either through embarrassment or fear, depending on the nature of the adjective. When a consensus of opinion arrives at the most likely name, the host reveals the identity of the guest. If the adjective was too abusive, it might be wise to have the victim's coat ready.

LINE WALKING

Players: Any number

You will need:

Masking tape, a pair of binoculars

This is the ideal game to play before everyone finds out whether they're sober enough to walk out into the night air. Lay a strip of masking tape in a straight line across the floor and ask players to walk along it. A few drunkards may fall by the wayside after a couple of staggering steps, but the majority will probably manage it reasonably well. Now ask them to repeat the journey, this time looking through the wrong end of a pair of binoculars. Suddenly, it's not as easy… and they begin to wish they hadn't had that tenth can of lager after all.

TRICKS

Within this section you will find over 250 tricks, ranging from simple tricks with playing cards and everyday objects to cunning and practical jokes. The beauty of the tricks is that anyone can perform them – there are no grand illusions with complicated, expensive equipment.

There are tricks for every occasion — for the kitchen, at work or even in the bank queue. Other tricks are tailored for the pub where you can baffle your friends with your skill at doing unnatural things with ice cubes, beer mats and small change. In addition, there are classical practical jokes for everyone. The key to success with practical jokes is the timing. A hand rising up mysteriously from the ground may appear hilarious after an all-night party, but may be received with less enthusiasm at a funeral. The best practical jokes should cause an embarrassment that can be overcome by means other than an extensive course of therapy. It is important to choose the right victim — someone with a good sense of humour rather than a person who reacts to any setback by roaming the streets wielding an axe.

To help you choose the tricks best suited to your abilities, each is numbered with a Skill Level from 1 to 10. The higher the number, the more difficult the trick. Similarly the practical jokes are given an Embarrassment Factor of 1 to 10.

Have fun!

PRACTICAL JOKES AND TRICKS CAN BE DANGEROUS AND HAVE SERIOUS CONSEQUENCES.

THE INCLUSION OF A JOKE OR TRICK IN THIS BOOK SHOULD NOT BE CONSIDERED RECOMMENDATION FOR ITS USE. IN UNDERTAKING ANY TRICKS YOU SHOULD THINK CAREFULLY ABOUT POTENTIAL DANGERS.

PRACTICAL JOKES AND TRICKS

THE INVERTED MATCHBOX

Skill Level: ❶

Embarrassment Factor: ❹

Practical jokes comes in all shapes and sizes. Some operate on the grand scale and require the sort of elaborate planning which used to be the preserve of shows like 'Candid Camera' and 'Beadle's About'. With others, the charm is in their simplicity. This prank falls into the second category. Choose a victim who is a smoker and wait for him to leave the room for a while. He will invariably leave his box of matches lying on the table. In his absence, swap the box around so that the closed side of the tray is now on the same side as the picture. Leave the box picture-side up for his return so that he won't suspect anything. Then when he comes to open the box, all the matches will fall out on the floor. This spectacle can cause far greater embarrassment if timed to occur at an important business meeting, but your motives might be open to question.

LAGER SHOWER

Skill Level: ❶

Embarrassment Factor: ❹

Warning: This trick could be dangerous. Take care!

Certain customs go with certain drinks. Fine wine is swilled lovingly around the palate, dry Martini is shaken but not stirred and meths is accompanied by three choruses of 'I Belong to Glasgow'. Canned lager is shaken so vigorously that whoever opens it is covered in a sea of foam. As with everything, the timing is crucial. If at all possible, you should hand your friend the shaken can so that the grand opening coincides with him attempting to chat up the girl you fancy. By the time he has gone to clean himself up, you will have moved in. Even if he decides to press on regardless, the chances are she won't want to get too close to someone who stinks like a brewery, unless of course she's got a part-time job as a shire horse.

SAY IT WITH FLOWERS

Skill Level: ❶

Embarrassment Factor: ⑩

Warning: This trick could be dangerous. Take care!

If you don't mind spending money in your eternal quest to embarrass your friends, an outlay of about £10 can secure you a potential marriage-wrecker! But make sure that it is a friend on whom you play this trick, so that you can patch things up afterwards. You need to wait until your friend has spent a few days away alone — perhaps a business trip or the UK Solitaire Championships — and on his return, send him a big bunch of flowers with a romantic message on the card. Time the flowers to arrive when you're certain that his other half will be at home so that he can't bury them at the bottom of the dustbin and pretend they never arrived. If you're a real sadist, you could casually drop by that evening so that you can witness the mayhem you've caused, but there's always the danger that your expression might give the game away too quickly. Besides, his mood the next time you talk to him will be a sure sign as to whether your plot has had the desired effect. If the acrimony lingers, you will need to own up, preferably before solicitors become involved.

HIDE AND DON'T SEEK

Skill Level: ❷

Embarrassment Factor: ❺

Ever since the news story about the Irish hide and seek champion being found dead in a cupboard, this age-old pastime has been deemed too dangerous for some households, but it can still be incorporated into a cruel practical joke. When the evening is really going with a thud, you've run out of lager, there's no football on the telly and the only video left to watch is of your sister giving birth, why not suggest a game of hide and seek? One person will be unbearably enthusiastic, insisting that he knows a place where none of you will ever find him. So you tell him to go and hide and then you all disappear down to the pub. By the time he realizes he's been tricked, it will be his round.

CATCH THE EGG

Skill Level: ❷

Embarrassment Factor: ❼

You will need:

An egg, a ball

Eggs are very versatile, not least because there are so many practical jokes you can play with them. One of the easiest – and messiest – involves secretly substituting an egg for a ball during a game of catch. On summer afternoons, parks are full of groups of lads trying to offset their steady diet of lager and fast food with a spot of healthy exercise. For some, this entails nothing more than a few arm jerks in recognition of a passing girl, but for the more energetic it could entail kicking around a football, an impromptu game of cricket or volleyball, hurling a frisbee or simply throwing a tennis ball among themselves. Unless you are confident of your ability to make an omelette impersonate a frisbee, the egg substitution trick is best performed with a tennis ball. It is most effective when there three or four of you playing. Keep the egg in your pocket for the first few rounds so that you have all built up to a point where you are throwing and catching at speed. At an opportune moment, bring the egg into your left hand. As you catch the ball right-handed, quickly switch egg and ball and toss the egg to the next catcher. By now, he will be operating on automatic pilot and probably won't notice anything out of the ordinary about the projectile hurtling towards him. Even if he does spot that it's an egg, his natural instinct will still be to catch it. Either way, it will make an unholy mess as it splatters into his hands.

MINEFIELD

Skill Level: ❷

Embarrassment Factor: ❸

You will need:

Six plates, a blindfold

This is a daft trick for parties. Suggest a game of Minefield, a slight variation on the party game Obstacle Course, and scatter half a dozen plates around the floor. Tell the contestant that each plate represents a landmine which, for obvious reasons, he must avoid. But then having blindfolded him, you secretly remove the plates, leaving him prancing around like a demented hop-scotch dancer trying to steer clear of imaginary obstacles. Prolong the agony for as long as possible with cries of 'Look out', 'Mind that one' etc. When his legs are about to drop off through exhaustion, remove the blindfold and let him realize what a fool he's been made to look.

THE THIN BLACK LINE

Skill Level: ❷

Embarrassment Factor: ❹

You will need:

A coin, a pencil, a piece of paper

Sometimes it seems unfair to take advantage of the extremely gullible or the extremely drunk, but there are occasions when you just have to abandon such lofty principles. This is one such instance. Tell your victim that you're going to make his hand really giddy and then see whether he can roll a coin down his nose. In the misplaced belief that he is neither stupid nor drunk, he will accept the challenge with relish. Place the coin on a sheet of paper and ask him to draw round the coin very fast 15 times. His hand won't be feeling in the least giddy after that mild exercise so the task of rolling the coin down his nose will be a mere formality. As he acclaims his feat, what he won't have grasped is that the pencilled coin will have left a nice black line right down the middle of his nose.

THE UNSPIKED DRINK

Skill Level: ❷
Embarrassment Factor: ❼

Your victim for this prank should be one of those underprivileged souls who are not accustomed to the pleasures of alcohol. You know the sort – the prim spinster of the parish who only ever drinks a single small sherry at social gatherings because 'any more makes me feel light-headed' or the quiet little man from the computer department who has half a shandy at Christmas and promptly sticks his tongue down the throat of Mrs Jenkins from kitchenware. Embarrassed by the disgrace (or at least constantly reminded of it by the graffiti on the wall of the gents' lavatory), he will sensibly order nothing stronger than an orange juice at the next leavers' do. But this is where you and your friends tell him that you have spiked his drink with vodka. You haven't really – you've just added a splash of water – but, seduced by the atmosphere and seeing everyone else enjoying themselves, he will soon be convinced that he's been knocking back the spirits. After the first orange juice, he will loosen his tie (the first time that it has been separated from his neck since the Queen's Jubilee) and after the second he will start slurring his speech. By the third, he will be singing and by the fourth he will have taken to the dance floor, swivel-ling his hips like a latter-day John Travolta. At the end of the evening, even though he won't have touched a drop of alcohol, he will probably have to be carried out horizontally while declaring his undying love for the barmaid. And no matter how many times you tell him the next day that all he was drinking was neat orange juice, he won't believe you. He had a good time – and so did you, watching him.

ONE GOOD TURN

Skill Level: ❶

Embarrassment Factor: ❿

You will need:

A playing card

This is quite a good wheeze for a party. Hand your victim a pack of playing cards, tell him to go into the next room, to close the door behind him and to turn over, one at a time, as many cards as he wants to. Announce to everyone that when he returns to the room you will immediately name the last card he has turned over. While he is in the adjoining room checking for bugging devices, moving pot plants and hidden cameras, you simply place a card, which you have secretly taken from the pack, on the floor so that it leans upright against the door. As he opens the door to return to the party, he will unwittingly turn over the card and you can claim the easiest of victories.

FANCY THAT!

Skill Level: ❷
Embarrassment Factor: ❻

Fancy dress parties offer enormous scope for the imagination – the prospect of Margaret Thatcher deep in conversation with Groucho Marx, Napoleon dancing with Catwoman, Fred Flintstone getting off with Marilyn Monroe, and in the kitchen Elvis chatting to Ronald McDonald. They also provide an ideal opportunity for the practical joker, particularly when it comes to sending out the invitations. For just about the most embarrassing thing that can happen to anyone at a party is to be the only one who turns up in fancy dress. So feed your warped sense of humour by telling just one person that it is a fancy dress affair – tell the rest to come in ordinary clothes. However, you need to let them in on the joke in case the victim rings them to compare outfits. Having lit the blue touch paper, you retire and wait for that magical ring of the doorbell when Julius Caesar in all his finery steps into a room full of people in T-shirts and jeans.

FATAL FOOTWEAR

Skill Level: ❷

Embarrassment Factor: ❺

You will need:

Carpet tacks or drawing pins

None of us would ever dream of looking inside our shoes, trainers or slippers before putting them on because, fortunately, in Britain we don't have to worry about deadly spiders and snakes deciding that our sweaty footwear offers an ideal resting place for the winter. Indeed the biggest threat posed is the emission of noxious fumes from yellowing insoles. The ozone layer has crumbled from less. Taking all of this into account, the toes of footwear make ideal hiding places for all manner of mean tricks, guaranteed to give the wearer a nasty shock. The scattering of a few carpet tacks or drawing pins in the toes of a friend's slippers is assured of waking him up as he staggers out of bed in the morning. Sturdy trainers or shoes also make admirable receptacles for certain semi-liquid substances. Runny rice pudding and creamy porridge are particular favourites, giving that lovely squelchy feel as the toes slide in. Another trick to play on someone who is renowned for his laziness is to tie the laces of his trainers together. If he leaves them tied up every night and simply steps into them the next morning, his first attempt at walking will see him fall flat on his face. This can be strangely rewarding for spectators.

THE RELUCTANT BALLOON

Skill Level: ❷

Embarrassment Factor: ❶

You will need:

Two balloons, sticky tape, a pin

To the uninitiated, the balloon is a harmless creature, but to nervous souls and Americans a sudden unexpected burst can mean a lifetime in therapy. So this jolly jape can be a good one to play just to see your victim cowering behind the sofa or under the bed waiting for a bang that never comes. To set up the joke, produce an ordinary inflated balloon and ask your victim to stick a pin in it without bursting it. No matter how gently he probes the outer skin, it bursts with an almighty bang, reducing him to a quivering wreck. Tell him he's not trying hard enough – it's easy. Say you'll show him how it's done. Produce a second blown-up balloon but, as you pat it to make sure that it's properly inflated, slip on a piece of transparent sticky tape which was hidden in your hand. Stick the pin through the sticky tape into the balloon and watch as he dives for cover. When nothing happens, he'll feel more than a little foolish, particularly as he emerges to see the big grin on your face.

BLACK EARS

Skill Level: ⑨

Embarrassment Factor: ⑦

You will need:

Ink, a piece of cloth

This one is much loved by office workers during those quiet moments when the boss is away, the bar isn't open and there's no racing on the telly. Wait for one of your colleagues to leave the room and, while he is out, smear some ink on the receiver of his phone with a piece of cloth. As he returns to the office, greet him at the door and tell him that there's an urgent call for him on his extension. Depending on his personal circumstances, this could be his wife, lover, bank manager or impotency consultant. Obviously the ink is best concealed on a dark-coloured phone but, with the right incentive, his haste to pick up the receiver should be such that he won't even notice the ink on a pale phone. Of course the first thing he'll realize is that there's nobody on the other end of the line, a situation you explain by saying they must have rung off. But the damage has been done and his ear is now smeared with ink. You can leave him like this for as long as you like, until he looks in the mirror or starts wondering why everyone keeps giving him funny looks.

ROOM SERVICE

Skill Level: ❸

Embarrassment Factor: ❾

Warning: This trick could be dangerous. Take care!

Spending a couple of nights locked in a hotel on some business course can teach you a few truths about the people you work with, particularly those who steadfastly refuse to buy a round at the bar. They come up with all manner of inventive excuses: 'Sorry, I appear to have left my wallet in my room'; 'I've just been mugged in the lift'; 'What do you mean, you don't accept pesetas in Bridlington?' However you can exact revenge by acquiring a sheet of the hotel's headed notepaper and writing a bogus letter of complaint from the manager to one of your colleagues. The hardest part is actually getting hold of the headed notepaper. Once you've overcome that obstacle, you can get down to the fun part of writing the letter. Something along these lines might be appropriate:

Dear Sir

It is my duty to inform you that I have received a complaint from the hotel chambermaid about the state of room 132 following your stay there on the nights of 18th and 19th February with the group from Wells Electronics. Whilst I appreciate that to an extent what you do in the privacy of your own room is your business, my staff (all of whom are happily married women) were nevertheless alarmed to discover several items of a sexual nature. Quite apart from the used condoms in the litter bin, there was the matter of the literature in the top drawer of the bedside cabinet. Beneath the copies of What's On in Bridlington and Fun at Filey were two extremely dubious magazines, the covers of which showed leather-clad ladies brandishing whips. Finally there was the question of your bed linen. Some of those stains may never come out so I am writing to request that you make a financial contribution of £25 towards a new set of sheets. I look forward to receiving a cheque from you for that amount and suggest that in future you take your trade elsewhere.

Yours faithfully

(Manager)
cc: Mr D. Harding, Managing Director, Wells Electronics

All you have to do now is post the letter near the hotel (to ensure the postmark is authentic) and watch your colleague's anguish as he opens it in the office. Will he be outraged? Will he turn scarlet when he next bumps into his boss? Or will he quietly write out a cheque for £25, explaining that he and his wife have been going through a difficult time and the girl meant nothing to him really?

THREAD BARE

Skill Level: ❸
Embarrassment Factor: ❹

You will need:

A cotton reel, cotton thread, a needle

Find a cotton reel with thread the same colour as one of your shirts. Keeping the thread on the reel, push it through the eye of a needle and then push the needle through the sleeve of your shirt. Take away the needle and leave a visible length of thread, something like a couple of inches, hanging on the outside of your shirt. With the reel secreted inside your shirt in such a way that it can be easily unwound, just go about your daily business as usual. Sooner or later, someone will kindly point out that you've got a thread hanging loose and will offer to remove it for you. As they pull, they will unwind the entire thread from the hidden cotton reel. Once someone has started pulling a thread, it's very difficult to stop – there's that natural curiosity to get to the end of it. But as yard upon yard of thread emerges from your shirt, they will be horrified that they've ruined your favourite item of clothing. Any second, they'll be expecting the entire arm to fall apart. No matter when they stop, the feelings of guilt will remain with them until you confess that it's all a joke.

EGGSTRA ORDINARY

Skill Level: ❸
Embarrassment Factor: ❺

You will need:
An egg

If your flatmate is planning to make an omelette for dinner, here's a way of inject-ing a little entertainment into the proceedings. When you're home alone, hard-boil an egg and replace it in its box. So that your friend is sure to choose the boiled egg, remove any others (you can always claim you fancied a big fry-up earlier). Then cherish the moment as the would-be chef tries in vain to crack the hard-boiled egg on the side of the bowl. There is more chance of the bowl cracking first. As tem-pers rise, the awful truth will dawn, at which point you can ease the blow by pro-ducing an ordinary egg so that nobody need starve. But be warned: you'll probably have to do the cooking for the rest of the week.

THE CLINGFILM TRAP

Skill Level: ❸

Embarrassment Factor: ❾

You will need:

A roll of clingfilm

Clingfilm is among the great modern products, yet it is highly doubtful whether its inventors envisaged some of the more unusual – not to say notorious – uses to which it has been put. These include a joke which should only be performed in the home of a very close friend and even then only on condition that you are willing to disinfect the area afterwards. The set-up is simple. Lifting the seat of the toilet, you stretch the clingfilm across the open bowl, making it as smooth as possible to avoid detection. Then you wait for some hapless drunk to stagger to the loo and urinate in the vague direction of the bowl. When you hear a strangulated cry of anguish, you know it's time to get going with the disinfectant.

MR LYON

Skill Level: ❸
Embarrassment Factor: ❸

This is really silly and the bane of switchboard operators at almost every zoo, but it never fails to get a laugh in the office. Leave a message on a colleague's phone pad for him to call Mr Lyon and put the number of your nearest zoo or wildlife park. When the long-suffering switchboard operator answers and hears yet another call for Mr Lyon, they will probably politely inform him that he's been the victim of a practical joke. And he will slam down the phone, muttering darkly about having to work with a load of silly kids, while everyone else confirms his views by sniggering like fourth-formers. The more ambitious prankster might try Mr C. Lyon or, for the incurably gullible, Mr L.E. Fant, but don't overdo it so that the joke wears thin. And remember there are dial-back facilities on phones these days so calls can be traced. Your boss wouldn't be too thrilled if the zoo retaliated by depositing two tons of elephant manure outside his office window.

EXCALIBUR

Skill Level: ❸
Embarrassment Factor: ❻

Strange things can happen when you have the builders in – like they actually work for five minutes before taking a tea break – but none stranger than the hand which mysteriously rises out of the sink. You need a certain set of circumstances for this trick to work. The sink must be in place, but without a plughole/drainer or any pipes underneath. There must also be a cupboard under the sink where you can hide. Ideally you could do with the assistance of a third person (maybe one of the builders if he can tear himself away from his Earl Grey) to persuade your partner into taking a closer look at the sink. When she gets near enough, thrust your hand up through the hole in the sink and give her the shock of her life. It is also worth checking in advance that the water is switched off at the mains lest she be tempted to exact immediate revenge.

HOT LIPS

Skill Level: ❸

Embarrassment Factor: ❺

You will need:

A blindfold

Warning: This trick could be dangerous. Take care!

Every party has its self-styled stud, a ridiculously smooth operator overripe for sending up. In the Seventies, he wore an open-necked shirt and a medallion, and in the Nineties… he still wore an open-necked shirt and a medallion. He sees himself as the consummate ladies' man and enjoys nothing more than a game where he can come into physical contact with the fairer sex. And naturally he assumes that the feeling must be mutual. So make his dreams come true by telling him that you are going to line up all the girls, blindfold him and ask him to identify each one by the way they kiss. He can hardly contain himself. Once he is blindfolded, though, you have a nasty surprise in store for him, for you quickly substitute men for the girls. As he struts over, lips puckered, to where he thinks the first beauty is awaiting his charms, little does he know that he is about to kiss a 15-stone rugby player. The moment when he realizes to his horror that the person with whom he has just locked lips is not a girl but a burly man is one to dine out on for weeks to come.

BANANA MUNCH

Skill Level: ❹

Embarrassment Factor: ❺

You will need:

A banana, a blindfold

At a party, suggest a game of Banana Munch, explaining that it involves nothing more complicated than three blindfolded players each racing to devour a banana. Blindfold your victim and give him a banana and then pretend to do the same to the other two participants, but instead merely instruct them to remain silent. On the word 'Go', the victim starts to guzzle his banana as rapidly as is humanly possible, convinced that he is part of a race. He will be encouraged in this belief by the shouts of onlookers, all urging him to go faster and telling him that his rivals are catching up. When he has finally swallowed and probably almost choked on the fruit, he triumphantly removes the blindfold, only to be greeted by a sea of grinning faces and the realization that it was a one-horse race.

THE LOADED UMBRELLA

Skill Level: ❸

Embarrassment Factor: ❺

You will need:

Confetti or flour

We come to take certain things for granted: that the supermarket queue we choose will always be the slowest, that Pub comedians will never be funny and that when we open our umbrella nothing will suddenly fall on our head. It is this supreme confidence which makes umbrella-owners a natural target for practical jokers. In their absence, you can place all manner of objects into a rolled-up umbrella – confetti, flour, paper clips, corn flakes, perhaps even a portion of white-bait – and virtually guarantee that the owner will open the umbrella oblivious to the contents. The first thing he'll know is when a shower of confetti or a shoal of fish comes raining down on his head. The key to obtaining maximum enjoyment from this joke is to make sure you're around when it happens, although the look on his face when you next see him will be a fair indication of whether or not it was successful. Another umbrella trick is to tie up the spokes with tough string, rope or masking tape. When he steps out in the pouring rain and tries to put up his umbrella, he'll find that no matter how hard he tries, it won't open. First he'll get wet and then he'll probably try to get even.

THE FALSE HAND

Skill Level: ④

Embarrassment Factor: ❷

You will need:

A glove, paper tissues

A lot of adults are just big kids at heart so it is appropriate that some of the best and silliest practical jokes have their origins in the school playground. The much-loved false hand routine definitely falls into that category. The preparation is simple. You fill a glove (including the fingers) with paper tissues so that it looks as if a hand is inside it, then pull down your sleeve over your hand and hold on to the glove by its open end. Do a tour of your friends, offering to shake each one warmly by the hand. As they reciprocate the gesture and shake your hand, it drops off. My, how they'll laugh! Obviously there is a time and a place for such a joke. A high-powered Japanese business delegation might not see the funny side and don't try it out on a little old lady with a dodgy heart. Somehow a joke loses its edge when the victim is rushed to hospital in an ambulance.

WATER TORTURE

Embarrassment Factor: ⑤

You will need:

Two glasses of water

This is another good prank for a party. Select your victim and say: "I bet you can't recite 'Little Bo Peep' while balancing a glass of water on each hand." Such a challenge will be hard to resist, even when you point out that the glass of water must be placed on the back of each hand. He will still hold his arms out willingly. And as he begins the earnest tale of the poor girl and her lost sheep, a full glass balanced on the back of each hand, you and your friends simply get up and go out. Suddenly the awful truth dawns on him – he has been abandoned without any way of depositing the glasses. He is stuck there, high and dry, although as he becomes increasingly desperate, maybe not so dry. You can, of course, merely pretend to shut the front door and hide in the hall instead. The effect will still be painful enough. It is best to play this joke before your victim has had too much to drink, otherwise he won't be capable of balancing a glass on the back of his hand in the first place.

THE MOVING FINGER

Skill Level: ❹

Embarrassment Factor: ❸

You will need:

A cardboard box with a lid, cotton wool, glue, tomato ketchup

This is another joke which owes its conception to the likes of Just William. In those days, it would be guaranteed to send squeamish, pigtailed schoolgirls screaming to the nearest teacher, but in these times of Girl Power you're more likely to receive at least a tongue-lashing or even a severe case of GBH. In the United States, you'd probably be sued for causing unnecessary distress. So this is very much a trick for the brave. Take a small cardboard box and in the bottom cut a hole large enough to accommodate a finger. Glue cotton wool to the bottom of the box, but leave a space over the hole. Close the lid and, holding the box in your hand, push one finger through the hole and bend it over so that it is lying there limply. Tell your victim that you have something interesting to show them, a line which has worked for everyone from Henry VIII to Hugh Grant. Open the box so that they can see the finger and, when they are least expecting it, suddenly wiggle it. You can either have your finger plain or with relish. The addition of tomato ketchup makes the sight of the moving finger all the more horrific and will ensure a spectacular reaction. Once again, there are certain sections of the community on whom it is unwise to practise this trick, notably anyone who has recently lost a finger in a chain-saw accident.

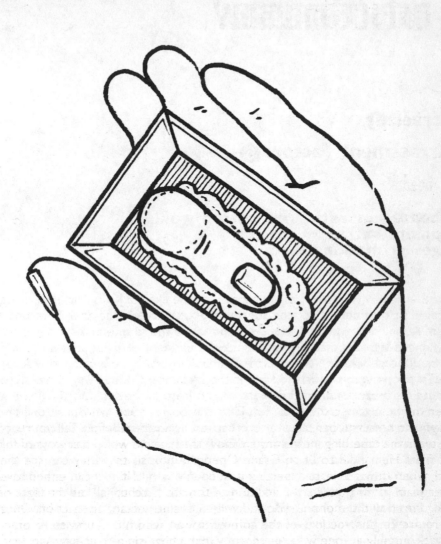

THE OFFICE MUMMY

Skill Level: ④

Embarrassment Factor: ⑥

You will need:

Bandages or masking tape

It needs at least two people to execute this practical joke successfully. The aim is to catch a work colleague unawares while he is on the phone and tie him to it, using either bandages or masking tape. Since the element of surprise is so important, you need to choose the call carefully. Probably the best time to strike is when he is on the phone to his girlfriend and his thoughts are drifting away aimlessly to a far-off land of romantic candlelit dinners and holidays in the sun. Or of course he may be having a blazing row with her. Either way, his mind will be elsewhere, enabling you and your accomplice(s) to creep up unnoticed. Before he can react, furiously wind the tape or bandage around his head (but not eyes, nose or mouth), the phone and his hand so that he is firmly wedged in position with his ear to the receiver. For good measure, tie his other arm to the arm of the chair. An additional advantage of timing your raid to coincide with a personal call is that his anguished cries down the phone won't alienate a business client. You can leave him like that for as long as you like – you can even spoon-feed him his lunch. Another office jest – one which merely requires the victim to be seated rather than actually on the phone – is to tie him to his chair, using plenty of string or rope. As he sits there helplessly, you can answer all his phone calls with the immortal line: 'He's a bit tied up at the moment ...'

NELSON'S EYE

Skill Level: ❹

Embarrassment Factor: ❻

You will need:

**A chair, a stuffed stocking, a marble,
an overripe strawberry or peach, a blindfold**

This party trick offers a history lesson with a tour of the anatomy of Admiral Nelson. Having been blindfolded, your victim is asked to 'feel Nelson's good leg' and her (this one probably works best with a female victim) hands are steered towards someone's leg. Then she is asked to feel Nelson's bad leg whereupon her hands are brought into contact with a chair leg. Next she is asked to feel Nelson's good arm and finds herself fondling an arm before being asked to feel his bad arm, at which she gropes a stuffed stocking. Nothing to get worried about so far, but, in the words of the Caped Crusader, the worst is yet to come. For finally there is the matter of Nelson's eyes. First she must feel Nelson's good eye, whereupon a marble is slipped into her hand, and then it is time for his bad eye. At this moment, her fingers are guided towards a horribly mouldy overripe strawberry or peach and as she feels the squashy mess, her screams will be heard in the next hemisphere. One thing is certain – she'll make sure that history doesn't repeat itself.

SOMETHING FISHY

Skill Level: ④

Embarrassment Factor: ⑧

You will need:

A piece of uncooked fish

'Put a haddock in your tank.' As an advertising slogan, it stinks. But the result can be more devastating than anything a tiger can produce. It really needs two of you to carry out the plan effectively. First you need to gain access to the engine of the victim's car. This can be done under the pretence of admiring the working parts (for some reason men with new cars are always keen to show off their sumps and carburettors although, as a topic of conversation, it must rank alongside the drainage system of Birmingham or the history of the nail). While your victim is praising his new engine, have your accomplice distract him momentarily – the suggestion (erroneous as it turns out) that there may be a speck of oil beneath the car will guarantee his undivided attention. With his back turned, pull the piece of wet fish from its newspaper wrapping and slip it into the engine near the radiator. When your victim reappears to resume the discussion, bring it to a rapid conclusion by saying that you'd better get back – you've got jobs to do, fish to fry! Now you just let nature take its course. With any luck, the first whiff of fish from the engine will occur while he's on a hot date with a new girlfriend he really wants to impress. On the aphrodisiac scale, the smell of fish comes just above chronic diarrhoea. As a passion-killer, it is comparable to having a policeman knocking on your car window. From then on, the more he drives, the worse the smell will get. Unless you're particularly vindictive, confess your sins before it completely wrecks his love life or before he spends a fortune on garage bills while mechanics search for the fault. As a goodwill gesture, you could always present him with a bag of chips.

EGG ON THEIR FACE

Skill Level: ❹

Embarrassment Factor: ❼

You will need:

One egg per person

One of the most popular games for the dying embers of a party is Russian Omelette in which players take it in turns to crack an egg over their own head. All bar one of the eggs are hard-boiled, the excitement being to see which poor partygoer will leave with egg on their face. But if you are a particularly devious host, you can play this game with a minor alteration. The rules are the same – everyone cracks an egg over their head – but to save time and for a grander spectacle, here they will all do it simultaneously. Oh, and there's one other thing which you will omit to mention – none of the eggs have been hard-boiled! Introduce the event by explaining the rules of Russian Omelette, but don't actually say that is what they are about to play. Merely lead them to believe that all but one of the eggs are safe. On the count of three, get them to smash their eggs on their skull. By the time they realize they've been tricked, it will be too late. With all of your guests sitting there with egg streaming down their faces, it is a handy way of bringing the party to a quick conclusion – but don't be surprised if not everybody comes to your next one.

SPOONERISMS

Skill Level: ⑤

Embarrassment Factor: ⑥

You will need:

Three spoons

Warning: This trick could be dangerous. Take care!

You need three people to carry out this practical joke – two accomplices and your stooge. Inform the stooge and one accomplice that they are going to play Spoonerisms while the third person acts as umpire. The two participants kneel facing each other, each with a spoon handle in his mouth. They then take it turns to hit the bowed head of their opponent as hard as possible with the spoon. Since it is difficult to exert much force from such a position, the blows should be relatively soft but, unbeknown to the stooge, he is being hit quite firmly by the umpire who has a spoon secreted behind his back. He can be left in ignorance until someone takes pity.

STRUNG ALONG

Skill Level: ⑤
Embarrassment Factor: ⑦

You will need:

A long piece of string

Frighteningly simple, this practical joke relies on your finding two gullible victims in the street. Armed with a length of string, you stop someone who doesn't look in too much of a hurry and, explaining that you are a surveyor whose colleague hasn't turned up, ask him whether he would mind holding one end of the string for a moment while you take the other end for the measurement. You then disappear round a corner with the string and tell the same story to another passer-by, whereupon you vanish into thin air leaving two complete strangers holding a piece of string. If they're still there when darkness falls, you'll know you picked the right men for the job.

THE GLASS EYE

Skill Level: ⑤
Embarrassment Factor: ⑤

You will need:
A marble, a handkerchief

Hour after hour stuck on the M25 and nothing to do but stare at the bumper of the car in front and listen to Tony Blackburn on the radio. No wonder we have road rage. From time to time, you'll find yourself exchanging sympathetic glances with the driver in the next lane and here's something to do which will really catch his eye. Put a marble in the same pocket as your handkerchief and lift them out together, concealing the marble in the handkerchief. Then, when you're sure you've got his attention, pretend to remove your eye from its socket and to put it on the handkerchief. Keeping the replaced eye tightly shut, produce the marble and polish it furiously with the handkerchief. Your fellow driver will look suitably aghast as you complete the performance by flourishing the marble and appearing to push it back into the socket. When you open your eye, keep the marble hidden in your hand. Even if he realizes that it's a joke, it will relieve the tedium an iota, and if he doesn't, the bumper of the car in front had better watch out.

PUBLIC HUMILIATION

Skill Level: ⑤

Embarrassment Factor: ⑧

Warning: This trick could be dangerous. Take care!

Shopping with your partner can be a tedious experience, so what better way to liven it up than with a spot of public humiliation? Find the most public spot available – in a busy shop or a bank – then suddenly turn to your partner as if you haven't seen him or her for ages (actually this is a joke which is best performed by women on unsuspecting boyfriends or husbands). In an unnaturally loud voice so that nobody within a two-mile radius can fail to hear, say something like: 'It's Gerry, isn't it? Fancy seeing you. The last time I saw you, you were just about to start your sex addiction therapy...' Alternative greetings might include:

'You've got a nerve. You go off and screw my mother and now you expect to come crawling back to me and the children.'
'Simon, I haven't seen you for years. Did you get off on those bestiality charges? Wouldn't the sheep give evidence?'

Watch with glee as your friend wishes he could crawl in a hole.

FINGER THREAD

Skill Level: ⑤

Embarrassment Factor: ②

You will need:

A bandage, a piece of thread

This trick is of a gentler nature, but will still work well if you choose a caring, compassionate victim… which immediately excludes lawyers, agents, tax inspectors, traffic wardens, taxi drivers, lorry drivers, bus drivers and anyone carrying a clipboard. To achieve the desired effect, first pierce two small holes in a bandage, placing the holes so that when the bandage is wrapped around your finger they will be on opposite sides of your digit. Then insert a piece of cotton thread through one hole and out the other before wrapping the bandage around your finger. Now all you have to do is go up to that nice lady in the next office and ask her whether she's heard about how you trapped your finger in the filing cabinet. Keeping the bandaged finger behind your back, really lay it on thick about how you had to be rushed to hospital and how the doctors had to sew the tip of your finger back on. At this, produce the bandaged finger for viewing and, sliding the thread up and down so that it looks as if it's going straight through your finger, explain that it doesn't hurt too much if you do it slowly. At the very least, she'll choke on her digestive.

ALL SEWN UP

Skill Level: ⑥

Embarrassment Factor: ⑥

You will need:

Needle and thread

Are you fed up with your boyfriend going out with his mates five nights a week? Have you had enough of them commandeering the TV to watch the football while you wanted to see the new Brad Pitt movie? Well here's a way of gaining a degree of revenge without shredding his clothes or chopping off his manhood. It does involve tampering with his wardrobe, but nothing more permanent than sewing up the ends of the sleeves of all his shirts and trousers. In the early morning stupor that passes for being wide awake, he won't notice anything amiss until he wonders why his feet aren't appearing out of the bottom of his trousers. In panic, he may think it's something medical but, when he discovers that his shirts have met a similar fate, it will dawn on him that there is treachery afoot. Tell him you'll unpick them in the evening as long as he agrees to stay in and watch. And in the meantime he could start a new fashion for bank employees wearing T-shirts and shorts to the office…

BANANA SLICE

Skill Level: ⑥

Embarrassment Factor: ④

You will need:

A banana, needle and cotton, scissors

Perhaps it has something to do with the shape, but bananas are always the funniest fruit. Any fruit jokes are invariably about bananas, never about apples, oranges or grapes. A banana comedy gig could pack out the Royal Albert Hall whereas a strawberry in concert would struggle to fill a phone box. And when was the last time you had a good laugh with a mango? This prank reinforces the banana's position as the king of fruity comedy. You begin by threading a needle with cotton and pushing it through the skin of the banana along one of the flat sides. Pull plenty of thread through, then push the needle back into the hole and along the next side. Keep going until the needle comes out again through the first hole. Pull both ends of the cotton and the banana will be sliced inside its skin. Repeat this four or five more times, depending on the size of the banana, so that the fruit is sliced from top to bottom. As long as you remember to remove all the threads of cotton, there will be no hint of anything untoward having taken place. Offer your victim the rigged banana and sit back while he peels it... only to find that it is already sliced. One of two things will happen – either the banana will collapse in pieces to the floor or he will simply stare at it in disbelief.

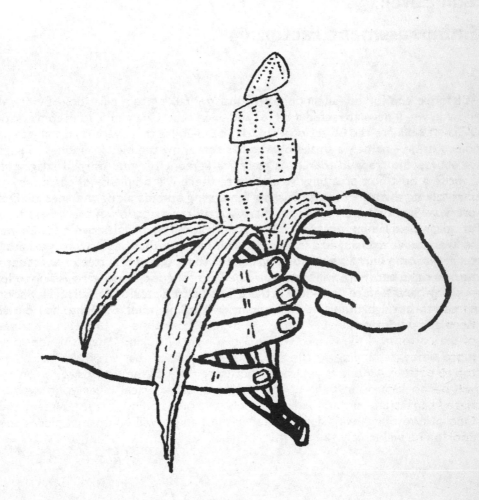

CONVERSATIONS WITH A PILLAR BOX

Skill Level: ⑥

Embarrassment Factor: ⑦

At a loose end for the afternoon? Why not try talking to a pillar-box? Before you know it, you'll have attracted a bigger audience than Channel 5. Your conversation with an inanimate red object operates on the premise that there is an animate pink object inside — namely a small boy who has somehow tumbled in amongst the mail. Of course the trapped toddler is merely a figment of your warped imagination. Choose a post-box on a busy street where there will be plenty of passers-by and start talking through the slot, making reassuring sounds along the lines of 'Don't worry, we'll soon have you out of there.' Draw the attention of the others to the lad's plight, explaining that you were first attracted by his plaintive cries for help. Say that you've exchanged a few words with him, but that he's now too exhausted to speak. Some uncharitable souls will either think you're a nutter or say it serves the boy right, but there will always be a quorum of good Samaritans willing to lend a helping hand. Before you know it, there'll be half a dozen of you all making soothing noises through the flap. At that point, you calmly melt away into the crowds, your day's work done.

THE TASTY GOLDFISH

Skill Level: ⑥

Embarrassment Factor: ⑤

You will need:

A slice of carrot, a goldfish bowl or fish tank

An old favourite, this is nevertheless still a highly effective joke when performed for an unsuspecting public. For maximum effect, it is best carried out in front of a constant stream of passers-by such as in a shop window where it first gained notoriety on 'Candid Camera' some 30 years ago. But, failing that, it still works well on a one-to-one basis with a goldfish owner who thinks you've just devoured their pet. The secret of the trick is to conceal a thin, flexible slice of carrot, about three inches long, in the palm of your hand. Dip your hand into the fish bowl or tank and, as you pull it out, produce the piece of carrot and waggle it around as if it were a wriggling goldfish. Before your startled victim can protest, slip it into your mouth and swallow it with a gulp and a licking of your lips. The reaction you get will rarely disappoint.

THE BUCKET OVER DOOR

Skill Level: 6

Embarrassment Factor: 8

You will need:

A bucket of water, a chair

Warning: This trick could be dangerous. Take care!

The bane of every maths teacher since children were invented, the bucket over the door trick remains a classic practical joke. The fact is that nobody expects to open a door and get soaked so the element of surprise makes it a natural winner. Leaving the door slightly open, stand on a chair or step-ladder (you're still trying to trace your real ladder) and balance the bucket of water on the top of the door frame. As soon as the victim pushes open the door, the contents of the bucket will come tumbling down on his head, amid much merriment from all bar one. For the more timid, you could substitute confetti or scraps of paper for water – this has the advantage of not drenching any carpets. At the other end of the scale, there's always baked beans… Just don't use a metal bucket.

CALL BOX

Skill Level: ⑦
Embarrassment Factor: ⑥

This is another innocuous little pastime to while away those long hours at the office between lunch and going-home time. For the trick to work, your office window must overlook a public telephone box. The first thing you need to do is pop down to the box and write down the number of the phone there. As you see somebody approaching the box, dial the number so that the phone rings when they open the door. Timing is vital – if you leave it too late, they'll have started dialling their number before you get through and you'll just hear the engaged tone. A smart move is to dial every number except the final one when you first see the person going over to the box and then to press the last digit as they actually enter. Whoever answers the phone will naturally sound puzzled – after all, nobody expects the phone to ring in a call box. Once you've got their attention, you have to give them a task to perform. With any luck, there'll be someone hanging around waiting, maybe for a bus or a lift. Describe that person to them ('fifties, wearing a plastic rain hat, floral coat and wheeling a shopping trolley'), explain that it's your wife, that you knew she'd be outside the supermarket and could they get a message to her? Make it something simple like, 'Your husband says, will you get another pork chop for dinner?' At first, the person on the other end is bound to protest, but if you plead convincingly enough, they'll do as you say just to get rid of you so they can use the phone. When you've finally persuaded them, you can watch from the safe haven of your third-floor window as the person in the call box accosts a complete stranger about pork chops. There will be a lot of bemused expressions and arm waving, probably culminating in a suggestion that the poor woman with the shopping trolley comes to speak to you on the phone, in which case you simply hang up. By then, you'll have had your fun. Whilst this may seem a good lark, you have to be sensible about it. Remember that people use call boxes in an emergency so if the person on the other end sounds too harassed, hang up and let them get on with it.

WATERWORKS

Skill Level: 7

Embarrassment Factor: 8

You will need:

A broomstick, a goldfish bowl

Warning: This trick could be dangerous. Take care!

Fill the bowl with water (if there is already water in it, remember to remove the goldfish) and promise your victim an astonishing spectacle if he will hold the broomstick while you climb on a chair to reach the ceiling. Carefully place the bowl against the ceiling – open end up, please – and tell the victim to press the broomstick against the base of the bowl, thereby wedging it against the ceiling. Then you climb down from the chair and leave him to get on with it. By the time you return, you'll find either a friend with severely aching arms or a wet carpet.

THE BLANKET GAME

Skill Level: ⑥

Embarrassment Factor: ⑨

You will need:

A blanket

The success of most practical jokes is dependent on the reaction of the victim, so selecting someone with the right credentials for victimization is of considerable importance. The Blanket Game will work with anyone, but it is much more satisfying played on somebody meek and mild rather than a natural extrovert. It is best played at a party when everyone has had a few to drink. Even your victim may have downed one or two. You explain patiently that it is nothing more than a guessing game which requires him to sit fully clothed under a blanket. What could be more innocuous? He is told that all the other guests have in mind a certain article which he has about his person and that he must try to guess the article in question by taking it off and displaying it above the blanket. Only then will he be told if he is right. This could be the most risqué thing he's done since handing that library book back a day late in 1967. Item by item, he hangs things over the blanket – watch, beige socks, sensible shoes, Postman Pat tie (to make him look wild and reckless) – and item by item, they are rejected. Eventually he finds himself stark naked and utterly confused. It is now that everyone joyously confesses that the item they were thinking of was the blanket itself. At this point the blanket may be ceremoniously removed to reveal the poor chap's embarrassment to the full, but a kinder option is to let him keep it on, gather his clothes and scurry to the bathroom... and then probably straight out of the front door.

WATER BED

Skill Level: 7

Embarrassment Factor: 8

You will need:

A bottle, a cork, a piece of string, water

For reasons best known to themselves, this trick was apparently once popular with soldiers of the French Army. It works by the theory of frustration. One evening, you slide a bottle full of cold water between the sheets in your victim's bed. Irritated, he will remove it and go to sleep. The following night you do the same, and so, in all probability, will he. On the third night you again insert the bottle of cold water between his sheets, but with a minor adjustment in the form of a piece of string tied from the cork in the bottle to the end of the bed. Angry at discovering the bottle for the third night in a row, he will yank it out of the bed, in the process releasing the cork and a pool of water all over his sheets. It might be an idea to arrange to stay at someone else's house that night…

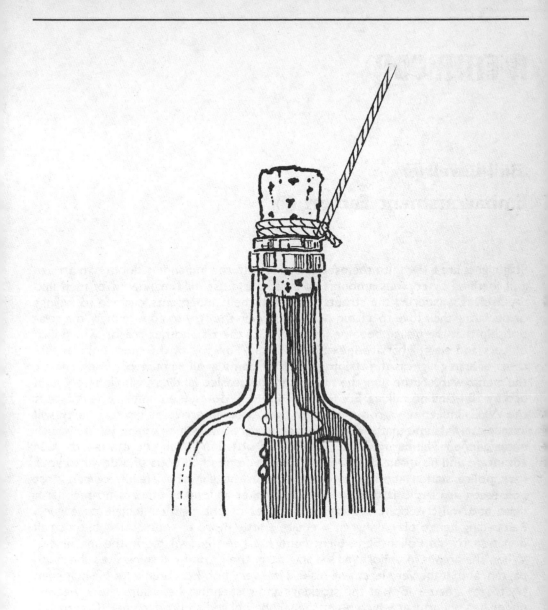

A FAIR COP

Skill Level: ⑦

Embarrassment Factor: ⑩

Stag nights are a law unto themselves. Faced with the impending doom of marriage and fortified by copious amounts of lager, the most mild-mannered of men find themselves wandering the streets at night in their underpants, chained to railings or declaring their love to a lamp-post. (It is when they try to consummate the relationship that the police become involved.) But there's another reason why police officers and stag nights are inextricably linked. For one of the most popular features of a stag night is the strippagram. They come in all manner of guises. There's the traffic warden, the nun, the nurse, and the seaside landlady, who'll have you in bed by 10 – and no talking. But for most future grooms, the number one choice is the WPC. Indeed any groom seeing a policewoman arrive at his stag party will immediately assume that she's a strippagram, particularly if he's been told that such entertainment will be provided, and this is a situation which you can use to your advantage and his intense discomfort. What you need to do is pop down to your local police station and have a quiet word in the ear of a friendly officer. Most policemen are enthusiastic about practical jokes as long as there is no real harm done and will cheerfully suggest the services of one of their female colleagues. Persuading her to play along may require a little more of your charm, but a small donation to the Police Benevolent Fund has been known to oil the machinery. When she arrives in uniform at the stag party, the groom will think she's the strippagram and, at the very least, will make a few very non-PC comments. He may even try to get a better look at the stockings and suspenders he is sure she is wearing under her uniform, at which point she will be obliged to produce her ID card and her male colleague. If the groom is still not convinced that he has picked on a genuine officer, the sight of the police car waiting outside should sober him up rapidly.

JUMP!

Skill Level: ⑧
Embarrassment Factor: ⑤

You will need:

A stool, a blindfold, a hard-backed book or a tray

For this trick to be at its most effective, you need a macho man for your victim – someone who reads books about the SAS and keeps pit bull terriers. If your group is composed solely of men who read books about flower arranging and keep toy poodles, try another joke. First you blindfold your victim and perch him on a high stool. Two strong men stand in front of the stool, one at either side, allowing the victim to rest his hands on their shoulders. They then raise the stool off the ground a couple of inches while at the same time another accomplice taps the victim's head firmly with a hard-backed book or a tray. Disorientated by the blindfold, the victim will be certain that the bump was his head hitting the ceiling and that the stool must be high in the air. The two strong men then gently lower the stool to the floor, but the victim's confusion will be such that he'll still think he's several feet off the ground. As everyone urges him to jump, his bravado will almost certainly desert him and he'll decide it's too dangerous. Only when his blindfold is removed will he realize that he's been made to look somewhat foolish.

APPLE-PIE BED

Skill Level: 8
Embarrassment Factor: 5

After a heavy night, there is nothing more welcoming than your own bed… that is, unless it is an apple-pie bed. To those ignorant of the genre, an apple-pie bed is one which it is impossible to penetrate, with the result that the person, frustrated and exhausted, ends up sleeping on top of the bed rather than in it. Begin by tucking in the bottom sheet all around the bed and then add the top sheet, tucking it in at the top and the upper sides. Put the pillow on top of the top sheet and then fold the top sheet back from the bottom of the bed so that it covers the pillow. Fold back the top sheet to reveal the pillow, add blankets and tuck everything firmly in place. From the outside, the top sheet will look like two sheets, but there is nowhere for the victim's legs. You have created something which is harder to get into than Fort Knox.

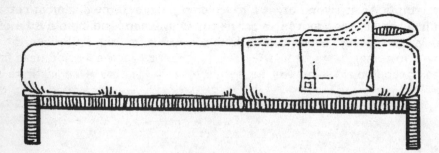

MOVING GNOME

Skill Level: ⑧
Embarrassment Factor: ⑤

Garden gnomes used to be the prerogative of elderly couples living in seaside bungalows with names like 'Dunroamin' and 'Bayview', but in recent years they have spread alarmingly to other parts of the country and different sections of the community. Nowadays when you walk along any suburban street, you are more than likely to stumble across a gaggle of the bearded chappies peering out from behind a bush or perched on a rock. Clearly they are of limited intelligence – what is the point of holding a fishing rod over a patch of dry soil? – but their simple charm seems to delight their owners. To non-worshippers, the placement of the gnomes may seem haphazard, but we are led to believe that their position in the garden is determined by where they are likely to be happiest – maybe in the sun or near another gnome, or simply a place where next door's tom cat won't spray all over them. So if they were suddenly to start moving around, seemingly of their own accord, it would cause their owners considerable consternation. This is where the practical joker comes in, but remember any such japes should only be carried out on a friend's gnomes. All manoeuvres will have to be performed either in the dead of night or when your friends are out. At first, just move one gnome a couple of feet and wait for any reaction. If, a few days later, the gnome has reverted to its original position, you know that you are getting through to the owner. You can then become bolder in your moves, swapping two of them around. By now the owner will be so perplexed he will probably start confiding in you. And when the next morning he comes down to find Gerald, his favourite gnome, buried head first in the herbaceous border, he will be beside himself. He may even instigate night patrols or erect a barbed-wire fence and searchlights. Meanwhile your deeds become ever more outrageous with gnomes popping up in the strangest places. By the time you have two of them performing an indecent act in the ornamental wheelbarrow, it is probably time to stop.

375

PRESS GANGED

Skill Level: ⑨

Embarrassment Factor: ⑦

Warning: This trick could be dangerous. Take care!

This trick is a real test of your ability to carry out a hoax. Your victim needs to be someone with an unusual hobby. Most offices have them – the little man from accounts who boasts the county's largest collection of pencil sharpeners; or the secretary who goes lawnmower racing at weekends; or the boss who hangs around street corners at night (but that's another story). Collectors, in particular, are always keen for their passion to reach a wider audience. Someone with a room full of toe-nail clippings of the rich and famous can't understand why the rest of the world isn't equally fascinated with the subject, especially as he's hoping to acquire one of Elvis's any day now. Therefore these people are the perfect target for the newspaper hoax. To carry it out effectively, you will need a partner-in-crime, someone with a mobile phone who is willing to pose as a newspaper reporter. Let us say your chosen victim's hobby is collecting toasters. Get your friend to phone him up, pretending to be a reporter with the local paper, saying that he would like to do a story about his collection. Your victim will be only too eager to co-operate, particularly when the 'journalist' sounds genuinely interested in toaster collecting. At the end of the first exploratory call, your reporter friend should leave the number of his mobile phone – you don't want the victim phoning up the real paper and finding that no such person exists. The sting will be the photo session. Rather than do this at the victim's house, the paper would much rather take the photos at his workplace where he could be surrounded by appreciative colleagues. The session is fixed for Tuesday and the victim has been asked to bring in as many of his 500 toasters as he can manage. With the aid of his car and two large suitcases, he manages 104. Told that the shoot is to take place in the office at noon, he spends most of the morning hauling toasters upstairs, only to receive a phone call from the bogus reporter at 11.45 telling him that the photographer has been called out on another job. The shoot will be rearranged for Thursday, same time. Not trusting security at work, the victim has little option but to take all his toasters home. He brings them in again on Thursday and again the shoot is cancelled at the last minute as the photographer has suddenly been taken ill. The victim's anger at another cancellation might thus be softened by concern for the photographer's health. Your reporter friend must promise faithfully that he will get a photographer for Monday, adding that the editor is so keen on the story that he would like the avid collector to wear a chef's hat and apron so that it can make a lively front-page picture. Flattery will get you everywhere. Come Monday and the toasters reappear once more. At noon, your victim is standing resplendent in chef's hat and apron, 105 toasters (he managed to cram an extra one in the boot) laid out before him, waiting for the photographer. You have temporarily absented yourself due to an urgent call of nature. You return in one of those disguises so adored by Noel Edmonds, brandishing your daughter's Instamatic. It dawns on your victim that he has been set up. When a toaster flies through the air in your direction, you realize perhaps he can't take a joke after all.

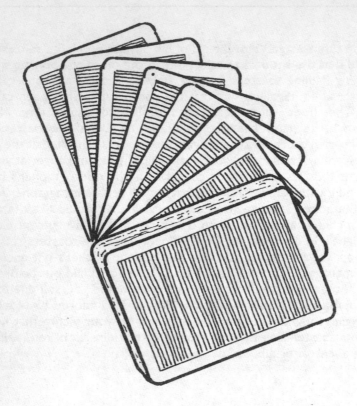

CARD
TRICKS

THE HAIRY ACE

Skill Level: ❶

You will need:

Glue, a hair

Card tricks don't come much easier than this. All you have to do is take a hair (if you're a bit short yourself, borrow one from a friend) and glue it to the back of the ace of hearts so that it is just visible against the background. Since the idea is for the hair to be undetectable to all but yourself, choose a fine strand in preference to a great clump of dreadlock. Select five cards from the pack (including the hairy ace) and ask your friends to lay them face down on the table. By the magical powers invested in you, tell them that you can find the ace of hearts without even touching any of the cards. Although you can spot the ace straight away by the presence of the hair, make a great play of locating the correct card – you don't want everyone to know how easy it is. After your first success, have the five cards rearranged and repeat the feat. You can carry on ad infinitum, the only threat to success being if one of your houseproud friends decides to 'get rid of that nasty little hair on the back of one of the cards.'

ROYAL FAMILY

Skill Level: ❶

Put all 12 court cards (jacks, queens and kings) together somewhere in the centre of the pack and ask a member of your audience to try and split them up by cutting the cards a dozen times. With each cut, take at least three cards off the pack. Even after the 12 cuts, the entire royal family will, barring divorce or skiing holidays, still be together in the pack.

ODD ONE OUT

Skill Level: ❶

You will need:

A paper clip

This is extremely silly, but can lead to immense frustration. Indeed people have been known to come to blows over it. All you do is pluck five cards from the pack – two pairs and an odd one. For example, you might choose the two of spades, two of diamonds, 10 of hearts, 10 of diamonds and queen of spades. Hold all five cards together in your hand with the odd card in the middle of the five. Show the faces of the cards to your volunteer and then reverse them so that he is confronted with the backs of the five cards. Tell him you're going to ask him to do the easiest thing in the world, a task which is even within the intellectual capabilities of the average amoeba: would he kindly attach a paper clip to the odd card? With confidence oozing from his pores, he slides the clip on to the middle card but, when you reverse the cards once more to show them face up, it transpires that he has put the paper clip on the front card by mistake. He's bound to demand another go... and another... and another, and as he continues to meet with abject failure, that's when matters can become a little heated. What make it all the more galling is that you are clearly not interfering with the cards or the clip in any way. It's just one of those irritating little tricks.

SECRET SIGNALS

Skill Level: ❶

You will need:

A table

By squatting under a perfectly ordinary table, with no view of proceedings, you are somehow able to name the cards which are being dealt on top of it. The secret of the trick is that one of the dealers is your partner-in-crime and the pair of you have concocted a series of signals which he will relay to you under the table with his right hand. If the card is a spade, he will tap once on his right knee; if it is a club, he will tap twice; for a heart, he will tap three times; and for a diamond, four times. After he has indicated the suit, he will move on to the actual number with the jack counting 11, the queen 12 and the king 13. Thus two taps followed by a display of 12 fingers tells you that the card which has been dealt is the queen of clubs. If your accomplice is subtle with his signals, the rest of your friends will be baffled by your prowess. Their initial suspicions will fall on the cards, so make sure they shuffle them to their satisfaction before dealing, and on the table. Perhaps there is a hole in it. So allow them to carry out a thorough inspection of the table for woodworm or any other boring parasite. They will find nothing untoward and will be left with little option but to acknowledge your brilliance… until someone starts wondering why your accomplice suddenly seems to have such an itchy right knee.

SNEAK PREVIEW

Skill Level: ❷

Ask someone to pick any card from the deck and then tell them to show it to the rest of the gathering, but not yourself. While all eyes are focused on that card, take a sneaky glance at the bottom card in the deck... and whatever you do, don't forget it. Ask your volunteer to put the selected card back on top of the deck face downwards and then, as you deliver your well-honed patter, casually cut the pack anywhere you like. Square off the deck so that there can be no suspicion of an improper cut, fan through the cards and the selected card will be immediately beneath the one you glanced at earlier. It's as easy as that.

BOTTOMS UP

Skill Level: ❷

Even if the only deck of cards you're familiar with is the old Max Bygraves classic (15 weeks in the charts in 1973), you should be able to master this simple trick. Before you begin, secretly turn the bottom card of the pack face upward. Then fan out the cards in your hand face down, making sure you don't show the rogue end card, and invite your guinea pig (metaphorical, not literal) to pick a card. At this point, it is a neat diversion to proffer a particular card whereupon your guinea pig, smelling a rat, will think that the trick revolves around a hidden card and will deliberately select another. This will make the eventual dénouement all the more stunning. When the person has chosen a card, close the pack and swap it into your other hand, in the process turning the pack over so that the odd card is now face down on top. After asking the person to remember the selected card, get him or her to return it to the pack. Turn your back on proceedings, fan open the cards and you can easily identify the chosen card as it will be the only one, apart from the top card, which is face down. With the sure-fire scent of victory in your nostrils, turn around and demand: 'Is this your card?' When the gasps of amazement have subsided, savour the moment as your friends applaud wildly and, with any luck, start writing cheques.

TALKING CARDS

Skill Level: ❷

You will need:

12 identical envelopes, a pencil

Your friends may long have suspected that there was something strange about you – perhaps it's your back collection of Songs of Praise videos or your bedroom poster of Judith Chalmers. Now you can confirm their worst fears as you claim that playing cards are able to talk to you. Before carrying out this trick, you need to lay your hands on a dozen identical envelopes. Mark four with a tiny pencil dot on the left-hand corner of the flap, four with a dot on the right-hand corner of the flap and leave the remainder blank. Then put the envelopes in a pile, the left-dotted on top, the right-dotted in the middle and the blank underneath. With the preparation complete, it's time for the magic. Remove the four jacks, the four queens and the four kings from the pack and put a jack in each of the top four envelopes (those with the dot on the left), a queen in the next four (those with the dot on the right) and a king in the last four blank ones. Turn the envelopes over so that nobody can see the dots and get someone to give them a good shuffle. It is now that, picking up one envelope at a time, you claim to hear voices from within. If the dot is on the left, you could claim the voice is 'Jack Nicholson or maybe Jack (sic) Villeneuve, but whoever it is, it's definitely a jack.' You then open the envelope to reveal the jack and prove your amazing psychic powers. Continue through as many of the remaining envelopes as your audience can stomach and wait for the men in white coats to take you away.

TELEPHONE TELEPATHY

Skill Level: ❷

With this trick, you can achieve the seemingly impossible by transferring your thoughts of a particular card down the phone so that the person at the other end names it correctly. Shuffle the pack thoroughly and allow your audience to inspect it in order to verify that the cards are perfectly ordinary and are not marked in any way. Thus assured, they will find what follows all the more remarkable. Ask one person to select absolutely any card from the pack and to show it to you. Let's say it's the six of diamonds. Then you boldly declare that you will telephone your friend Vic and, without you giving him any clues whatsoever, he will tune in to your telepathic powers and identify the card. Needless to say, it's all a big con. When you ring up, Vic, who has been thoroughly briefed, answers the phone and, speaking slowly, says: 'Clubs, diamonds, hearts, spades.' When he reaches the correct suit (here it would be diamonds), you speak, saying something like: 'Is Vic there?' (Cue song). He then counts through the numbers, slowly and deliberately, starting from the ace and working up to the king. When he gets to the correct number (in this case the six), you speak again, saying: 'Hi, Vic, I've got a call for you.' You then pass the phone to whoever chose the card in the first place and Vic promptly declares that the card is the six of diamonds. Impressive, eh?

BERMUDA TRIANGLE

Skill Level: ❸

You will need:

A Pritt stick

With this trick, you demonstrate how a perfectly ordinary card can vanish completely from the pack. The trick is in the preparation. While your fans are still paying at the turnstiles, smear the four edges of the back of the top card with a Pritt stick (and maybe a blob in the middle for luck). When everyone is seated and a hush has descended on the auditorium (all right, your bed-sit), ask a volunteer to take a card, to show it to the rest of the audience and to put it on top of the pack. Under no circumstances must your volunteer be allowed to take the original top card. As you pick up the pack, casually press the chosen top card down on to the sticky back of the card beneath. They will now be as one. Cut the pack a few times and deal out the cards face up. Handling the two glued together cards carefully, express concern that there is absolutely no sign of the selected card – it has simply vanished into thin air. At this point, some over-zealous members of your audience may demand a body search lest the missing card be secreted about your person. This should be actively encouraged unless the audience is:

a)   composed entirely of serial killers on a care in the community day-release scheme

b)   a Women's Institute party

c)   the Dale Winton Appreciation Society

KINGS AND QUEENS

Skill Level: ❸

This trick comes complete with its own fairytale – the story of a group of travelling kings and queens who are forced to swap coaches because of insufficient legroom. Begin by removing all of the kings and queens from the pack and arrange the eight cards in suits so that they alternate king, queen, king, queen. Deal out the first pair – the king and queen of hearts – face down and ask someone to turn them over. While this is happening, craftily switch the top card of the six remaining in your hand to the bottom, thereby changing the order of the royal rulers. With the king and queen of hearts still face up, deal out the other six cards alternately face down so that the audience, unaware of your sleight of hand, will think that all the kings are in one group and all the queens are in the other. Then you can tell your tale of how the various royals set off to a ball in two separate coaches, divided by sex. After a while, the king of hearts, who, although married to the queen of hearts, was having an affair with the queen of diamonds and also had a secret love child by the six of spades, felt that travelling with three men was cramping his style and his legs, so he decided to switch to the queens' coach. At this point you move the king of hearts face up to the other pile which supposedly contains four queens. However, the queen of hearts didn't want to share a coach with her errant husband. She knew all about his flings and anyway she was about to 'come out' about her relationship with the queen of clubs, so she decided to move over to the kings' coach. At this point, you move the queen of hearts (face up) to the other pile, that which is thought to contain three kings. Thus you have one pile with the king of hearts face up and three cards face down and the other pile with the queen of hearts face up and three cards face down. Everyone thinks the queen of hearts is with three kings and the king of hearts with three queens. But, as with most royal romances, nothing is quite what it seems and you turn over the cards to reveal that, in fact, all the kings are in one coach and all the queens are in the other.

MISTAKEN IDENTITY

Skill Level: ❸

Take the four aces from the pack and, when nobody is looking, slip the ace of diamonds into your pocket. Hold up the other three aces in a fan shape with the ace of hearts in the middle but so that its true identity is hidden by the ace on either side. As far as the audience are concerned, it is the ace of diamonds in the middle. Boldly announce that you are going to make the ace of diamonds disappear. Gather up the three aces, put them in different parts of the pack, give them a good shuffle and deal them out face up. To everyone's surprise, there is no sign of the ace of diamonds. Complete the illusion by producing the ace of diamonds from your pocket.

RHYMING CARDS

Skill Level: ❸

All you need to do for this trick is memorize the following rhyme:

'Eight kings threaten to save

95 queens for one sick knave.'

It is utterly meaningless until you translate it into cards – eight, king, three, 10, two, seven, nine, five, queen, four, ace, six, jack. So, before attempting this feat of memory, arrange the cards in the pack in that order and in alphabetical suit order of clubs, diamonds, hearts and spades. Thus the first card will be the eight of clubs, followed by the king of diamonds, then the three of hearts, 10 of spades, two of clubs, seven of diamonds, nine of hearts and so on. In this way, you can predict the order of every card in the pack. Your suspicious friends can inspect the cards to their hearts' desire, but will find nothing to explain your powers. For the cards are not marked in any way and, to the untrained eye, appear stacked totally at random. The experience will leave them completely mystified… and asking for your help with next week's Lottery numbers.

SPOT THE DOT

Skill Level: ❸

You will need:

A pencil

To prepare for this trick, use a soft pencil to draw a diagonal line across the side of the shuffled deck of cards. Your audience will attribute the pencil line to everyday wear and tear, little suspecting that it is all part of your fiendish plan. For the trick itself, ask one person to pick a card and, without showing it to you, to memorize it and replace it anywhere in the deck. The chosen card will now show up as a small dot in the side of the deck and is thus easily identifiable, allowing you to brandish the card triumphantly to your new-found fan club

IN A FLAP

Skill Level: ❸

You will need:

Two extra cards, scissors, glue

Cut a small square from the middle of one spare card, fold it in half and stick one half to the back of the other extra card. This gives that card a small flap. Press down the flap so that it is invisible (for this reason the cards must have identical patterns on the back) and put it on the top of the pack. Now announce that you are going to suspend the cards in mid-air. Place the top card face up in the palm of your hand, secretly pull out the flap and grip it between your fingers. Put a number of other cards on your hand, cunningly inserting them beneath the card with the flap. Then when you turn your hand over, instead of falling to the floor, the cards will be held in place by the trick card. You don't get tricks like this with David Copperfield...

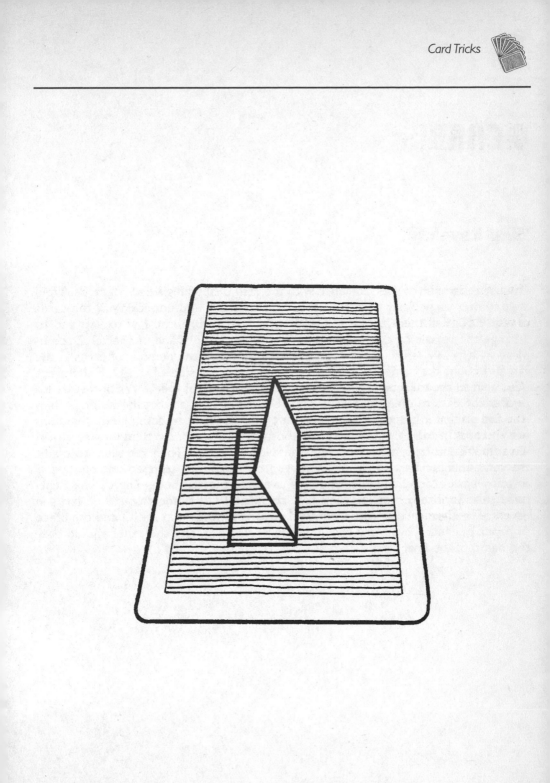

Q CARD

Skill Level: ❸

Entrust a member of your audience with the task of shuffling a pack of cards. Avoid anyone of a particularly nervous disposition, or you'll end up picking all the cards off the floor. Tell them to cut the pack in half, to return one half to you and to arrange the remaining cards face up on the table in the shape of a letter Q, complete with tail. When the Q is complete, silently count the number of cards in the tail and count the same number of cards up the right side of the Q. If there are five cards in the tail, count five cards up the right side of the Q. Write the identity of that fifth card on a slip of paper, fold the paper over so that the writing is hidden and place it in the centre of the Q. Ask your assistant to count aloud the number of cards in the Q, beginning at the bottom of the tail and then moving clockwise up the left-hand side, stopping wherever they wish. Then get them to count the same number backwards around the Q, the card they stopped on counting as 1, going back around the left-hand side, avoiding the tail, and going up the right-hand side. So if they stopped their first count at 12, they must count 12 cards in reverse. The final card of this second count is removed from the Q and the piece of paper opened. If everyone has done their sums properly, the paper should bear the name of the final card.

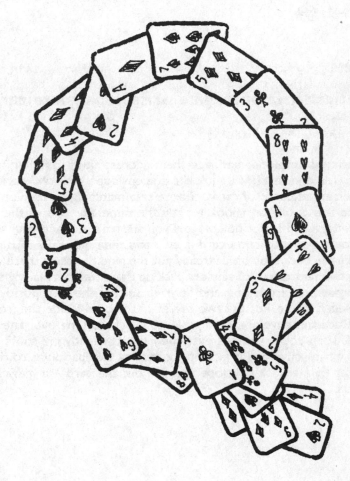

THE DOUBLE ENVELOPE

Skill Level: ❸

You will need:

Two identical envelopes, glue, scissors, a spare card

Take two identical envelopes and glue them address sides together so that there is no overlap. The end result will look like one envelope with two backs. From two identically patterned packs of cards, choose two matching cards – say, the nine of hearts. These two cards must look exactly the same. Put one of the cards inside the back envelope and seal it down. Now you are ready to face your audience. Tell them that you're going to cut a card in two and then magically repair it. Take the top card from the deck (you have already put the nine of hearts there), hold it aloft and cut it in two with a pair of scissors. Pick up the envelope, making sure that the audience only see the front one, and tip it up so that they are positive that there is nothing hidden inside. Put the two halves of the card inside the front envelope and seal it. Place the envelope on a table, cunningly turning over the envelope as you do so. You can count yourself extremely unlucky if anyone spots your deception. Now the back envelope is face up. Expressing trepidation as to the outcome, unseal the flap of the back envelope and pull out the card – a magically repaired nine of hearts.

POCKET CALCULATOR

Skill Level: ❹

Before facing your audience, slip two cards into your pocket. For the purposes of this trick, it might be an idea to wear a jacket since the sight of men rummaging around in their trouser pockets can be unnerving. Added to which, there's always the danger that the cards could get stuck to a 1979 blackcurrant Spangle. Get someone to shuffle the pack and, after this has been done to mutual satisfaction, deal the top three cards face up. Ask your volunteer to concentrate on any one of the three cards. Meanwhile make a mental note of the three cards and in which order they occur. Put them in that order in your jacket pocket behind the other two cards already there and announce that you will predict which card the volunteer has chosen. Take the two cards from the front of your pocket (the ones hidden there before the trick) and replace them in the pack. Ask the person, who now thinks there's only one card in your pocket, to name the card which he or she has been thinking of. As long as you have correctly remembered the order of the three cards left in your pocket, you should have no trouble in producing the right one.

DOUBLE DEALING

Skill Level: ❹

Here you can astound your friends by changing one card into another without any visible chicanery. Ask someone to choose a card, to show it the rest of the gathering without letting you see it, to remember it and put it back on top of the deck. Create some diversion so that nobody looks at your hands (a fire alarm is probably excessive), hold the pack in your left hand and use the index finger and thumb of your right hand to bend the top two cards upwards, lifting them off as one. Show the audience what they think is the top card (in reality it is of course the second card) and study the look of bewilderment on their faces. Put the two cards back on top of the pack, give the deck a magic tap and this time turn over the top card only... and it will be the chosen card. Given the innate simplicity of this trick, it is best to perform it either to an audience of dullards or to people who are all too drunk to care.

LOOKALIKES

Skill Level: ❹

For this trick you need two sets of pairs which look similar – such as the seven of clubs and seven of spades and two of diamonds and two of hearts. Remove all four cards from the pack. Place the seven of clubs on top of the pack and the two of diamonds at the bottom. Keep the other two face down to one side. Announce that without any physical interference or mental coercion, you will predict the precise place in the deck at which your volunteer tells you to stop dealing and that you will mark the spot in advance with two lookalike cards. Sounds impossible, doesn't it? Read on. Deal the cards face down, telling your associate to say 'Stop' whenever he or she wishes. When the call comes, pick up the two of hearts and lay it face up on top of the dealt cards. Place the rest of the pack on top of the two of hearts. Deal from the top of the pack again and this time when the call to stop arrives, put the seven of spades face up on top of the dealt cards. As before, put the rest of the pack on top of the seven of spades. Cut the cards at the upturned two of hearts and reveal the card immediately above it – the two of diamonds. Then do the same with the seven of spades, the card above it being the seven of clubs. Eat your heart out, Mystic Meg.

PARTNERS

Skill Level: ❹

Magician's assistants are a breed apart. Where else would you find a woman prepared to smile sweetly whilst being sawn in half? For this trick, your assistant is indeed your most valuable prop as you hang on her every word to bemuse, baffle and bewilder the audience. It all revolves around a secret code concocted beforehand between the two of you. The trick begins with you leaving the room. In your absence, someone picks a card and your assistant shows it to all present before carefully placing it face down on the table. The card is not marked in any way, but the first clue from your assistant is in the direction the card is facing. Beforehand the pair of you have agreed that the suit shall be determined by the table representing an imaginary clock. If, from the door, the card is pointing on a 12 o'clock/6 o'clock axis, it means the card is a spade; a 9 o'clock/3 o'clock axis denotes a club; 2 o'clock/8 o'clock indicates a heart; and 10 o'clock/4 o'clock suggests a diamond. So the moment you enter the room you know what suit the card is. Now watch your assistant's movements very closely. If she flicks imaginary dust from her knee, your pre-arranged code will tell you the card is an ace, a two or a three; if she touches her hair with her right hand, it's a four, five or six; if she touches her hair with her left hand, it's a seven, eight or nine; if she casually crosses her arms, it's the 10, jack, queen or king; if she starts fidgeting on the spot, she's probably waiting to go to the loo. To identify the precise card, you need to indulge in a spot of carefully rehearsed conversation with your assistant, but try and make it sound as natural as possible instead of like a school nativity play. Each of your assistant's replies carries a hidden meaning. When you ask cautiously, 'Is the card a club?' or whichever suit you know it to be, if she answers 'Yes', it is the first card in the group indicated by her movements. If she answers 'It is', then it's the second card in the group. If she replies 'Right', it's the third in the group. And if she answers 'Correct', it's the fourth in the group. Therefore if you enter the room, see the card on the table on a 9 o'clock/3 o'clock axis, see your assistant touching her hair with her left hand and when you ask her whether the card is a club she replies 'It is', then you can immediately declare the mystery card to be the eight of clubs. This is not a trick to repeat too often in front of the same people as it's only a matter of time before someone cracks your code.

7 UP

Skill Level: ❹

Arrange the cards in advance so that the seven of hearts is reversed and placed seventh from bottom of the pack. Fan the pack, making sure that nobody can see the reversed card, and ask someone to choose any card, to remember it and to return it to the top of the deck. Cut the cards so that the reversed seven is now somewhere near the middle. Explain in hushed tones that one of the cards has somehow managed to turn itself over and that the value of that card will pinpoint the precise whereabouts of the selected card. Search through the pack until you find the upturned seven of hearts, count along another seven cards and, lo and behold, the seventh card will be the chosen one.

THE TAPERED DECK

Skill Level: ④

You will need:

A pair of scissors

This trick is best performed with a fairly old pack since the first thing you have to do is cut strips off all the cards. To produce what is known in the trade as a tapered deck, you have to make narrow sloping cuts down either side of every card so that one end of each card is slightly narrower than the other. This can be a time-consuming business, so if you have a low boredom threshold, move on to the next trick in the book. Making sure that all the cards are facing the same way (ordinary edge outwards), fan them out and offer them to a member of your audience. Ask him or her to pick a card and study it in total silence. Make sure they are fully aware that any attempt to speak will result in a severe punishment. While this thought process is taking place, put the cards back together, turn them around and fan them out again, this time with the narrow edge facing outwards. Tell the person to put the card back anywhere in the pack. Put the cards behind your back and regroup them into a neat pile. Say that you will only be able to find their card if they concentrate really hard on it whereas in truth all you have to do is feel out the card which is wider than the others at one end.

GRAINS OF TRUTH

Skill Level: ❹

This is another crafty way of recognizing a chosen card. Ask a volunteer (preferably someone who is not in possession of all their faculties) to shuffle the pack and to separate the cards into two piles. Tell him or her to choose any card from the first pile, study it and put it back on top of the second pile. As you do so, tap the top card on the second pile to indicate where you want them to put it, in the process cunningly releasing a few grains of salt you had concealed between your thumb and forefinger. Unless they are particularly alert, they will not spot the ruse. Then ask them to place the first pile on top of the second pile and to turn the whole pack face up. Tap the side of the pack with your finger (or a magic wand if you are treating all this seriously), warble some magic incantation, and the presence of the salt, allied to the tapping, will create a small gap immediately above the chosen card. You simply pull out the card beneath the space and take a bow.

SUIT ABILITY

Skill Level: ④

Beforehand, sort the pack into two halves, one containing spades and hearts, the other clubs and diamonds. Put the two halves together, but make sure that the top card of the bottom half protrudes slightly in order to act as a marker. Your friends will think this is a perfectly ordinary pack of cards – a random mix of red and black – but you know different. Now to baffle them. Using the marker card as your dividing line, separate the pack into your two carefully prepared halves. Ask someone to pick any card from one half of the pack, to show it to everyone else in the room except yourself and then to replace it anywhere in the other half of the pack. All you have to do is flick through the cards and spot which spade or heart has managed to infiltrate its way into the half reserved for clubs and diamonds, or vice-versa. To sustained applause (and maybe a few encores), hold the chosen card aloft.

TELEPATHY

Skill Level: ❹

You will need:

A blindfold

The actual degree of skill required to perform this trick is minimal – there is no sleight of hand – but as a memory test it takes some beating. For a successful result, you and your trusty assistant need to burn the midnight oil to think of a code which will enable you to identify any card in the pack – something along these lines:

ACE	=	TELL ME
TWO	=	CAN YOU TELL ME?
THREE	=	WILL YOU TELL ME?
FOUR	=	PLEASE TELL ME
FIVE	=	ARE YOU ABLE TO TELL ME?
SIX	=	NAME
SEVEN	=	CAN YOU NAME?
EIGHT	=	WILL YOU NAME?
NINE	=	PLEASE NAME
TEN	=	ARE YOU ABLE TO NAME?

JACK	=	**CONCENTRATE AND TELL ME**
QUEEN	=	**PLEASE CONCENTRATE AND TELL ME**
KING	=	**CONCENTRATE AND TRY TO NAME**
CLUBS	=	**THE CHOSEN CARD**
DIAMONDS	=	**THIS PERSON'S CARD**
HEARTS	=	**THE MYSTERY CARD**
SPADES	=	**THE CARD WHICH HAS BEEN SELECTED**

After committing that lot to memory, all you have to do is astound your audience by your telepathic powers. While you are blindfolded, your assistant asks someone to pick any card from the pack, shows it to the rest of the audience and then asks you to name it. And it is the way in which your assistant phrases the question that gives you the card's identity. For example, if the assistant says, 'Please name the mystery card', your memory should tell you that it's the nine of hearts. It doesn't always to pay to come up with the right answer too quickly – otherwise everyone will know it's a fix – so grope around in the dark for a while with comments like: 'I see a red card... I see eight dots... no, no, I see nine...', or 'I see a tall dark handsome stranger... it's the king of clubs.'

ODDS 'N' EVENS

Skill Level: ❹

Remove the court cards from the pack and put all the odd numbers (aces, threes, fives, sevens and nines) in one half and all the even numbers (twos, fours, sixes, eights and 10s) in the other half. Fanning out one half of the reduced pack face down, ask someone to select a card and study it. While this is happening, quickly square up that half and fan out the second half instead. Ask for the card to be replaced anywhere in those cards. By looking through the cards, you can easily spot the chosen one — it will be the only even-numbered card amongst the odds, or vice versa.

THE MARKED PACK

Skill Level: ④

You will need:

A pencil, a small box

The essence of a good card trick is for it to appear fiendishly difficult to perfect yet in practice be incredibly easy. With this trick, all of the hard work is done beforehand. Firstly, remove any card from the pack (let's say it's the king of hearts) and on the back of the card make a small pencil mark so that you will be able to identify it when the need arises. Then along the bottom border of the face of every other card write 'king of hearts'. Once you've recovered from writers' cramp, shuffle the cards and fan them out face down to your volunteer, making sure that the writing is hidden from view. While you are spreading the cards, you are mentally searching for the card with the pencil mark on the back. When you find it, casually remove it from the pack as if you have just plucked any card at random. Pretend to write on its face (but don't) and then put the card in the box without letting your volunteer see which card it is. Ask him to select any other card from the pack, but again make sure he doesn't see its face. Since they've all got 'king of hearts' written on them, it doesn't matter which card he picks. Drop the card into the box and move the rest of the cards out of the way. Now for the revelation. Take the two cards from the box and show the card supposedly chosen by you (in reality, of course, it's his). Across the bottom is written 'king of hearts' and, when the second card is turned over, amazingly it is indeed the king of hearts. In the words of David Coleman: 'Quite remarkable.'

PILES

Skill Level: ④

In spite of its name, this trick is extremely popular at parties. Rig the pack in advance by putting six picture cards at the top and the other six at the bottom. Then ask the audience to call out any four cards with values between one and 10 (i.e., not picture cards) and remove them from the pack to leave a deck of 48. Deal these cards into six piles of eight so that, unbeknown to the audience, the top and bottom card of each pile will be a picture card. Choose someone from the audience to take a card from near the centre of any of the six piles, to show it around (but obviously not to you) and to put it back on top of the same pile. Tell them they can stack the piles in any order. Announce that by looking through the pack, you will immediately be able to spot the mystery card. Since the chosen card was from the centre of a pile it will not be a picture card but, when replaced on top of a pile and stacked with the other piles, it will finish up between two picture cards. So all you have to do is flick through the pack and find the only non-picture card between two picture cards. The sole exception is if the person has arranged the pile with the chosen card at the top of the pack, in which case the top card will not be the picture card you are expecting, but the mystery card itself.

BLIND SUMS

Skill Level: ⑤

Discard the twos, threes, fours, fives, sixes and jokers from the pack to leave 32 cards. Explain that this trick operates under a points system whereby an ace counts as 11, a court card (jack, queen, king) as 10 and all the others as numbered. Turn your back on proceedings and ask three people to choose one card each from the reduced pack and to put them separately face up on the table. Then tell them to add the number of cards needed to bring each pile's points total up to 15. So if the upturned card is an ace, four cards should be placed face down on the same pile; if it's a king, five cards should be added face down; if it's an eight, seven cards should be added. They must then hand the remaining cards to you. Since your back has been turned throughout, you can have no idea which three cards were originally selected, but boldly declare that by counting the number of cards you have just been given and adding 16 you will arrive at the total points score of the three upturned cards. It never fails.

QUEENS BEHAVING BADLY

Skill Level: ⑤

Line up this trick by removing the four queens and two jacks from the pack. Fan out the queens in your left hand so that everyone can see them… but not the two jacks which are hidden behind the second queen. As far as everyone can see, you are only holding four cards. Gather up the cards and place them on top of the pack. Then spin some yarn about the househusband kings complaining about being left at home with the ironing while the queens are out enjoying themselves at a hen night down at the local. Say that, on the kings' orders, you're going to split the women up by putting one queen on the bottom of the pack, two well apart in the middle and the fourth one on top. Take the top card and put it on the bottom of the pack, making sure that all present can see that it is a queen. Take the next two cards and place them well apart in the centre of the pack, but keep their identities hidden as these are the two jacks. Show everyone the fourth card – a queen – and replace it on top of the pack. Ask a volunteer to cut the pack, but confess that, despite your best efforts, the four queens have somehow managed to gang up together again. Deal out the pack of cards face up and, somewhere around the middle, all four queens will be together.

JUMPING JACKS

Skill Level: ⑤

To set up this variation on Queens Behaving Badly, take the four jacks from the pack along with any three other cards. Show the four jacks to your audience in a fan with the three rogue cards hidden behind the third jack. Square the cards up and put them on top of the pack before dealing the first four cards (which the audience foolishly believe to be the quartet of jacks) into separate rows. Now deal the next three cards (which really are three jacks) on top of the first jack. Continue dealing out three cards on to each of the other rows so that you have four piles of four. The audience will think there is a jack at the bottom of each pile, but you know that the pile on the left consists solely of jacks while the remaining three piles are made up of random cards. Pick up the first pile and confirm the audience's misconception by showing them the jack at the bottom. Stack this pile on top of the next one, put these two piles on top of the third and then the three piles on top of the fourth. Make sure you don't let anyone see the bottom card of the last three piles. With all 52 cards together, get members of the audience to cut the pack as many times as they wish. Reveal that the jacks which, moments ago, were at the bottom of separate stacks are now magically reunited. And sure enough when you fan out the cards face up, all four jacks are together.

SLICED OPEN

Skill Level: ⑤

You will need:

A knife

Ask someone to pick a card and to show it to the rest of the audience. While this is happening, and Great Aunt Edie who has forgotten her glasses and thinks she's looking through old family photographs is consequently regaling all around her with tales of how she knew the queen of clubs when she was just a girl, you should secretly squeeze the cards so that they buckle a little. Then ask for the card to be put back on the bottom of the pile. Shuffle the cards repeatedly until everyone is satisfied that the cards are well and truly mixed up. Because all of the cards apart from the chosen one have been buckled, there will always be a discernible break, no matter how thoroughly they are shuffled. Pick up a knife and slide it into the pack at the point of the break. The card below the break should be the one chosen earlier. The amount of buckling required to perform this trick successfully comes only with practice. Obviously the less you need to bend the cards the better, as it won't be apparent to the audience what you are up to. If you bend them at right angles, it does tend to give the game away.

MIND READING

Skill Level: ⑤

In common with a number of tricks, this one relies on you snatching a quick glance at the bottom card in the pack when nobody is looking. The premise may be straightforward, but the result is highly impressive as you demonstrate powers of mind-reading which would put 'The Champions' to shame. You need to choose a member of your entourage to help you with this trick. Since it involves shuffling the cards, it is best to avoid a Captain Hook lookalike. Take two packs of cards with different designs on the back so that one pack is distinguishable from the other. Give one pack to your assistant and tell him (for the purposes of the performance, we'll assume your assistant is male) to copy every move you make. You can take this to extremes and have him licking the end of his nose or scratching his bottom (this being another reason for not choosing someone with a metal hook for a right hand). Shuffle the cards and, while your assistant is busy shuffling, sneak a look at the bottom card of your deck. You then swap packs and ask him to pick a card from his deck. It is here that you announce grandly that you are going to read his mind by selecting exactly the same card from your pack. This assertion will inevitably be greeted with much scoffing and ridicule, but you press on unbowed. Pick your card, but don't let him see what it is. Replace your chosen card on top of your pack and tell him to do the same. Now both cut your cards and swap packs again. You know that the card he chose will be immediately under the one you saw earlier at the base of your pack. Tell him to pull out the chosen card from his pack and lay it on the table. You pick out the card which is under the sneak-look card and, as if by magic, they're the same. You must be a mind-reader...

THE THREE PACK TRICK

Skill Level: ⑤

You will need:

A pencil

To get ready for this trick, choose any card from the pack and mark it lightly on the back with pencil dots in the top-left and bottom-right corners. Replace it in the pack so that it is the 26th card from the top. Now for the trick. Place the pack face down on the table. This is pile A. Ask a volunteer to lift off more than half the cards and to place them on the right to form pile B. It is essential that over half of the cards are lifted otherwise the trick won't work and you'll be left looking a complete dipstick. Now ask your associate to lift off about half of the cards on pile B and to put these on the right to form a third pile, unsurprisingly known as pile C. Next ask him or her to shuffle pile C, to look at the top card, memorize it and put it back on top of that pile. Then order pile C to be placed on top of pile B and ask for pile A to be shuffled and put on top of the B and C pile. Finally pick up the cards and spread them out face down from left to right. When you see the pencil dot on the marked card, count it silently as 1 and continue counting the cards to yourself until you reach 26. If you get to the end of the row before reaching number 26, go back to the left-hand end and carry on counting. Turn over the 26th card and, joy of joys, it will be your friend's chosen card.

ELEVENSES

Skill Level: ⑤

Shuffle the cards and deal out the top 21 alternately in three columns of seven. Ask your volunteer to choose a card from any of the three columns, to remember it and put it back in the same place. Ascertain which of the three columns the chosen card is in and gather up the columns, ensuring that the one containing the chosen card is in the middle. Deal the 21 cards out again in the same way, asking your volunteer to tell you which column the card is in. Once again pick up the 21 cards, taking care to put the column containing the selected card in the middle. Repeat the process for a third time, again placing the column with the mystery card in the middle as you pick them up. Finally deal out 11 cards from the top. Turn over the 11th card and, to everyone's surprise (including yours), it will be the chosen card.

EIGHTS

Skill Level: ⑤

For this trick, you need to arrange the pack so that the four eights are in 10th, 20th, 30th and 40th position. Ask someone to choose a number between 10 and 20. If the number is 18, deal 18 cards face down, then say: '18 is 1 and 8. 1 and 8 is 9.' At this, you deal eight cards back on to the pack, placing the ninth card face down to one side. Ask for another number between 10 and 20. For 13, deal 13 cards face down and after your little speech about 1 and 3 making 4, deal three cards back on to the pack and put the fourth face down to one side. Repeat this manoeuvre twice more so that you have four cards face down in a row. Remind your volunteer that all the numbers were chosen completely at random and then turn over the four cards. Unless your ability to add up has deserted you, they will be the four eights.

THE FORETELLING

Skill Level: ⑤

You will need:

A sheet of paper, a pen

Take an ordinary sheet of paper, fold it in half and then fold the top piece back on itself. Over the second fold write in large block letters the number of a playing card, such as 4 OF HEARTS, so that the writing protrudes on either side of the fold. When you open out the paper, you will have two rows of strange hieroglyphics. Add more shapes to the rows to make them look like some obscure Ancient Egyptian scriptures and, for extra authenticity, create a third row of writing between the other two. Place the four of hearts, or whichever card you have written on the paper, on the top of the pack and ask someone to think of a number between one and 10. Deal that number of cards face down from the top of the pack and show the person the bottom card of those dealt. That is his chosen card. It also happens to be the original top card – the four of hearts. Show him the obscure sheet of paper and promise that somewhere in the scrawl is the prediction of the card he would choose. Simply fold the paper so that the two halves of your initial writing are joined together again and sure enough it reads 4 OF HEARTS.

DOUBLE DISCOVERY

Skill Level: ⑤

This is another one of those tricks where the secret is in the preparation. The pack of cards is divided into two halves. One half contains all the odd-numbered red cards and all the even-numbered black cards (jacks count 11, queens 12 and kings 13). In the other half are all the even-numbered red cards and odd-numbered black cards. In finest magician mode, call for two volunteers to help you with this trick. Each volunteer is handed half of the pack to shuffle, the mix of cards in their grasp seemingly being so random (with cards of all four suits, high and low) as to convince them that there is no chicanery afoot. Tell them to select a card, memorize it and place it face-down among the cards held by the other volunteer. Further convince them that everything is above board by allowing them to shuffle their half as often as they like. Still keeping the two halves separate, ask the two volunteers to try and find the other person's chosen card which, unless they have got a Saturday job as a mind-reader or have read this book, they will be unable to do. Then calmly, but not too arrogantly, announce that you will do it for them. As you scan each pre-arranged half, it is easy for your trained eye to spot the interloper because it doesn't fit in with the odd-even, red-black sequence. Remove the offending card from each half and lay them face down on the table. Ask the volunteers to name their cards and, with a flourish, turn over the two cards on the table to reveal that they are the chosen pair.

NAME THAT CARD

Skill Level: ⑥

This trick is more a test of stamina than magic. Shuffle the cards, deal them face down into four piles of 13 and ask someone to think of any card. Pick up one of the stacks, fan the cards out and ask whether the mystery card is among them. If necessary, repeat this procedure with the other three stacks until the card is located. Please note that the person merely has to acknowledge the presence of the card – they must not blurt out, 'yes, that's it, the four of clubs'. When the card has been spotted, gather up the four stacks, making sure that the one containing the mystery card is the top stack so that you know that the card is among the top 13 in the pack. Once again deal the cards face down into four piles. Now you know that the card will be one of the three or four cards at the bottom of one of the piles. Fan the stacks as before. When you learn which stack the card is in, place that stack under the other three as you form them into a pack. Yet again deal the cards face down into four stacks so that the card will be at the top of one of the stacks. Fan the cards as before and, when you are told which stack the mystery card is in, put that stack face down on the table. Pick up one of the other stacks, sneaking a look at the bottom card as you do so. Put that stack on top of the one with the sought-after card. Put these two stacks on top of the remaining cards. Ask your patient volunteer (who by now is probably in pyjamas) to cut the cards a couple of times. Finally look through the cards, find the card you glimpsed and the card the person has been thinking of all this time will be the one above it.

ROWS OF FIVE

Skill Level: ⑥

Shuffle the pack and deal out 25 cards face up in five rows of five. Ask someone to concentrate silently on one of the cards and to tell you which row that card is in. You must then make a mental note of the card at the left end of that row. This will be your key card. Next you collect the cards, beginning with the card at the far right end of the bottom row and working upwards. When you reach the top of that column, go back down to the bottom of the next column along and continue in this way until you have gathered up all 25 cards. When you have done that, once again deal the cards face up into five rows. Locate your key card and ask which row the chosen card is in now. His card will be in the same column as the key card and, since you now know the row, you can readily identify the mystery card.

BOTTOM SHUFFLE

Skill Level: ⑥

After the pack has been thoroughly shuffled in full view of your audience, sneak a look at the bottom card. Holding the pack in your left hand, use your forefinger to pull the bottom card back a little from the front edge of the pack. Keep a firm grip on this card and begin dealing the other cards from the bottom of the pack face up as quickly as you can. While doing this, tell the audience to shout 'Stop!' whenever the fancy takes them. At the 'Stop!' command, produce the bottom card which you have been keeping back, put it face down on the table and call out what it is. When the card is turned over, they will see that you are right.

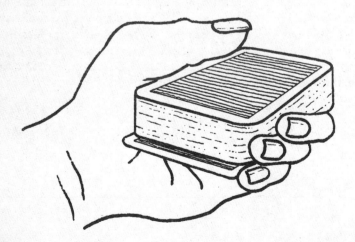

ALL FOURS

Skill Level: ⑥

This trick requires the services of four volunteers so it gives you the chance to impress a wider audience with your skills. Give the cards a good shuffle and remove any four. Show these to your first volunteer and ask him to think of one without telling you which it is. Place the cards back on the table aside from the main pack, take out another four from the pack, show them to volunteer number two and ask him to remember any one card. Then put these four cards into a pile on top of the first four. Repeat the process with two more people so that there are 16 cards on the table and each person has remembered a card. Next deal out the cards into four piles of four. Show the cards in all four piles to the first volunteer and ask him to say which pile contains the card he is thinking of. As a result of the way you have re-dealt the cards, his card will be the first in the pile he has indicated. So you can name it with supreme confidence. Do the same with the second person (his card will be the second in the pile he indicates). Similarly the third person's card will be third in the pile he points to and the fourth person's card will be the fourth in the pile he indicates. And even if more than one person happens to name the same pile, the theory remains the same. The first person's card will be first in the pile, the second person's second and so on.

STICKY FINGERS

Skill Level: ⑥

You will need:

Glue

To prepare for this trick, glue two cards together. If you don't want to ruin your pack, choose the jokers, and in any case use a light glue rather than superglue so that you can prise them apart afterwards if necessary. Put the two cards which have been glued together on top of the pack, fan out the cards and ask someone to pick a card and remember it. Your deception can only be uncovered if the person is stupid enough to pick the top card. Have the card replaced on top of the pack so that it is now immediately above the trick card. Cut the cards at random as many times as you wish and flick through the pack until you feel the snap sound that reveals the location of the thick glued card. The chosen card will be the one immediately above it.

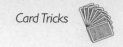

JACKS AWAY

Skill Level: ⑥

You will need:

A matchstick

Prepare the pack so that the four jacks are at the bottom. Hold the pack face down in your left hand (your thumb at one side, your fingers at the other) and ask one of your friends to use a match to push a group of cards a little way out of the pack. Grip the protruding cards between the thumb and forefinger of your right hand, but as you pull them away, use your thumb to slide out the bottom card of the pack too – one of the jacks. Place that pile (with the jack at the bottom) face down on the table. Repeat the process with the match three more times so that you have four heaps and, unbeknown to your audience, a jack at the bottom of each one. Finally you turn over the piles face up to reveal the four jacks.

X-RAY EYESIGHT

Skill Level: ⑥

X-ray vision would be a tremendous benefit if you could switch it on or off at will. After all, most of the male population would consider it a real boon for viewing Ulrika Jonsson on Gladiators, but few would relish the prospect of seeing Michael Fish's cold front while he is delivering the weather forecast. This trick will leave your friends with the distinct impression that you have somehow managed to acquire X-ray eyesight. As you cut the pack, take note of the bottom card, which we'll say is the five of clubs. Put the pack behind your back and switch the bottom card (the five of clubs) so that it is now face up on top of the deck. Show the pack to everyone, holding the cards in such a way that the five of clubs is facing them and they assume that the remaining cards are also facing forward. Stare meaningfully at the back of the pack and declare that you can see straight through to the five of clubs. In fact, you are looking at another card on the bottom of the pack, say the nine of diamonds. Shut your eyes, put the pack behind your back again and move the nine of diamonds face up to the front. Showing the pack to your audience as before, announce that the top card is the nine of diamonds, at the same time making a mental note of the new bottom card. You can carry on like this until everyone is convinced either of your X-ray vision or that you are a brazen cheat.

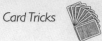
THE CHANGING OF THE CARD

Skill Level: ⑥

You will need:

Glue

Choose any three playing cards from the pack and fold two of them exactly in half so that they sit at right angles. Place the vertical pieces of each card back to back and glue them together and then stick the horizontal sections to the face of the third card. The result is a card with a movable flap which reveals one card when the flap is pulled up and a different card when the flap is pushed down. Use this card to baffle your friends by holding it in your left hand face up and then passing your right hand over it and secretly pushing down the flap. You can then, of course, reverse the procedure to reproduce the original card. To make the trick more dramatic, it is best to use two cards of different-coloured suits, say a spade and a diamond. But be warned: some people witnessing the five of spades changing before their very eyes into the 10 of diamonds can react in an alarming way. The next thing you know they're on the phone to Mulder and Scully and recalling the day when aliens descended and snatched Uncle Cyril's false teeth from the glass by the side of his bed.

A SHARP CUT

Skill Level: ⑦

Fan out the cards, ask one of your disciples to choose one and remember it, and then tell him or her to replace the card face down on top of the pack. You're now going to cut the cards, but the trick is to ramble on in true magician mode so that the audience is concentrating on your face rather than your hands. To perform the sharp cut, you hold the pack with both hands, ensuring that the fingers of your left hand exercise a firm grip on the top card. Still gripping the top card in your left hand, pull out the top half of the deck with your right, except the top card itself which will then slide into place as the top card in your left hand. Put the cards in your right hand under those in your left. You have thus performed a cut without changing the top card. Tap the top of the deck and say that you are going to bring the chosen card back up to the top and when you turn it over, the magic has worked. You can repeat this ruse over and over again – obviously the faster you are able to do it the better – and your audience will never cease to be amazed… although signs of tedium may set in by the third day.

THE LOST CARD

Skill Level: ❻

Here you do your best Sherlock Holmes impersonation to track down a missing card. Have the pack shuffled and, by riffling one end with your thumb, sneak a look at the top card. Pass the pack to a member of your entourage and, with your back turned so you can't see what he's doing, tell him to count out as many cards as he wants, to remember the number of cards he has counted and to remember the name of the next card in the pack. So if he has counted out eight cards, he must memorize the ninth card. Get him to replace the cards he has counted on the top of the pack so that they are immediately above the mystery card. Take the pack and seek out the card which you glimpsed at the very start. Remove that card and all the cards behind it and put them at the base of the pack. Hand the pack to your new-found assistant and tell him to count out the same number of cards as he had done previously. Get him to look at the next card and ask him whether it was the same one as the mystery card. When he says no, you have to pretend to look worried. Pick up the card he has just looked at and put it on top of the cards he has counted out. Then put this pile on top of the rest of the pack. Stress that you're not implying he can't count up to eight or whatever, but that you'd like a second opinion. Count out the same number again, turn over the next card and this will indeed be the mystery card. Another successful case has been solved.

FIVE CARD CHOICE

Skill Level: ⑦

Ask someone to deal you 15 cards. From these cards, pick five which contain a representation of suits – say a club, a diamond, a heart and two spades (if you don't get a decent cross-section, have the cards dealt again). It is important to memorize the order of the suits among the five so arranging them in alphabetical order is a definite help. Ask your friend to make a mental note of any one of the cards and, in addition, remember the last card yourself. Put your five cards in order on top of the pack and place the other 10 on top of them. Now move the top five cards to somewhere in the middle of the pack and then do the same with the bottom five cards. Finally put the new top five cards in the middle so that your original five are now back on top again. Hold those five cards behind your back and ask your friend to reveal his or her chosen card. Since you know the order of the suits and the identity of the last card of the five, you can produce the chosen card from behind your back without even looking.

LUCKY NUMBER

Skill Level: ⓪

Magicians can bring out the worst in human behaviour. Sometimes we only watch them in anticipation that one of their illusions will go spectacularly wrong. Just as we used to sit through ice skating on Grandstand in the hope that Torvill and Dean would suddenly plunge through the ice, so we watch magicians on live TV on the off-chance that one day the dutiful assistant will stagger out of the metal booth with a sword between her shoulder-blades, followed by a posse of elderly St John Ambulance men clambering frantically on to the stage to usher an early commercial break. Whilst this trick does not offer the same prospect of bloodshed (a paper cut from the jack of clubs is hardly comparable), it is one where you can pretend, Tommy Cooper-style, that everything has gone horribly wrong. It relies upon the sharp cut demonstrated earlier. Ask a friend to select a card, to memorize it without showing it to you and to replace it on top of the pack. Perform the sharp cut a few times to make it look as if the cards are well and truly mixed up whereas, provided you have done the cut correctly, the same card will still be on top. Then ask for a number between two and 10 and deal out the corresponding number of cards face down. If the number is six, deal six cards. In a state of blind panic, confess that you've forgotten the magic word and will be forced to abandon the trick. Gather up the six cards in order and put them back on top of the pack, the mystery card now being sixth from the top. Suddenly inspiration comes and you say you've remembered the magic word. Count out the chosen number of cards again (in this case, six) and your friend's original card will be the last one.

THE LADY VANISHES

Skill Level: ❼

You will need:

Scissors, sticky tape, a spare queen of hearts

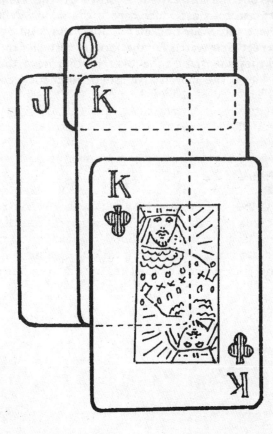

Your first task with this trick is to behead the queen of hearts. Imagine it as Cilla Black in full song and you'll have no problem. Cut the heads from either end of the queen and, with one piece face up and the other face down, join them together at the top using sticky tape as a hinge. Fold the hinged card (with the sticky tape hidden inside, on the back) and slide it over one end of the joker. All of this must be done in secret, away from prying eyes. For the trick itself, you place the imposter queen between two kings, showing the three cards to your audience in such a way that only the very top of the queen is visible. The audience must be able to see that it is a queen, but must not be able to see that from the neck down she is a joker. Close the cards by pressing them down with your finger and hold them face down, making sure that the hinged edge is nearest to you. Take out the bottom card (one of the kings) and place it face down on the table. Carefully place the next card (the joker) face down on the table, keeping the hinged section of queen's heads hidden in your hand. Finally put the last card face down on the table, swap the cards around and ask everyone to guess which card is the queen. While they are doing so, slip the hinged piece into your pocket. Naturally they will be supremely confident of guessing correctly, so watch for the look of disbelief on their faces when you turn it over and they see that it's the joker. Furthermore, the other two cards are revealed to be kings. The lady has vanished. Hitchcock couldn't have done it better.

A CUT ABOVE

Skill Level: ⑦

You will need:

A handkerchief

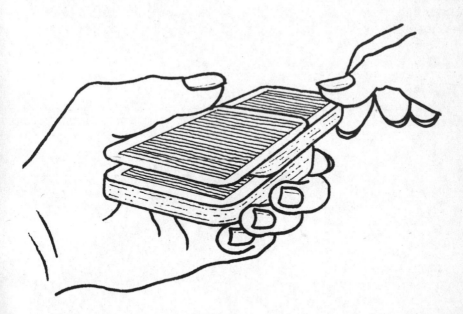

Make sure you know the identity of the top card in the pack and perform the sharp cut so that it remains on top. Hold the pack face down in your left hand and drape a handkerchief (clean, please!) over the cards. As you do so, secretly turn the pack face up in your hand. In order to conceal your subterfuge, avoid using a see-through handkerchief. Ask someone to cut the pack under the handkerchief and, as what is thought to be the top half is lifted and set aside, turn the cards in your hand over again. After all the cutting, the top card will be the same card as at the start of the trick. Ask your friend to look at the top card without showing you. He or she thinks that card has been cut at random whereas you know it has all been carefully arranged. Put both halves of the pack back together and have them shuffled thoroughly. Deal out the cards face up, announcing that you will stop at the card which your friend has chosen. To inject a little drama and give false hope to any doubters, you can deliberately go past the card before doubling back to it.

THE RISING CARD

Skill Level: ❼

You will need:

Scissors

The only drawback to this trick is that it requires the wholesale destruction of your pack of cards. If you want to split hairs, it's actually only half of the pack which is butchered, but you can't have much of a game with 26 cards. It's like playing Happy Families with some of the cards missing, when you end up with Mrs Bun the single parent or Master Chop the orphan. To make this trick work, you need to cut a hole in the back of 26 of the cards. The hole should be near the base of the card, in an identical position on each one and large enough to accommodate your fore-finger with a little to spare. Divide the pack into two – in one face-down pile are the 26 cut cards below an ordinary card, and in the other pile are the 25 remaining intact cards. Ask someone to choose a pile. If he chooses the genuine half, let him take it; if he chooses the holey half, pick it up and give him the other half. Either way you can't lose. That's the beauty of being a magician. Ask him to select a card from the ordinary half and to replace it in the other half which you are holding in your hand. Place the cut half on top of the ordinary half and turn the pack face up. Remove the bottom card, which was originally the uncut card on top of the fake pile, and put it somewhere in the ordinary half. Pick the cards up, square them and hold the pack out in front of you so that the audience can only see the face of the top card. Make sure that nobody can see the back of the pack. Grip the pack with your thumb on one side and three fingers on the other, leaving your forefinger free to probe the hole in the top card. Poke your finger through the tunnel formed by the holes in the cards until you come to a barrier. This will be the sought-after card. When you reach it, force it up with your finger so that it magically rises out of the pack.

TELEPHONE DIRECTORY

Skill Level: ⑦

You will need:

**A telephone directory, a handkerchief,
a piece of paper, a pencil**

Flick through the phone directory and find someone with a silly name – Blackadder, Snogworthy, Irritable-Bowel or Tibballs. Make a note of the page number and line number and choose the corresponding cards from the pack. So if it's page 79, line 18, choose a seven, a nine, an ace and an eight; if it's page 147, line 26, choose an ace, a four, a seven, a two and a six. After writing the chosen name on a piece of paper, which should then be placed in your pocket, place the cards in order on top of the pack. In the first instance (page 79, line 18), the seven would be on top, the nine would be the second card, the ace would be the third card and the eight would be the fourth card. Now for the trick. Tell your friend that you will somehow predict which name they are going to choose from the entire local phone directory. Add that their choice will be made via a random selection of cards. Place the cards face down in your left hand and cover them with a handkerchief. Repeat the skill demonstrated in A Cut Above, whereby you turn the pack over beneath the handkerchief, get your friend to lift off the 'top' half of the pack and set it aside and then you craftily turn the cards in your hand face down again. The net result of all this activity is that the top card is the same as when you started. Ask your friend to take the top two cards from those in your hand (if it's a three-digit page number, it will need to be the top three cards). In this example, it will be a seven and a nine. Tell them to turn to page 79 of the directory. Then ask them to take the next two cards from the pack – the ace and the eight – and to go down 18 lines on page 79. Ask them to read out the name on line 18 and at the same time produce the piece of paper correctly predicting the chosen name.

CHANGING ACES

Skill Level: ❼

Take the four aces from the pack with the ace of clubs on top, followed by the ace of hearts, the ace of diamonds and the ace of spades. Keep the cards face down. Close the cards, place them in your left hand and, as described earlier, lift off the top two cards as if they were one. Show everyone what they think is the top card – the red ace of hearts – then craftily put the real top card – the ace of clubs – face down on the table. Next reverse count the remaining three aces into your right hand so that the other black ace – the ace of spades – is now on top. Using the same double lift method, show the audience what they believe is the new top card – the red ace of diamonds – but instead deal the real top card – the ace of spades – on to the table. The audience think the two red aces have been dealt on to the table but, when you turn the cards over, they are the two black aces. The red and black cards have magically changed places.

MYSTIC LEG

Skill Level: ❼

You will need:

A piece of paper, a pen

This exhibition of uncanny prediction begins with you writing 'Your chosen card is the four of spades' on a piece of paper. Slip the paper down your sock – somewhere there is no chance of it being discovered (for weeks if need be) – and put the four of spades face down on top of the pack. Holding the pack behind your back, cunningly slide the top card off and slip it into the waistband of your trousers. Make sure you're not wearing baggy trousers or it could necessitate an unseemly strip to retrieve the four of spades. Give the rest of the pack to your friend and ask for the cards to be shuffled and handed back to you. Once again, hold the cards behind your back and coolly lift the four of spades from your waistband and put it back on top of the deck. Ask your friend to take the top card, to remember it and to put it back anywhere in the deck. Scan the cards and confidently take out any card except the four of spades. With a certain air of smugness (not an altogether alien trait in some magicians), say: 'Is this your card?' With great relish, your friend (perhaps soon to become your ex-friend) will snarl: 'No, you've got it wrong. I knew you couldn't do it. It was the four of spades.' But he who laughs last, laughs after he who laughs first or whatever it is. Still feigning dejection, reach into your sock and produce the piece of paper bearing the words: 'Your chosen card is the four of spades.' Gobsmacked doesn't begin to describe it.

DANCING QUEENS

Skill Level: ❼

You will need:

A spare jack of spades, two boxes, scissors, glue

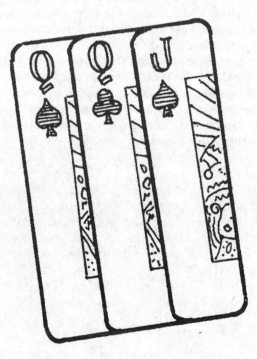

447

Since this trick requires the destruction of four cards, it is best to use an old pack, or better still, someone else's. To prepare, you need to glue the queen of spades and the jack of spades back to back. Then glue the back of the queen of clubs on to the face of the queen of spades, but a third of the way along so that they appear side by side. Trim the overlapping edge of the queen of clubs so that it is the same size as the queen of spades underneath. Next glue the back of the spare jack of spades to the face of the cut queen of clubs, again about a third of the way along. Trim the overlapping edge of the jack to the size of the queen of spades. You now have a normal-sized playing card with the jack of spades on one side and a third each of the queen of spades, queen of clubs and jack of spades on the other. Begin the trick by showing the audience two empty boxes. Let them have a good look so that they can see there are no secret flaps or compartments. Pick up a perfectly ordinary jack of clubs and hold it in your hand next to the montage card – when you show these to the audience, it looks as if you are holding four cards. Drop the cards into one of the boxes, but then declare your intention of removing the jack of spades. Pick up the special card and show the audience the face where only the jack of spades is visible. Make sure that nobody sees the cut and paste card on the reverse side. Drop the jack of spades into the second box. Next transfer the normal jack of clubs into the second box. Everyone will think that you've swapped the two jacks into the second box, leaving behind the two queens in the first box. But now you show them the first box and, incredibly, the two queens have done a runner. Furthermore when you go the second box and hold up the cards as before, showing two queens and two jacks, it can be seen that the queens have somehow danced across from one box to the other. Cue applause.

THE FOUR ACES

Skill Level: 8

The most baffling card tricks are the ones where your friends do all the work, thus apparently leaving no room for you to manipulate the pack. The key to this piece of deception is to have all four aces on top of the pack at the start. You can of course cut the pack to show good faith but, in doing so, perform the sharp cut so that the aces remain on top. Put the pack down and ask someone to cut the cards into four piles. Beginning with the pile on the left, being the pile furthest from the one with the aces at the top, ask for the cards to be mixed up by switching the top three cards of the pile to the bottom. Then ask for the next three cards on that same pile to be distributed one each on top of the other three piles. Ask for the left-hand pile to be put back. Have the same procedure repeated with the three remaining piles – top three cards to the bottom, next three cards on top of each of the other piles. Ask everyone whether they are happy that the cards have been well and truly mixed up. They will almost certainly all say 'yes' (anybody perverse enough to say 'no' should simply be ignored) whereupon you turn over the top card on each of the four piles to reveal that they are the four aces.

THE FINAL CARD

Skill Level: 8

This one's a corker. Take a well shuffled pack and sneak a look at the bottom card. Ask a friend to take a card and to remember it without telling you. Cut the pack and tell him to place his card on the top half, then lay the bottom half on top of that. Cut the pack a couple of times and then search through the cards, ostensibly in a hunt for his card, but what you're really looking for is the card that was on the bottom. When you find it, cut the cards again so that it reverts to its position at the base of the pack. It's play-acting time again, that time in a trick when you are overcome by gloom and despondency. You can't find his card, you whimper plaintively. Perhaps a tear starts to trickle down your cheek… particularly if he's just poked you in the eye because he's waiting to get down to the pub. Search through the pack once more, this time silently counting out 21 cards from the bottom. With another despairing shake of the head (people have won Oscars for less!), put the 21 cards on the top of the pack and announce that you'll have to resort to plan B. This involves dealing out all 52 cards into two piles (deal to your friend first). At the end of the deal, ask whether the card he chose is in his pack. He should say no (if not, it's back to the drawing-board), in which case you discard his half and deal out the remaining 26 in two piles. Carry on dealing like this until you are left with one card. Turn it over and it will be the card he chose.

THE SHORT CARD TRICK

Skill Level: ❽

You will need:

Scissors

This trick operates on the same principle as The Final Card, but involves the creation of what is known in magic circles as a 'short card'. To make a short card, you need to trim the top edge by about an eighth of a centimetre. This might not sound much, but when the pack is squared off neatly the short card is immediately identifiable to the magician and can thus serve as a key card to help with locating others. The amount cut off is so small that the audience can spot nothing untoward, even in close-up. Short cards may be used in all manner of tricks. Here you have to prepare the pack so that the short card is the 22nd card from the top. Spread the cards and allow your volunteer to pick one. While he is studying his chosen card (it's amazing how long it takes some people to remember the seven of diamonds), flick through the pack with your fingertips so that you can locate the short card. If he has selected a card from the part of the pack below the short card (cards 23–52, that is), divide the pack immediately above the short card and have the mystery card inserted there. That card now occupies 22nd position. If however he took a card from the part of the pack above the short card, you need to divide the pack at the short card and insert the chosen card immediately below that one to ensure that it is the 22nd card from the top. You now deal out the cards alternately into two piles – the first face up, the second face down. Ask your volunteer to tell you whether his card is in the face-up heap. If you have counted correctly, it won't be. Deal out the face-down pile as before (alternately face up and face down) and continue like this until there is just one card left face down. That will be the mystery card.

THE PAIR OF ACES

Skill Level: 8

For this exercise you need two packs of cards with identical colours and patterns on the back. Before unleashing your magical powers on an unsuspecting public, secretly take the ace of hearts and the ace of diamonds from one pack of cards and put one at each end of the other pack, giving you a pack of 54 cards. You don't need the remaining 50 cards of the first pack. Take the 54-strong pack and hold it in a fan, keeping the backs of the cards facing your audience so that they can't see the two aces at either end. Make a bold show of announcing that you want to find the ace of hearts and the ace of diamonds. Remove the duplicate pair (still leaving you with the aces on the ends) and hold them up so that the audience can see them. Then replace the two aces clearly somewhere in the middle of the pack, close the pack and grip it firmly between your fingers and your thumb. Now comes the tricky bit. Throw the pack to the floor while keeping hold of the two end cards. As the cards cascade downwards, you are left holding the ace of hearts and the ace of diamonds. Show them to the audience… and hope that nobody spots the spare aces lying somewhere in the pile on the carpet.

CASCADE OF CARDS

Skill Level: ⑨

You will need:

A small piece of double-sided sticky tape

The art of plucking a card out of thin air is nobly demonstrated in this spectacular trick. The only preparation is to place a small piece of clear, double-sided sticky tape on the back of your right hand. It might pull on the hairs when you remove it afterwards but, believe me, the trick is worth the pain. Ask someone to select a card from the pack and put it on top of the deck. Cut the pack, holding the bottom half in your left hand and putting the top half face down on the table with your right hand. Suddenly throw the cards in your left hand high into the air and, while everyone is watching them fall, quickly press the back of your right hand on to the pile on the table so that the top card sticks to the adhesive tape. As the cards descend, reach your right hand out into the middle of the cascade and emerge with the chosen card on the back of your hand. Everyone will think you have performed an amazing feat of magic... except the smart Alec who has read books like this and knows to watch your hands instead of the cards.

THE FLYING CARD

Skill Level: ⑩

In this variation of Cascade of Cards, you ask a volunteer to shuffle the pack, pick a card, memorize it and return it to the top of the deck. Having noted the bottom card as in previous tricks, you can cut the cards and thus know the identity of the secret card. Say that, because this is such a top-of-the-bill trick, you need a little more room. As you turn your back on the audience and walk slowly to your new location, find the secret card, slide it to the bottom of the pack and lick your right thumb. Turn round to face your audience once more and, holding the pack with its back to them and with your soggy thumb pressed against the face of the bottom card, throw the entire pack into the air. The bottom card will remain stuck to your thumb and you can reveal that it is indeed the mystery card. With further practice, you will even be able to convey the impression that you have plucked the mystery card out of thin air. As all the cards flutter downwards, you can jab out your arm (the one with the card stuck to the thumb) and everyone will think you have caught the card in flight. It is only when they come to shake you warmly by the hand that they start to wonder where your thumb's been...

HYPNOSIS

Skill Level: ⑨

You will need:

Two spare cards, scissors, a piece of elastic or a thin elastic band

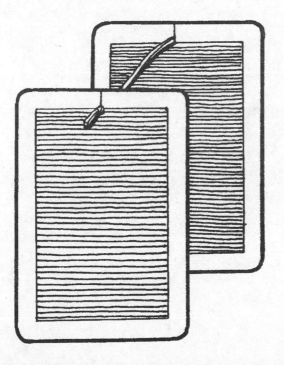

Take any two cards from a spare pack and make short vertical cuts in the top of both cards. Cut a piece of elastic about 10cm long and tie a knot near each end. Pass the elastic through the slits in the two cards, with the knots at the back, making sure the cards are facing the same way. After all that, you can get down to business. Put the linked cards at the bottom of the pack with the elasticated end nearest you, fan out all of the cards face down and ask somebody to pick one. But, by fair means or foul, steer them clear of the trick cards. Instruct them to remember the card and put it face down on the table. Cut the pack so that the trick cards move to the middle, pick up the chosen card and insert it into the pack in the elastic loop which links the trick cards. As you push the card in, the elastic stretches. Grip the pack firmly and hold it up. Ask your friend to name the chosen card and announce that you are going to hypnotize it into rising out of the pack. Mutter a few words of mystical gibberish, loosen your grip and the card will jump out of the pack.

THE MISSING CORNER

Skill Level: ⑩

You will need:

A handkerchief, an elastic band, a ball-point pen

The majority of card tricks can be performed just about anywhere (although the

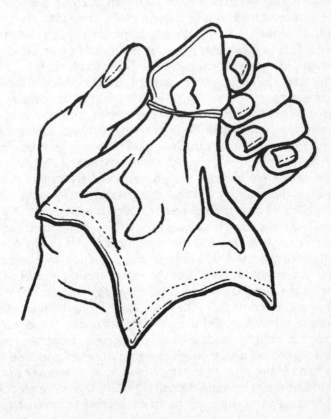

cards do tend to get a little soggy in the bath), but this trick is so baffling that it demands a grander backdrop – a smart lounge at the very least. Indeed it is so impressive that you might even care to dress for the occasion. But if you can't find magicians' white gloves, don't try to do it on the cheap with a pair of rubber gloves! As preparation, you need to tear off one corner from any card in the pack, approximately a quarter of the size of the card. Throw that piece away and put the torn card face down on the top of the deck so that the missing quarter is situated at the bottom left-hand corner. Place another card above it on the deck, relegating the torn card to second position. One more thing: you need an elastic band in your right-hand trouser pocket. Now hold the pack face down and ask someone to choose a card. After he has taken his card, put the pack face up on the table and nonchalantly remove the card at the bottom of the deck (this is the one that was earlier hiding the torn card). To justify your action, wave the card in the air, explaining that the person could have picked absolutely any card. Replace this card at the top of the face-up deck. The torn card is therefore now at the bottom. Take the card which your volunteer has chosen and tear off one corner, roughly the same size as you tore from the first card. Make sure that the piece you remove shows both the number and suit of the parent card. Hand the three-quarter section of card to him and ask him to write his initials on it. Holding the pack face down, you then put that card on top of the deck so that it is immediately above the first torn card. However the torn part of the chosen card should be at the top right-hand corner of the pack – in other words, the opposite way round to the card beneath it. Next hand him the piece you tore from the card he selected and ask him to sign that too. While he is preoccupied with doing that, you give the impression of dealing his torn card face down on to the table, but in reality you press your right thumb on the top right-hand corner of the pack and pull out the unsigned torn card from beneath the chosen card. By careful positioning of your hands, make sure that nobody can see that there is still a torn card on top of the deck. Cut the pack so that the signed torn card is safely tucked away somewhere in the middle. The next stage is to pick up the face-down torn card from the table (the one which everyone thinks is the signed card) and to rip it into three pieces, keeping the face of the card hidden from the audience. Take the signed corner of the chosen card and hold it on top of the other three pieces. The only face which will be visible to the audience will be that of the signed card. As far as they are concerned, all four pieces come from the same card. Hold the four pieces aloft in your right hand, drape a handkerchief over them and, under the cover provided, force the signed piece of card upwards so that it protrudes from the rest. With your left hand, grab the signed section through the handkerchief and hide the other pieces in your right hand. Bring your right hand down to your trouser pocket and pull out the elastic band, at the same time depositing there the three pieces of card. Tie the elastic band around the centre of the handkerchief to hold the piece of card in place at the very top (see illustration). Of course, the audience think there are four pieces of card in the handkerchief. Give the handkerchief to your volunteer and ask him to remove the elastic band. To his amazement, he will find only the torn corner which he signed earlier. Then you fan out the pack to produce the rest of his signed card, magically reassembled. When he matches the corner to this card, he will discover that it is a perfect fit. Everyone will be left scratching their heads in wonderment… as long as you haven't got a hole in your trouser pocket.

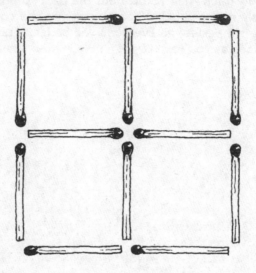

PUB
TRICKS

DIFFERENT STROKES

Skill Level: ❶

You will need:

Pencil and paper

This is the easiest trick in the world… once you know how it's done. On a piece of paper, you write six vertical strokes like this: I I I I I I. Challenge anyone to change the six strokes into three without rubbing any of them out, cutting the paper in half or similar cheating. When your friends look at you blankly, like losing finalists at Cruft's, and beg you to tell them the answer, you simply take the pencil and add to the strokes so that you end up with: T H R E E. Annoying, isn't it?

CROSS QUESTION

Skill Level: **1**

You will need:

Six coins

This is a good trick to sharpen everyone's wits before the pub quiz. Arrange six coins on the table in the shape of a cross – a vertical line of four and one placed either side of the second coin from the top. Tell your friends that, by moving just one coin, they must form two rows with four coins in each. While heads are scratched and brows are furrowed, you can show them how it's done. Simply move the coin at the bottom of the vertical column and place it partly over the coin which is second from the top. You thus make four coins across and four down.

ALL SQUARE

Skill Level: ❶

You will need:

12 coins

See whether they have learnt from the previous trick with another simple coin riddle. Arrange 12 coins on the table in a square, four coins on each side, and say that you want the same coins rearranged to form another square, but with five coins on each side. The idea is the same as before. You take one coin from each side and move it to a corner where you stack it partly on top of the coin already there. There are now two coins on each corner, leaving you with five coins on each side.

THE FINGER OF SUSPICION

Skill Level: ❶

This is really nothing more than a playground joke but, since a lot of pub conversations evoke memories of the fourth form, it is worth including. You tell one of your mates to put his hand flat on the table and then to bend his middle finger back. Now bet him that he can't raise the ring finger of the same hand without moving the other fingers and thumb. No matter how hard he concentrates, he will struggle. And so will everyone else. When hands are aching and fingers are sore, show them what to do. Put your hand flat on the table and bend your middle finger back as ordered before. Then use your other hand to lift the ring finger! Now is probably a good time to nip to the loo.

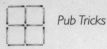

THE X FILES

Skill Level: ❶

You will need:

Four matches

Arrange four matches on the table in the shape of an X so that there is no space between the four where they meet in the centre. The matches of one arm will be touching, but the other two will be separated by the first two. The join of the two matches which touch should line up with one edge of the other two matches, not the centre of their join. Ask one of your friends to make a square by moving just one match. The words 'easy' and 'peasy' spring to mind because all you do is pull back the match which touches all three others, so that there is now a tiny square space where the four matches meet in the middle of the X.

WINE BLUFF

Skill Level: ❶

You will need:

A bottle of wine, a glass

If you've forsaken the pub for a wine bar, this challenge should ensure that you don't have to pay for the next bottle. When you're about halfway through the bottle and your glass is partly full, put the cork firmly back in the bottle and bet your friends that they can't drink from the bottle without removing the cork. Most will accept that it is impossible, although hardened drinkers may well opt to tip the bottle upside down and place a gaping mouth under the neck in the forlorn hope that a trickle may slither down the sides of the cork. When everyone has admitted defeat, bet them the next bottle that you can do it. Simply turn the bottle upside down, fill the cavity at the base of the bottle with wine from your own glass and drink from the cavity. No wine will ever have tasted better.

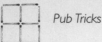

SEPARATION

Skill Level: ❶

You will need:

Salt, pepper, a piece of paper, a glass of water

Normally the amount of enjoyment that can be derived from a cruet set extends no further than using the salt and pepper pots to discuss football tactics. But you can also utilize them to play a neat scientific trick on your friends. Sprinkle roughly equal amounts of salt and pepper on to a slip of paper and mix them together with your finger. Bet everyone that you can separate the salt and the pepper just by one turn of your wrist. Seeing the mixture of salt and pepper, they will probably accept whereupon you take a glass of water, pick up the piece of paper and tip the contents into the glass. The salt will sink to the bottom while the pepper will float on the surface. All that's left to do now is collect your winnings.

THE SUM OF LIFE

Skill Level: ❷

You will need:

Pencil and paper, an envelope

Any faint knowledge of mathematical principles seems to desert us in the relaxed atmosphere of the pub, which is how we sometimes forget that a 16-stone thug and seven lagers add up to trouble. So a trick which relies on a fairly simple mathematical theory is unlikely to be challenged by any of your friends who will instead be utterly mesmerized by your remarkable foresight. You start by writing down a number on a piece of paper and getting someone to put it in an envelope and seal it. Allow them to check that there's nothing untoward about the envelope. The number you write should be exactly twice the number of the current year so if you are performing this trick in 2001, you write down 4002. Then call on your friends to choose someone to take part. The end result will seem even more impressive if the volunteer is a person you barely know. Hand the volunteer a pencil and paper and ask him to write down the answers to these four questions:

*   **THE YEAR OF HIS BIRTH**

*   **THE YEAR HE FIRST STARTED WORK**

*   **HIS AGE AT THE END OF THIS YEAR**

*   **THE NUMBER OF YEARS SINCE HE STARTED WORK.**

Ask him to add up the four numbers. The total will always be twice the current year, so when your volunteer opens the sealed envelope to reveal your prediction, the two figures will tally.

THREE SQUARES

Skill Level: ❷

You will need:

Eight matches

There is always a tremendous sense of anticipation associated with the first pint of the day. You get down to the pub for opening time, with a throat like sandpaper, and you watch the barman pull that first heavenly pint. And what happens? There is a violent gurgling sound and what should be something approaching amber nectar comes out looking like the product of a rabid dog. You have a pint of foam, at which point the barman suggests that the lager may need changing. While he sets off to do his duty, you are left in limbo. Anticipation has turned to frustration. By now, there are two or three other customers in the same boat, all equally impatient. To keep tempers under control and to pass the time while waiting for the barman to return, demonstrate a quick trick. Challenge anyone to make three squares from just eight matches. It will be just your luck if the guy next to you has seen the trick before, in which case it will take him approximately 10 seconds to lay out the matches in two squares, but so that they overlap, thereby forming a third smaller square. Well, it was worth a try...

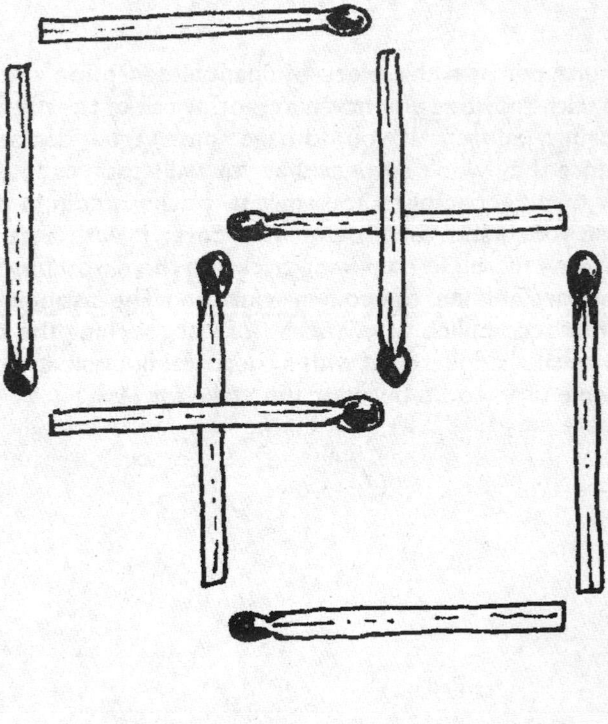

FRAUD!

Skill Level: ❶

You will need:

A coin, a handkerchief

For the best results, perform this piece of financial deception after you've done a few other coin tricks. Provided you haven't made a hash of the previous tricks, your friends will grudgingly admit that you do have some vague idea as to what you're doing and therefore they won't suspect that you will stoop as low as this. Success depends entirely on an accomplice. You start by placing a coin in the palm of your hand. Partly close your hand, turn it over and cover it with a handkerchief. Then ask all of your friends (if you keep playing tricks on them, you probably haven't got many) to step forward and feel the coin in your hand. The last person to come forward must be your accomplice who, instead of just touching the coin, removes it. You then toss away the handkerchief with a theatrical flourish and reveal your hand to be empty. People used to be burnt at the stake for less...

HEADS OR TAILS

Skill Level: ❷

You will need:

Some coins

Loose change is always handy in a pub with a decent jukebox. But if the afore-mentioned jukebox is dedicated solely to Pan Pipe Favourites (including such pan pipe classics as 'Born To Be Wild', 'Paranoid' and 'Anarchy in the UK'), not only is it time to find a new pub, but you need something to do with your change. There is a limit to the number of packets of chicken tikka flavoured crisps which you can devour in one evening. So, by way of a change (no pun intended), get your friends to put some loose coins on the table for a quick demonstration of 'Heads or Tails'. You need a reasonable number of coins to make it interesting – say half a dozen. After the coins have been laid out, make a mental note of how many are heads side up. Turn your back and ask someone to turn over any even number of coins. He can do this more than once in an attempt to confuse you, but he must never turn over a single coin. Then ask him to cover any one coin with his hand. When you turn back to face the table, you are immediately able to tell him whether the coin under his hand is a head or a tail. The rule is simple. If the number of heads at the start was odd and is still odd now – or was even at the start and is still even – then the covered coin is a tail. However if the number of heads at the start was even but is now odd, or vice-versa, then the hidden coin must be a head. Everybody will be so impressed they won't notice you pocketing the props.

471

SOMETHING UP YOUR SLEEVE

Skill Level: ❷

You will need:

Four matchboxes, an elastic band

Despite protestations to the contrary, magicians always seem to have something up their sleeve – whether it be a string of silk scarves, a flock of doves or a herd of wildebeest. The object here is marginally less exciting – a half-full matchbox – but the result can still be amusing. The matchbox is hidden up your right sleeve, tied to your wrist with an elastic band. You start the trick by putting three empty matchboxes on the table. You shake each box in turn – two with your left hand which produces no sound – and the other with your right hand. As a result of the hidden box, when you shake your right arm the audience hears the sound of matches. You then swiftly jumble up the boxes and ask any of the spectators to identify the box which contains the matches. Only you know that they are all empty. When their efforts meet with abject failure, you shake the three boxes again – two with your left hand and one with your right – before mixing them up once more... and so it goes on. Their attempts to find the right box will continue to prove spectacularly unsuccessful until they work out that you really do have something up your sleeve.

MATCHING SHAPES

Skill Level: ❷

You will need:

12 matches

Arrange a dozen matches in a block of four squares as shown. Challenge your friends to remove any two matches so that they leave exactly two squares. You simply remove two of the inner matches so that you are left with one large square and a smaller square within.

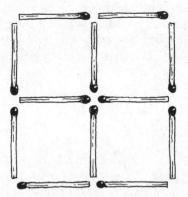
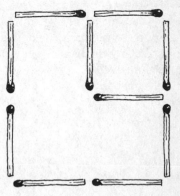

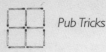

THREE BLIND DICE

Skill Level: ❷

You will need:

Three dice

Even with your back turned, you are able to calculate a player's dice throws. Turn away from the table, ask him to roll three dice and to add up the total, keeping the figure to himself. Let's assume he threw 6, 4, 1 and ended up with 11. Tell him to turn any one of the dice upside down and to add that number to the total. We'll say he turned over the 6 to get a 1 and so his running total is 12. Again he mustn't tell you the score. Ask him to roll the same dice again and to add that new number to his total. If he rolls a 5, his grand total will be 17 although the dice on the table (5, 4 and 1) only add up to 10. You now turn back to face the table with no knowledge of what numbers he threw on his first and second goes. But by adding up the dice in front of you (10) and adding 7, you will always come up with his secret grand total, in this case 17.

DOTTO

Skill Level: ❷

You will need:

Pencil and paper

As a nation, we love a bet. We'll bet on anything – that the Loch Ness Monster will be discovered before Scotland win the World Cup; that the Teletubbies will split up this year, citing artistic differences; and that Elvis will eventually be discovered hiding away somewhere he thought no one would find him – working as Director of Tourism for a small Midlands town. So the moment you say, 'I bet you can't…', you are assured of any number of takers. For this bet, you need a pencil and a piece of paper, the challenge being to draw a circle with a dot in the middle without taking the tip of the pencil off the paper. There will probably be all manner of squiggles as people try and fail, but the solution is quite simple really. You draw your circle in a corner of the paper and leave the pencil tip on the circumference of the circle. With your other hand, you fold over the corner of the paper into a triangular shape so that the point reaches the centre of the circle. Finally you retrace the pencil's journey around part of the circumference and then go across the folded triangle of paper and make a dot next to the point. When you pull back the fold, you have a circle with a dot in the middle and your pencil never once left the paper.

THE CHANGING TRIANGLE

Skill Level: ❷

You will need:

10 coins

For this coin puzzle, you arrange 10 coins in a triangle – one at the top, two on the second row, three on the third and four at the bottom. The object of the exercise is to turn the triangle upside down by moving only three of the coins. First you move the top coin down to a position beneath the middle two coins on the bottom row. You then move the coin at either end of the old bottom row up two rows and the result is an inverted triangle.

BEER MAT BALANCE

Skill Level: ❸

You will need:

Two beer mats, a glass, a penknife, glue

This one will bemuse even the most cynical of observers… for at least a minute. To prepare for it, take two identical beer mats, both of which should be in pristine condition. Score one mat from top to bottom down the middle with a penknife. Glue half of the face of that mat to the back of the other mat. Allow the unstuck half to lie flat against the back of the mat in front. Now announce that you are going to balance an ordinary glass on an ordinary beer mat. Hold the mat at the unstuck side and show everyone the back and front. They should all think there is just one mat. With the audience in front of you, place the glass on the top edge of the mat, at the same time pulling out the flap at the back so that it forms a right angle with the rest of the mat. This creates a platform on which the glass can balance. At first, appear reluctant to let go of the glass for fear that it will fall, but eventually pluck up courage and allow the glass to stand unaided. They will all think you've performed a miracle until they insist on inspecting the mat a little more closely, so don't perform this trick more than once to the same circle of friends. It is also advisable to use an empty glass for this trick as a full one might prove too heavy for the card and not only will you incur the wrath of the landlord, more importantly you'll lose your drink.

SECRETS

Skill Level: ❸

You will need:

A pocket calculator, pencil and paper

Warning: This trick could be dangerous. Take care!

There are two things a woman likes to keep secret – her age and the number of men she's slept with – so to prise such information from her is a veritable feat. Here's how it's done. Hand her a pocket calculator and ask her to key in the number of men she's slept with over the years. Tell her to multiply this figure by two, add five and multiply the total by 50. She should then add her age to the total, add 365 and subtract 615. This will leave a final sum which should be written on a piece of paper and handed to you. Unravelling the secrets is now easy for you. The last two numbers in the final total are her age and the preceding figures are the number of men she admits to having slept with. An eight-digit calculator should suffice for this task, but if you're dealing with someone who has led a particularly colourful life you may need a larger model.

TUG O' NAPKIN

Skill Level: ❸

You will need:

A paper napkin

Hang Tough, Pyramid, Run the Gauntlet… Pull the Napkin? No, somehow trying to pull a paper napkin in half is unlikely to earn a place among the tests of strength on Gladiators, but it requires more physical exertion than you think… unless, of course, you know the secret. Take an ordinary paper napkin, twist it diagonally from one corner to another and roll it tightly so that you end up with something resembling a piece of rope. Challenge any of your friends to break it in half by pulling both ends simultaneously. Hard though they may try, it will all be to no avail. Some egos may even be damaged beyond repair. While everyone's eyes are on macho men being reduced to quivering wrecks by a mere paper napkin, secretly wet your fingers. Now you can step in. Place your wet fingers over the centre of the napkin, an action which has the immediate effect of weakening it. Once the water has taken hold, it is a simple task to pull the napkin apart at that point. Nobody will ever kick sand in your face again.

THE TRAVELLING COIN

Skill Level: ❸

You will need:

Two small coins

For this trick, the sheer speed of movement deceives the eye. You start with your hands placed on the table, palms upwards, slightly less than a foot apart. On each hand rests a small coin. On the left hand, it is placed in the centre of your palm, but on the right hand, it is situated at the base of the first and second fingers. This positioning is essential, otherwise the trick won't work. Without raising your hands from the table, swiftly turn both hands over and inwards. This movement has the effect of throwing the coin from the right hand over to the left where it is caught by the left hand as it hits the table. Unless you are particularly clumsy, the speed of the transfer will be too quick for the naked eye. Then you ask your spectators to tell you how many coins are under each hand, and they should say one. You promptly astound them by revealing two coins under your left hand and none under your right. If you are left-handed, you will probably find it easier to swap things around by putting one coin in the palm of your right hand and the other at the base of the first two fingers of your left hand so that the coin travels from left to right.

DICE CHALLENGE

Skill Level: ❸

You will need:

Two dice

Turn your back on the table and ask one of your mates to throw two dice without telling you the numbers. Let's say he throws 6 and 2. Now tell him to double the number on one of the dice (if he chooses the 6, that's 12), to add 5 (that makes 17), multiply the answer by 5 (giving a total of 85) and then to add the number on the other dice (2). So he ends up with 87. Ask him to subtract 25 and to tell you the resulting number (62). This figure denotes the numbers on the dice he originally threw – 6 and 2 – which means you've worked out what he rolled with your back turned throughout.

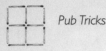
POCKET MONEY

Skill Level: ❸

You will need:

A pocket calculator, pencil and paper

By doing this mathematical challenge, you can find out whether someone has enough money in their pocket to buy the next round. Actually, unless their idea of a round is a packet of crisps split four ways, the answer will be no because the trick only works on sums under £1. It operates on the same principle as Secrets. Tell your friend to write down his age, double it, add five and multiply by 50. Next he must subtract 365 and add the amount of change in his pocket, in pence. If he is 28 and has 75p, this will give a grand total of 2760. Now you take over by adding 115 to give a final figure of 2875. The first two digits represent his age and the last two denote the amount of change in his pocket. The formula will always work as long as your friend isn't too rich.

GUESS THE NUMBER

Skill Level: ❸

You will need:

A set of dominoes

More fun with dominoes! What more could you want from life? Unlike most tricks, this one begins with a visit to the loo. No, you're not going to make all the toilet paper disappear out of the men's cubicle – that's probably been done already – nor are you going to make the hand-drier operate at a temperature where it doesn't barbecue your skin. Instead quietly announce that you're just going off to answer a call of nature and, in your absence, you want one of your friends to pick a domino from the set and to put the rest of the set back in the box, hidden from view. When you come back, there is no possible way you can know which domino has been chosen. Yet, without peeking, you are going to name that domino. It's a bit of a struggle at first, so tell whoever chose it that he is going to have to do a quick sum. Get him to look at the higher of the two numbers on the domino (if it's a double, then obviously either number will do) and to multiply it by five. He must then add seven and double the answer. Next he must add on the lower of the two numbers on the domino and subtract 14. The two-digit answer will be the numbers on the mystery domino. So if the domino is 5:1, it works like this: 5 x 5 = 25 +7 = 32 x 2 = 64 + 1 = 65 - 14 = 51. The numbers are 5 and 1.

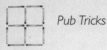

THE EMPTY GLASS

Skill Level: ❸

You will need:

Four matches, a coin

Arrange four matches into the shape of a wine glass (see illustration) and place a coin between the two vertical matches which form the sides of the 'glass'. Challenge any of your friends to move the 'glass' in such a way that the coin finishes up outside it. Only two matches may be moved. The first move is to slide the horizontal match (the one forming the base of the 'glass') half its length to the left. The second move is to switch the detached vertical match (the one which originally formed the right-hand side of the 'glass') down to below the left-hand end of the horizontal match. The 'glass' is now upside down and the coin is outside.

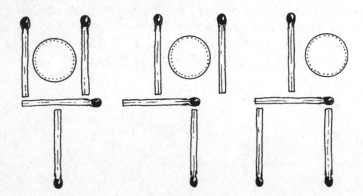

X STATIC

Skill Level: ❸

You will need:

A £1 coin, a match, a plastic comb

Stand a pound coin on its edge on the table and balance a match across the top of the coin. The aim is to move the match off the coin without touching either object. To do this, you need to create static electricity. Rub a plastic comb through your hair or on to the sleeves of your pullover if it's made of wool. Hold the comb next to the match and the static electricity from the comb will cause the match to drop off the coin.

PLAYING WITH FIRE

Skill Level: ❸

You will need:

A lighted cigarette, an ice cube

Warning: This trick could be dangerous. Take care!

Why do people choose to eat fire for a living? After all, career openings are rather limited. As a result of government cutbacks, most councils no longer even have a fire-eating department. Yet we still marvel at those who appear to swallow fire without burning away the insides of their mouth. Fire is exceedingly dangerous and is definitely not something to be toyed with, but you can demonstrate your ability to defy pain in a relatively innocuous way which you should be able to perform without having the pub evacuated. Pick up a lighted cigarette and hold the burning tip between your fingers for a few seconds. Do not let anyone take a puff. You should be able to do this without suffering any adverse effects. The secret is that just beforehand you have placed those same fingers on an ice cube or something equally cold. This serves to numb the pain. Now you can pass the lighted cigarette to the next brave contestant while you move on to the bed of nails.

THE DOMINO EFFECT

Skill Level: ❸

You will need:

A set of dominoes, a bag, pencil and paper, an envelope

The game of dominoes has undergone something of a renaissance in recent years, and is no longer played solely by men who wear cloth caps and race whippets. This trick with dominoes is deceptively simple, but is guaranteed to impress anyone who knows nothing at all about the game. To set up the trick, you must secretly remove any domino except a double. If the one you pick is 3:2, you then write 3 and 2 on a piece of paper and pop it in a sealed envelope. Begin the performance by handing the envelope to one of your friends, along with a bag full of dominoes (minus, of course, the one you have already taken out). Tell him to set the dominoes out on the table in game fashion, but don't let him count the tiles in case he discovers your villainy. Announce that the envelope contains a prediction as to which numbers will be at either end of the line when all of the tiles have been laid out correctly. When he finishes, ask him to open the envelope and, sure enough, the numbers on the piece of paper will be those at either end of the row – in this case 3 and 2.

BRIDGE BUILDING

Skill Level: ❸

You will need:

A piece of thick paper, three glasses

Stand two empty glasses of the same height on the table and cover them with a piece of strong paper – something like blotting paper. You then boast that you can perch a third empty glass upright on the paper bridge, thus creating a pyramid shape, but the question is: can anyone else? No matter how carefully they position the glass, the paper will give way, so make sure someone is on hand to catch the falling glass. Alternatively, use a plastic glass – one of those awful things you get in downmarket clubs. It still won't balance, but it will prevent everyone being covered in broken glass. Finally you show them how it's done. Take the piece of paper and fold it several times lengthwise so that you form a row of pleats. Put this on top of the two glasses and then balance the third glass on the corrugated paper. This time it will hold.

BOTTLE IT

Skill Level: ❸

You will need:

An empty bottle, a banknote, a pencil

If you should ever find yourself in a life-or-death situation where your only hope of salvation is to remove a banknote from beneath an upside down bottle without lifting the bottle, remember this trick. Place the banknote on the table and stand the inverted bottle on top of the note. Lay a pencil across the end of the note nearest to you and roll the note around the pencil towards the bottle, keeping the roll as tight as possible. The note will edge towards you and eventually slide out from under the bottle which remains perfectly upright. As you become increasingly adept at this trick, you will probably be able to dispense with the pencil altogether. But always carry one with you... just in case.

TEN INTO FIUE WILL GO

Skill Level: ❸

You will need:

A piece of paper, pencil, scissors, a 5p coin, a 10p coin

Place a 5p coin in the centre of a square piece of paper and draw a line around the circumference of the coin. Cut out the hole which should therefore be exactly the same size as the 5p. Now challenge your friends to push a 10p coin through the hole without tearing the paper. In case any of your friends are a little too enthusiastic about these challenges, it is worth pointing out that hiring a chainsaw to slice the 10p piece in half is also forbidden. In fact, the trick requires no use of force whatsoever. You just fold the paper in half so that the hole is in the middle of the crease, put the 10p over the hole and lift the top corners of the paper. This has the effect of widening the hole, allowing the 10p to slip through unhindered.

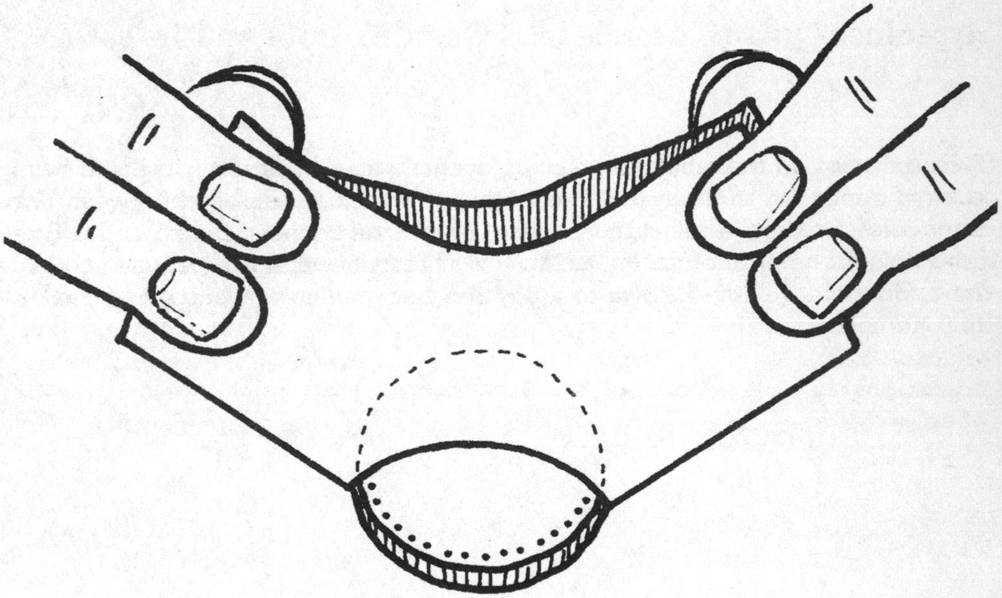

MONEY RING

Skill Level: ❸

You will need:

Six coins

Place six coins on the table in two rows of three (see illustration), the aim being to form a circle in three moves. Each coin moved must be placed between two other coins. First move coin 4 to a position below and between coins 5 and 6. Then move coin 5 one position to the left so that it rests beneath and between coins 1 and 2. Finally move coin 1 down to a position between coins 5 and 4 and the circle is complete.

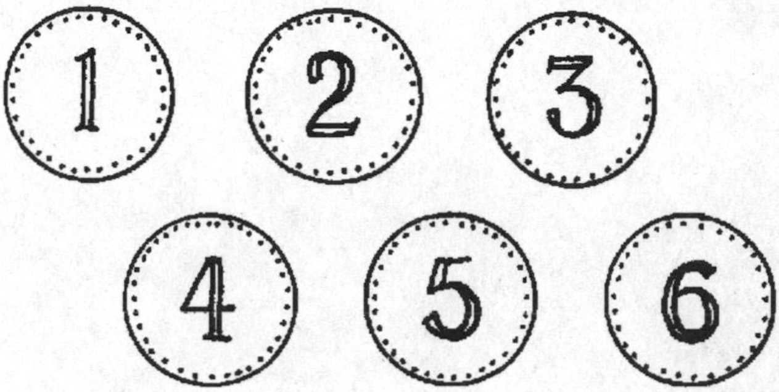
1
2
3
4
5
6

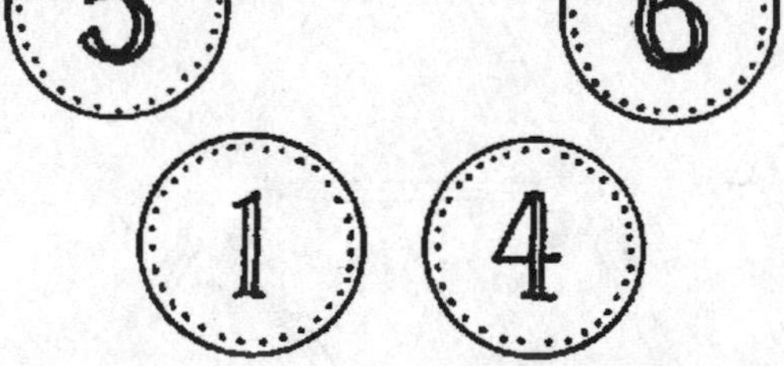
2
3
5
6
1
4

SPORTING TRIANGLES

Skill Level: ❸

You will need:

Nine matches

This is another ingenious puzzle with matches. Arrange nine matches in a row on the table so that they form three adjoining triangles. Now challenge anyone to make five triangles from the set-up by moving just two of the matches. All you do is take one match from each of the inside struts of the middle triangle and form a new triangle on top of the other two. You end up with four small triangles and one large one.

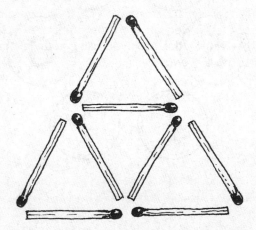

COIN THROUGH THE TABLE

Skill Level: ❸

You will need:

Two coins, pen and paper, sticky tape

Produce two coins and ask one of your group to put his initials on a tiny scrap of paper and to stick the paper on to each coin so that, in the wake of your trickery, they will be readily identifiable as the originals. Place the coins on the table, one near the edge closest to you and the other a few inches away. Pick up the farther coin in your left hand and give the impression of picking up the coin by the edge in your right hand. Instead you use your right hand to knock that coin into your lap where it is gathered by your left hand which is then placed underneath the table. Your left hand is now clenched under the table and your right hand is on top of the table. The audience believe there to be a coin in each hand whereas in truth there are two coins in your left hand and none in your right. Announce that you are now going to make the coin in your right hand work its way through the table to your left hand. After a pregnant pause, you clink the two coins together in your left hand as if one has just landed on the other and open your right fist to reveal that the coin there has vanished. Finally you bring your left hand out from underneath the table and show the two coins.

COCKTAIL SHAKER

Skill Level: ❸

You will need:

A cocktail menu, pencil and paper

Sometimes you need a break from your local. Maybe the new landlord's chosen Basil Fawlty as his role model, or they've stopped serving your favourite lager or they've painted over your graffiti in the toilets. So you seek out pastures new – perhaps that quiet little pub where they show the Shopping Channel instead of Sky Sports, or the pub by the train station with its Wet Anorak competitions, or that trendy Australian theme bar where, for complete authenticity, the bar staff are all ex-cons. There will also be an extensive cocktail list with names like Kangaroo Kick, Melbourne Cup and Echidna Surprise, none of which have ever been drunk by Australians. If the cocktail list boasts 18 or more items, you can indulge in a quick prediction game based on the numbers trick. Find the 18th cocktail on the menu – let's say it's Platypus Punch – and tell your drinking partner that's the one you're going to choose and you hope he does the same. He is undecided so you suggest a simple way of making up his mind for him. Give him a pencil and paper and ask him to write down any three-figure number, as long as the digits are all different. Tell him to reverse that number and to subtract the smaller total from the larger. Lick your lips saying you can almost taste that Platypus Punch and then ask him to add up the three digits he is left with. The answer will be 18 and so you count down 18 items and order him a Platypus Punch. You knew he'd come round to your way of thinking.

SALT AND PEPPER

Skill Level: ❸

You will need:

Salt, pepper, a plastic comb

This trick also relies upon the ability of a plastic comb to form static electricity. Pour a little salt on to the table and sprinkle a few grains of pepper on top. Now announce that you are going to separate all the salt and pepper in just 10 seconds. Run the comb through your hair to create static electricity and pass it over the salt and pepper pile. As you do so, the grains of pepper should leap up into the teeth of the comb, leaving the salt behind on the table. But don't try using the comb on your hair again for a while unless you want the sort of dandruff which makes people sneeze.

FOLDING MONEY

Skill Level: ❸

You will need:

A banknote

People are always impressed by tricks involving money, particularly when it's not their money that's being used. And since the chances of getting £5 out of most of your friends are pretty remote, you might as well use your own money for this trick. Take a £5 note (you can use any denomination, but the lowest is safest just in case anything goes wrong) and hold it upright so that everyone can see the Queen looking regally ahead towards the fruit machine and the jukebox. Fold the note in half by folding the top edge down towards you. Take the right edge and fold that over to the left edge so that the note is now folded in quarters and then fold it again from the right so that it is now in eighths. Next unfold the two doubled corners from the back by taking them to the right (the note is now back in quarters) and then open to the left the part of the note facing you so that your £5 note is folded in half. Finally lift the front half of the note and the Queen will be seen to be upside down. You have somehow made her stand on her head without turning the note over.

MATCHING NUMBERS

Skill Level: ❹

You will need:

A box of matches

Place a closed matchbox on the table, rattle it and ask one of your friends to bet whether it contains an odd or even number of matches. The beauty of it is that whichever he guesses – odd or even – will be wrong. The secret is in the preparation. Before you do the trick, put four matches in the matchbox tray and lay a fifth match diagonally across them so that it is wedged against the sides. When the tray is tipped upside down, the four matches below the diagonal one will not fall out. Then put another 10 matches on top of the diagonal match, making a total of 15 in all, and slide the tray back into the cover. Now you can perform the trick. Ask your friend to nominate odd or even. If he says odd, tip the tray upside down and only the top 10 matches will fall out into the table, the rest being held in place by the immovable diagonal match. Quickly slide the tray back into the box so that the remaining matches stay unseen. Therefore he will have called odd when the number is even. If, however, he says even, gently squeeze the sides of the tray to dislodge the diagonal match and all 15 matches will come tumbling out. So he is wrong again. Provided you allow yourself time to prepare the diagonal match, you can carry on like this with any number of challengers, safe in the knowledge that you are invincible.

THE SECRET PACKET

Skill Level: ❹

You will need:

A coin, a square piece of paper, a pencil

Magicians love nothing more than making your money disappear and this trick presents another opportunity for them to fritter away your hard-earned cash. Place a coin on a square of paper and fold the bottom edge of the paper to within about 1cm of the top. Fold both of the sides behind the paper and finally fold that top centimetre strip back and away from you. From their viewpoint, the audience will think that the coin is safely pocketed with no visible means of escape, but your folding has created an open edge at the top. Turn the packet over so that the open edge is now at the bottom, gripping the paper so that the coin can't fall out. Tap the coin with a pencil to show everyone that it is still there. Then pass your left hand over the paper to conceal the movement of the coin, at the same time releasing your grip on the packet with your right hand and allowing the coin to fall into your palm. Keep the coin hidden there and tear up the packet amidst great pomp and ceremony. To widespread amazement (with perhaps a little apathy thrown in), the coin has vanished.

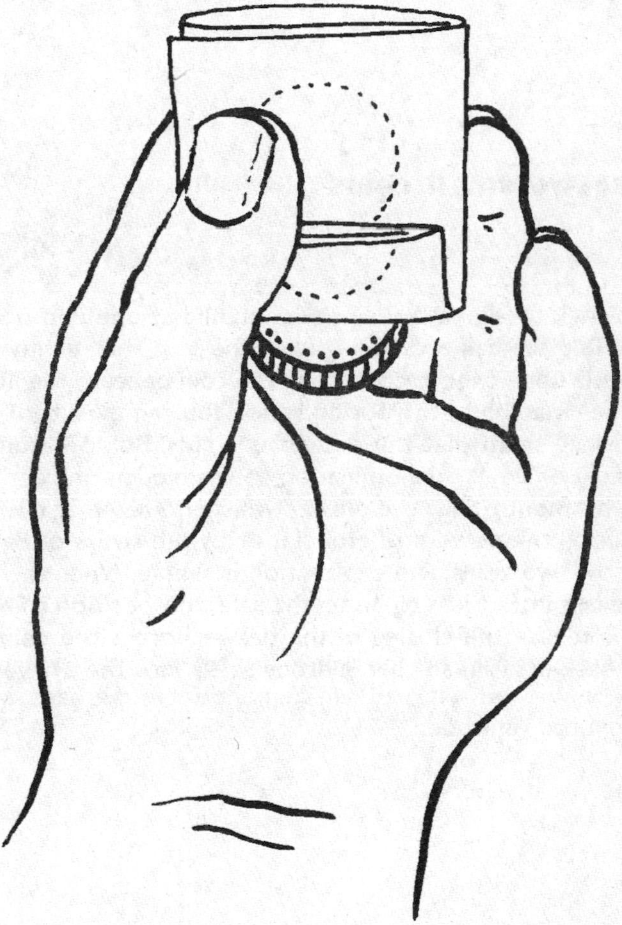

DOUBLE YOUR MONEY

Skill Level: ❹

You will need:

A matchbox, two small coins

Prepare for this trick by sliding a coin under the lid at one end of a matchbox so that it is wedged in place half protruding from the box. Then gently slide the drawer of the box partly open over it, concealing the coin beneath the lid. Now you can show the half-open matchbox to your audience. You can even turn it upside down in order to convince them that the drawer is empty. Borrow from a member of the audience a coin of similar denomination to the hidden one and tell him you're going to double his money. Shut the drawer, whisper a few magic words and, when you open it again, by the powers of Houdini or by the rivers of Babylon or whatever, there are now two coins. The explanation is simple. When the drawer is shut, the wedged coin falls in. But just to be on the safe side, position a finger at the back of the matchbox in case the closing of the drawer forces the coin out. That way, you can push it back in again so that it drops safely into the drawer.

COIN BLUFF

Skill Level: ④

You will need:

Three small coins

Every pub has its bore – the guy who reckons he knows everything but really knows nothing. He is a mass of wild rumours, all so unlikely that even the Sunday Sport wouldn't give them much credence. Over the past few months, he has collared you at the bar with definite news – 'it's gospel, I swear' – that Keith Richards is Barbara Cartland's secret love child; that Apollo 11 never went anywhere near the Moon and landed in a remote part of Mongolia by mistake; and that Lassie was really two Yorkshire terriers stitched together. Since he claims to be the fount of all knowledge, he will claim to know exactly how a magician does a particular trick even though, inevitably, he'll be hopelessly wide of the mark. There's nothing he likes more than catching someone out. So he'll be rubbing his hands with glee while you do this trick, only to discover that it has a nasty sting in the tail which might just reduce him to silence for a second or two. He sees you holding two coins flat on top of each other between your thumb and forefinger and claiming that by rubbing them together, you will produce a third coin. What he can't see is that you do have a third coin, tucked away in the palm of your hand near the base of your thumb. Anyway you rub away frantically and the speed of movement does create the impression that there are three coins. But he won't fall for that and will denounce it as just an optical illusion… whereupon you casually toss the three coins on to the table.

THE FALLING POUND

Skill Level: ⑤

You will need:

A glass, a 10p coin, a match, a beer mat

The title of this trick is a little misleading because, unless you possess a very large match – the sort which could have been used to light Apollo 11 – it is better to perform it with a lightweight 10p piece rather than a pound coin. Take a beer mat (preferably one that is dry and not sodden in ale) and place it across the top of an empty glass. The best part of the trick is making the glass empty in the first place. With the edges of the mat overlapping the rim, rest a match on the card and on top of the match, balance a 10p coin. As the tension builds to an unbearable crescendo, flick the mat forward (taking care not to send the glass flying as you do so) and the coin should drop into the glass while the match doesn't. It's all to do with the coin's inertia. Instead of a coin on a match, you can do the trick with an egg on a matchbox, but it's a lot messier. Anyway, who wants to spend most of the evening with an egg in their pocket?

THE THREE GLASS TRICK

Skill Level: ❺

You will need:

Three empty glasses

Here's a nice little puzzle to play just before closing time when everyone is in the mood for intellectual stimulation and the table is stacked with empty glasses. Take three glasses and stand them in a row, turning the glasses at each end upside down. Only the glass in the middle is upright. Explain that the challenge is to turn all three the right way up in three moves. Even the old drunk who's been propping up the bar for the past five hours could just about manage that (although he might incur a few breakages en route), but you then casually add that each move must involve two glasses being turned over simultaneously. Suddenly it's not so easy, but it can be done. If everyone is struggling and the bar staff are waiting to collect the glasses, keep them in suspense no longer. The first move is to turn over one end glass and the middle glass. Then you turn over both end glasses and finally the same two glasses from the first move (end and middle). This will leave you with all three glasses standing upright, which is more than can be said for the bloke at the bar.

CLUNK CLINK, EVERY TRICK

Skill Level: ⑤

You will need:

A coin, a napkin, a glass

Show your friends a coin and a napkin and then place the coin in the centre of the napkin and hold it aloft so that you are gripping the coin through the napkin. In your left hand, take a glass and cover it with the napkin. Once the glass is hidden from view, tilt it forward slightly. Now release the coin and it should clink against the side of the glass and drop into your left hand, but, on hearing the clinking sound, everyone will assume that it has fallen into the glass. Place the covered glass on the table with your right hand, keeping the coin concealed in your left hand. Finally, remove the napkin from the glass to universal disbelief that the coin has disappeared.

FANTASTIC ELASTIC

Skill Level: ⑤

You will need:

Two different-coloured elastic bands

With the palm of your left hand facing you, put a yellow elastic band over your forefinger and middle finger and a red one over your other two fingers (the colours may of course be changed according to availability). Hook the red band with the forefinger of your right hand and then do the same with the yellow band. Stretch both bands down and also put your right middle finger inside the two stretched bands. Use the two fingers to open the bands wide and then bend all four fingers on your left hand and slip them inside the two elastic bands. Quickly straighten out the fingers on your left hand, keeping them inside the bands, and the bands should change positions so that the red band is now on your left forefinger and middle finger and the yellow band is wrapped around the other two fingers.

RAPID COIN MOVEMENT

Skill Level: ⑤

You will need:

A coin, a ring

For this trick, you should wear a ring on your left hand – not for any show of marital solidarity, but because of the sound effect it will create. Hold a coin up for all to see and pop it into the palm of either hand. You now transfer it rapidly from one hand to the other, ultimately keeping it in your left hand while pretending to pass it back and forth. Eventually you clench your right fist in an exaggerated manner as if holding the coin. All eyes will now be focused on that hand, enabling you to let the coin slip quietly from your left hand into your lap where you can either cover it with your pullover or cross your legs so that it is tucked under your thigh. Then you slam your right hand down on the table. As you do so (and here synchronization of sound and movement is all-important), you knock the ring on your left hand against the side of the table. Everyone will immediately assume that the sound is that of the coin in your right hand hitting the table. So when you ask them which hand the coin is in, they'll nominate the right. That is when you raise your right hand and show them that there is no coin. But there will always be someone who thinks he can outsmart you and that person may well take one look at your clenched left hand, see the ring and put two and two together. 'I know where the coin is,' he'll announce grandly, whereupon you open your left hand to reveal a distinct absence of money. Cue egg on face. Even if your spectators are not blessed with inquisitive minds and don't ask about the ring, you will still have made the coin disappear.

DOUBLE COIN LIFT

Skill Level: ⑤

You will need:

Two coins, a glass with a stem

If one of your number is brave enough to drink pub wine or rich enough to drink brandy, try this trick with their glass. Balance two coins opposite each other on the rim of the glass and challenge anyone to pick both coins off the glass at exactly the same time using just the thumb and index finger of one hand. This is how you do it. You put your thumb over one coin and the index finger of the same hand over the other coin. Moving your fingers in unison, you slide both coins down the sides of the glass and around the base. Then you squeeze your finger and thumb together until the two coins meet and you snatch them off the glass in one movement. Although this trick may sound simple, it does require a steady hand and therefore becomes increasingly difficult – and entertaining – the longer the evening wears on.

THE DISAPPEARING NOTE

Skill Level: ⑥

You will need:

A banknote

In the finest traditions of Blue Peter, this is a trick you made earlier. The secret is all in the preparation. Far from prying eyes, you need to fold a banknote so that, when held in a certain way, it will look as if there are two notes. Here's how you do it. First fold the note in half vertically and towards you (A). Open out the note and fold it horizontally towards you (B). Open out the note again and make a diagonal fold away from you (C). Then, after unfolding the note, make another diagonal fold away from you, this time in the opposite direction (D). Unfold the note once more and repeat the earlier horizontal fold towards you (E). By holding the note at the sides and pushing inwards, it should now form two distinct flaps. Move one flap to the left and the other to the right and you should be left with a V-shape seemingly consisting of two separate notes. If you've made a mess of it, it will always make a nice bracelet. Assuming that you have perfected the folding process, you take the contraption down to the pub with you. At an opportune moment – just when somebody says it's your round – you produce the V-shape note from your pocket and announce that you will pay for the drinks with these two notes. You then open out the note and drop it dramatically on to the table. They will see that instead of the two notes they thought you had in your hand, there is only one. You have somehow made one of the notes disappear. Any grudging admiration will quickly evaporate when you explain that you can now only afford to buy half a round.

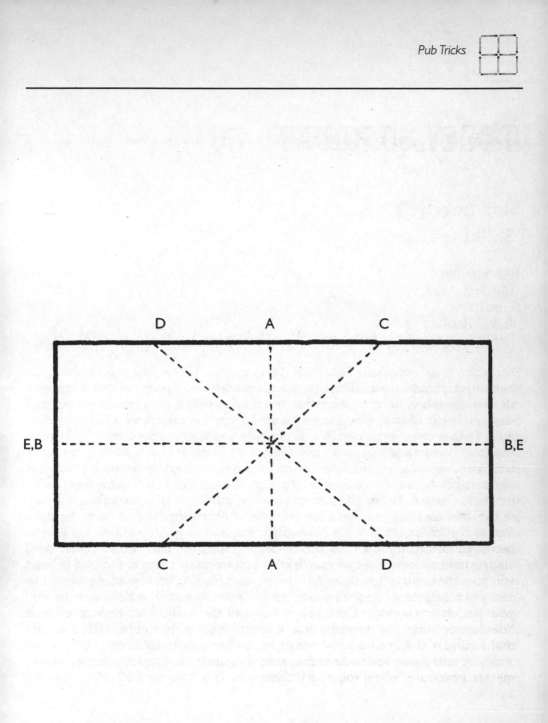

MONEY GO ROUND

Skill Level: ⑥

You will need:

A coin

Deception is an important feature of the magician's repertoire, making the audience's eyes deceive them. This trick, which creates the impression that a coin has travelled from one hand to the other and then vanished (whereas in truth it has been in the first hand all along), is very much part of the magician's staple diet. Hold a coin (or any other small object such as a ring or a key) in your left hand between your thumb and middle finger so that everyone can see it clearly. Announce that in your right hand you've got some priceless, magical disappearing dust which has only ever been used three times before – on Shergar, Lord Lucan and the crew of the Marie Celeste. You're going to sprinkle this dust over the coin to make it vanish into thin air. Bring your right hand down and, obscuring the coin from the audience with your fingers, give the distinct impression that you have taken the coin in that hand. In fact, the coin has merely slipped into the palm of your left hand. Keeping the coin concealed in your left hand, pretend to squeeze the coin in your right hand, seemingly manoeuvring it with your fingers. Then suddenly open the palm and fingers of your right hand to the audience to reveal that the coin has disappeared. With your right hand, search high and low for it – under beer mats, in shoes, under ashtrays – before announcing that you've spotted it. With your left hand, rummage in someone's hair and produce the coin (which, of course, has been lurking in your palm). The audience's appreciation might not run to a drink, but you may get a packet of crisps for your trouble.

BANK ROLL

Skill Level: ⑥

You will need:

A bread roll, a coin

This trick is a good surprise to play at the start of a pub meal. When the waitress comes round with her basket of bread rolls, take a roll and slip a coin into the palm of your right hand where nobody else can see it. Using your thumbs, break open the roll from underneath and then, as you push your fingers into the centre of the roll, press the coin into it. At the same time, move your thumbs up to break open the top of the roll and reveal the coin nestling within. Simply look surprised and pocket the coin whereupon everyone else will start searching inside their rolls in the hope of striking it rich. The drawback, of course, is that you shouldn't eat any roll which has had a coin inside. Oh, how we suffer for our art...

LINE 'EM UP

Skill Level: ⑥

You will need:

Three empty glasses, three full glasses

With most tricks, there is a definite purpose – a raison d'être – but the only probable result from this charade is that your beer is likely to go flat before you've had a chance to drink it. Still, here goes. Line up six pint glasses on the table, three empty and three full – although surely nobody would begrudge you that first comforting sip. The full glasses (which, for the purposes of the exercise, we will call 1, 2 and 3) should be together, followed by the empty glasses which we will call 4, 5 and 6. Thus the opening line-up is 1, 2, 3, 4, 5, 6. The aim is to swap the glasses around so that full and empty pints are positioned alternately, but you have only three moves and each move must involve moving two glasses and these must be adjacent to one another. It's a tricky one, but here's how it's done. Move full glasses 1 and 2 to the other end of the line so that the order is now 3, 4, 5, 6, 1, 2. Next move empty glass 6 and full glass 1 to the far right of the line, making the order 3, 4, 5, 2, 6, 1. Finally switch full glass 3 and empty glass 4 to a position between empty glass 5 and full glass 2. So you end up with an order of 5, 3, 4, 2, 6, 1 – empty, full, empty, full, empty, full. Now that's over, you can get on with your pint.

A FINANCIAL RIDDLE

Skill Level: ⑥

You will need:

Two 2p coins, one 1p coin

You need to be at your most alert to solve this problem – a mind befuddled by alcohol will struggle all the way through happy hour. Place a 1p coin on the table and then put a 2p piece on either side so that both of the higher-denomination coins are touching the 1p. The challenge is to move one of the 2p coins to a position between the 1p and the other 2p whilst adhering to three strict rules – the 2p on the left must not be touched; the 1p can be touched, but must not be moved; and the 2p on the right, being an exceedingly emotional coin, may be touched and moved. After the sum of intellects present have proved hopelessly unequal to the task, you can step in and show them how to do it. You put a finger from your left hand on the 1p and a finger from your right hand on the 2p on the right. With your finger, you move the 2p a little to the right and then bring it back and knock it against the 1p. Since the 1p and the 2p on the left are touching, this move creates a knock-on effect, forcing the 2p further to the left and creating a gap between it and the 1p. As you are allowed to move the 2p on the right, you can now swing it round into the space between the other two coins. Cue everyone else muttering: 'I wish I'd thought of that…'

TEN MATCH LIFT

Skill Level: ⑥

You will need:

Eleven matches

The challenge here is to use a solitary match to pick up another ten. To do so, you need to arrange the matches carefully on the table. Lay one match horizontally and nine more vertically across it, alternate matches facing in opposite directions. In other words, the heads of the odd-numbered matches will face one way and the even-numbered matches will face the other way. Finally place another match horizontally on top of the arrangement so that it is directly above the very first match to have been laid, but pointing in the opposite direction. Using the thumb and forefinger of both hands, you now firmly grip the ends of the two parallel matches and the matches sandwiched in between will also be raised from the table. Thus you have accomplished your mission of using one match to lift the other ten.

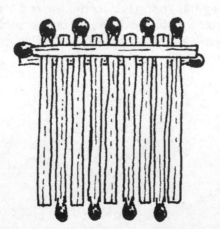

THE JUMPING BAND

Skill Level: ❼

You will need:

An elastic band

It sounds impossible – the stuff of which dreams are made – but, with practice, you can make an elastic band jump from one finger to another. Loop an elastic band around the forefinger of your left hand and, with your right hand, stretch it across so that it passes behind the middle finger of your left hand. Then, while taking care not to twist the band, pull it back down around your middle finger so that it now loops on to your forefinger again. Pause for a second and announce that you are now going to make the elastic band leap from your forefinger to the middle finger. Bend your middle finger slightly and the movement should cause the band to jump the divide and land on your middle finger. However, more than likely it will end up on the floor… in which case try again. Remember, nobody goes home until you get it right.

ROLL WITH IT

Skill Level: ❼

You will need:

A bread roll, a fork, a napkin

If you take the precaution of saving a bread roll, here's another stunt you can perform at the end of a pub meal. While the others are wrestling over custody of the one after-dinner mint, quietly stick the prongs of your fork into the roll at an angle and slip the roll and its new handle on your lap under your napkin. When the fuss has died down, say you're going to make your roll walk the tightrope. Taking a corner between the first two fingers of each hand, hold the napkin aloft so that it forms a small screen between you and the others and at the same time pick up the handle of the fork between your right thumb and forefinger. Keep the fork hidden behind the napkin and position it so that the roll appears balanced on top of the napkin. By moving the fork, you can make it look as though the roll is walking along the edge of the napkin.

THE GREAT ESCAPE

Skill Level: ❼

You will need:

A glass, a beer mat, a coin, a piece of paper

Declare your intention of making an ordinary coin burrow its way through a beer mat into a glass below. Follow the procedure in The Secret Packet by putting a coin on a square of paper and folding the paper so that you leave an unseen gap at the top. When you turn the packet upside down, the coin slides out into your hand. Place an empty glass on the table and pick up a beer mat between the thumb and forefinger of your right hand, keeping the coin hidden in the same hand. Rest the mat over the mouth of the glass, at the same time using your thumb to force the coin forward and to wedge it between the mat and the rim of the glass where nobody can see it. Now set the paper packet, which everyone thinks contains the coin, on top of the mat. Open your hand to show that it is empty and tap the beer mat. The vibration will cause the coin to drop into the glass and your stunned audience will think that it has somehow worked its way out of the packet and penetrated the beer mat.

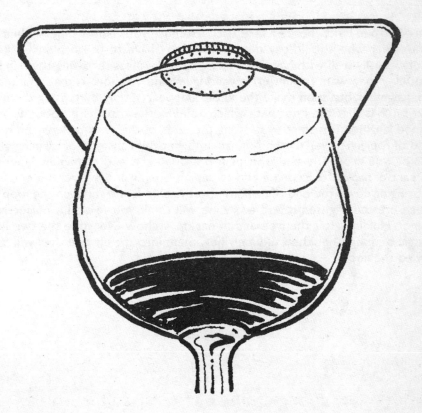

FLYING NAPKINS

Skill Level: ⑦

You will need:

Two napkins

After a good pub lunch, here's a neat trick to amuse your fellow diners while you're agonizing over who should pay the bill. You don't have to use napkins – the trick will work equally well with handkerchiefs – but it involves throwing them in the air and not everyone wants your germs wafting around. The idea is that you knot two napkins together, but then make the knot disappear simply by tossing them in the air. The catch is that the knot with which you link the napkins is about as genuine as canned laughter. You start by twisting the ends of the two napkins and crossing the end of napkin A over the end of napkin B, but then, instead of forming an ordinary knot, you cross the end of napkin B around the end of napkin A above the lower part of napkin B. Pass the end of napkin B over and across the end of napkin A, bringing down the end of napkin A over napkin B and through the loop which has been created. Tighten it and everyone will think you've tied a perfectly ordinary knot. Holding aloft the free end of napkin A, show everyone the two napkins seemingly tied together then suddenly hurl them into the air and they will fall separately to the floor.

WHAT A CORKER!

Skill Level: ❼

You will need:

An empty wine bottle, a cork, a drinking straw

As we have discovered, even if you desert the pub for a wine bar, your scope for trickery is by no means diminished. First you need to relieve the wine bottle of its contents (there will be no shortage of volunteers willing to undertake this task) and then ask the bar staff whether they would be so kind as to furnish you with a drinking straw and a cork which is slightly too small for the bottle you have. The cork must be large enough to rest in the neck of its own accord. You then announce the aim of the trick – to blow the cork into the bottle. It may seem a fairly pointless exercise, but it's surprising what people will do after they've guzzled a bottle of wine. The natural tendency will be to blow as fiercely as possible, creating the sort of gust which brings havoc to Florida from time to time, but they will soon discover that blowing hard simply makes the cork pop out of the bottle. When everyone is breathless, produce your drinking straw and show them how it's done. For if you place the straw against the centre of the cork and blow steadily, the cork will drop into the bottle.

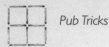

FORK BENDING

Skill Level: ⑦

You will need:

A table fork

Uri Geller's ability to bend all manner of cutlery has made him the bane of waiters everywhere. And with this stunt you can convince your friends that you too are blessed with the powers of Mr Geller. Hold the fork upright in both fists, left hand at the top and right hand at the bottom, just above the prongs which are pointing towards the audience. Press down the fork on to the table. Your actions should suggest that you are exerting great force, a feeling which could be communicated by shaking hands, the odd grimace and a bead or two of sweat. As you press down, allow the handle to fall back through your fingers so that it assumes a position approximately parallel to the table. Your fists and wrists obscure the dropping handle which is held in place solely by the little finger of the right hand, but, from the audience's head-on view, it will appear that you have bent the fork at right angles. When everybody looks suitably amazed, release your two-handed grip and show them that the fork hasn't bent one degree, let alone 90. They might not be too thrilled by your deception, but at least the waiter will be relieved.

TOPPLE THE BOTTLE

Skill Level: ❸

You will need:

A bottle, a paper bag

When you've exhausted every possible topic of conversation – football, music, politics, football, "Coronation Street", religion, football, the history of Pot Noodle, the 10 best places where you've thrown up, and football – here's a trick guaranteed to breathe life into a flagging evening. Produce an empty bottle from a paper bag – everyone had been wondering why you had been carrying them around all evening – stand the bottle on the table and the bag to one side and invite anyone to try and blow over the bottle. Their efforts will result in nothing more than sheer exhaustion which is when you step in to show them how it's done. Stand the bottle on the corner of the paper bag and blow into the bag. As the bag inflates, it knocks over the bottle. With everyone looking disgusted, it will be only a matter of seconds before someone asks: "So who do you fancy for the FA Cup?"

THE PENNY DROPS

Skill Level: ⑦

You will need:

An empty bottle, a match, a small coin

The preparation for this is actually more difficult than the trick itself. Bend a match into a V shape without breaking it and lay it across the top of an empty bottle which in turn is standing on a table. Place a 1p coin on top of the match and explain to your friends that they must try to get the coin into the bottle without touching the match, the bottle or the coin with any part of their anatomy and without rocking the table or blowing frantically. After a few have tried unsuccessfully (with predictable resorting to cheating), you can put them out of their misery. Simply pour a few drops of water on to the match at the centre of the V and, given a modicum of good fortune, it will open, allowing the coin to drop into the bottle.

WATER, WATER EVERYWHERE

Skill Level: ❼

You will need:

Two identical long-stem wine glasses

You should only attempt this trick if you are on extremely friendly terms with the landlord. Otherwise the sight of you balancing one of his precious wine glasses in your mouth might encourage him to order the rottweiler that passes as a door-man to feel your collar and eject you into the night air. In truth, this is more of a stunt than a trick. To set it up, you need two long-stemmed wine glasses, the sort in which the landlord serves his warm Chardonnay. Partly fill one glass with water. You can use any liquid but, in the likely event of spillage, the loss of water is less traumatic, not to mention cheaper, than scotch. Stand this glass on the table and then balance another identical glass, this time empty, upside down on top of it so that the two glasses are rim to rim. The challenge is to pour the contents of the lower glass into the upper glass without anyone touching the upper glass with their hands and without setting the upper glass on a firm surface (floor, table or chair) until the contents of the lower glass have been transferred into it. The way to do it is to bend over, pick up the base of the upper glass with your mouth and, stand-ing up, to tilt your head back slightly so that the glass is upright and the bowl of the glass is kept in position by your nose. Your hands are still free so you are able to pick up the other glass and pour the contents into the glass held between your teeth. It's not a pretty sight and is probably not something to perform on a first date, unless you want it to be your last.

STICKY DICE

Skill Level: ❼

You will need:

Three dice

Put the three dice down on a table and ask one of your fellow revellers to pick them up between tip of thumb and forefinger. Then tell him or her to drop the middle dice while still keeping hold of the dice on either side. It sounds easy, but it's not and attempts will invariably end in failure – until, of course, you show how it's done. Before your turn, sneakily lick your finger and thumb (this can be done under the pretence of removing a lump of pork scratching from your teeth). The moisture provides extra adhesion to your digits when you press them firmly on to the sides of the dice. Open your finger and thumb quickly, let the middle dice slip out and close them again immediately. You may wish to practise this trick for hours on end in the privacy of your own home, but only if you're a particularly sad individual.

CANDLE IN THE WIND

Skill Level: ❼

You will need:

A candle, a bottle

Unless you frequent a pub which has candles on the table, this trick is more suited to a wine bar. You position a sizeable bottle between yourself and the candle, press your face up to the bottle and blow against the surface. With any luck the candle should go out as if you have blown right through the bottle. The explanation is that when you blow on the surface of the bottle, your breath divides into two air currents which travel around the bottle and join up again on the other side to extinguish the candle. The really ambitious performer may care to try this trick with two or three bottles lined up between himself and the candle.

MATCHSTICKS

Skill Level: ⑦

You will need:

A book of matches

To set up this trick, take a book of matches and bend one match away from its original position, strike its head and blow out the flame. Place the book of matches inside your jacket pocket and head for the pub. When the conversation starts to flag, tell everyone that you are about to amaze them with a feat of magic. With your right hand, remove the book of matches from your pocket, holding the base between the finger and thumb so that the spent match, which is still attached to the book, is concealed by your thumb. Show the contents to your audience so that they can see all of the matches in the book are live. Now with your left hand, remove one of the live matches and strike it against the book. Close the book from front to back, pivoting the bent match so that it is now inside the book. Secure the cover and wave the lighted match around the book. Then pull back the cover to reveal that one match magically appears spent. While everyone tries to work out how it was done, say you'll put them out of their misery if somebody will refill your glass.

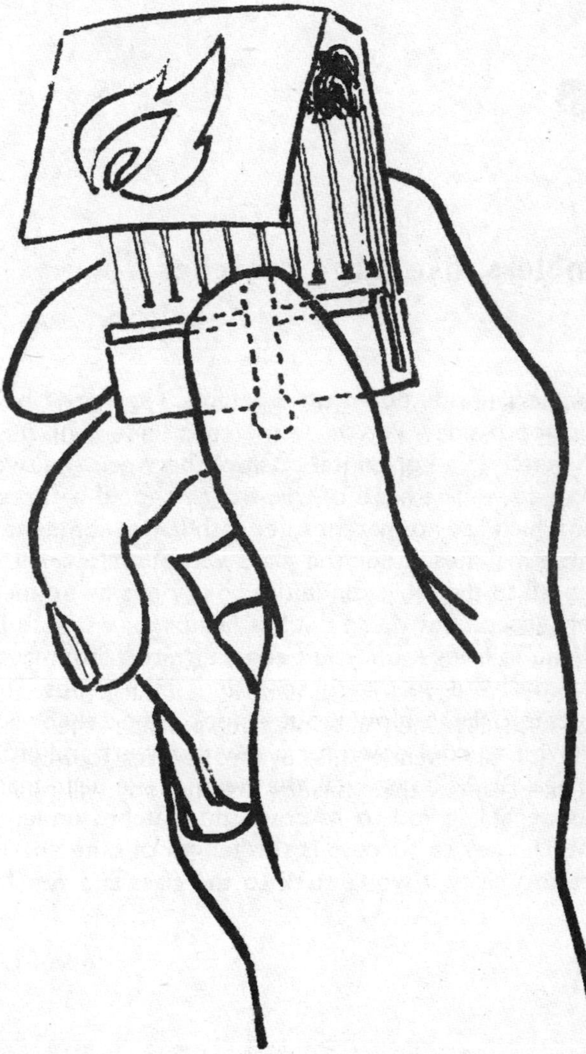

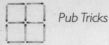

THE BIG MATCH

Skill Level: 🎱

You will need:

Two glass tumblers, five large matches

Place two glass tumblers upside down on the table. They don't have to be identical, but should be smooth-sided. Put three matches under one tumbler and carefully set the fourth match in a horizontal position between the two glasses, about a quarter of the way down. The head of this match should be pressed against the side of the tumbler which has no matches beneath it. Bet someone a pint that you can remove the three matches under the glass without allowing the match which forms the bridge to fall to the table. Since the solution is by no means obvious, he will almost certainly accept. But there's still a fair bit of work to be done before you can taste that pint. To bring it off, you need to ignite a fifth match and hold that against the head of the wedged match so that it too ignites. The moment the wedged match bursts into flame, blow it out – not too fiercely or you may dislodge the match. Then allow it to cool down for a few moments and lift the glass which its head is pressed against. All being well, the head of the dead match will stick to the side of the glass, enabling you to remove the matches under the other glass and claim your pint. The key to success is the length of time you leave the match to cool – if you are too hasty, it won't stick to the glass and you'll stay thirsty.

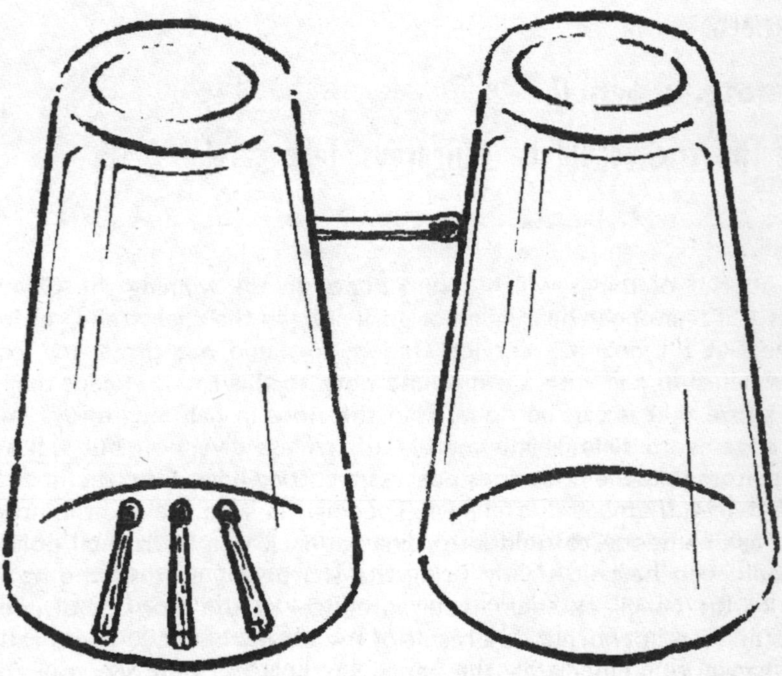

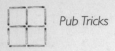

SNAP!

Skill Level: ⑧

You will need:

A banknote, a pencil

Warning: This trick could be dangerous. Take care!

There is no end of things which sound impossible – winning the Olympic 100 metres on a Spacehopper, hearing an original song in the charts, and getting a half-decent meal at a motorway service station, to name but three. You could add breaking a pencil in half with a five-pound note to this list… except that you are about to prove that it can be done. Fold the note in half lengthways, making as sharp an edge as possible. This is merely a harmless diversion, but will help convince spectators that the note does possess a cutting edge. Grip the note firmly at one end between thumb and forefinger (keeping the latter behind the note, out of sight) and ask someone to hold an ordinary pencil in a horizontal position. The pencil should also be held tightly. Bring the sharpened edge of the note swiftly down on to the pencil, extending your forefinger at the moment of impact. The pencil should snap in two, but as a result of the blow from your finger rather than from the banknote. Immediately the pencil has broken, withdraw your forefinger and nobody will suspect any subterfuge… unless a large bruise suddenly appears on your finger.

THE JAMAICA BOTTLE STUNT

Skill Level: ⑧

You will need:

A long-necked bottle

Warning: This trick could be dangerous. Take care!

If you're about as good a limbo dancer as Bernard Manning, you are advised to give this one a miss because it requires a great deal of athleticism. It is definitely not for someone whose idea of physical exertion is a game of chess or who has to have a lie down after reading the Sporting Life. The equipment consists of a long-necked bottle placed upright on the floor. Then, with your left hand holding your right ear, your right arm behind your back and your right hand holding your left foot, you have to bend down and pick up the top of the bottle in your mouth before straightening up again without losing either bottle or balance and without releasing your grip on your right ear or left foot. Phew!

RAISING THE MONEY

Skill Level: ⓫

You will need:

Five straws, a 5p coin

If you have the misfortune to find yourself in one of those large, modern feature-less chain pubs which serve identical meals and not only welcome families, but virtually refuse to serve you unless you've got children with you (it would be no surprise to see a sign: OVER-18s WILL ONLY BE SERVED WITH ALCOHOL IF ACCOMPANIED BY SOMEONE UNDER 10), you can at least pass the time with a trick or two involving drinking straws. For the one thing you can be certain of at such establishments is that there will be no shortage of free fun packs, badges and straws. So, after you've suffered the indignity of ordering Percy the Puffin's Kiddies Special, pluck five straws from a container and a 5p coin from your pocket and challenge anyone to lift four straws and the coin, using just one other straw. The secret is to build a solid construction. Place the first two straws in an X-shape on the table and put the coin on top of them where they meet in the middle. Put another straw vertically down either side of the X so that these two straws pass over and under the existing straws, but at opposite ends. Finally thread the fifth straw through the centre of the contraption horizontally so that it supports the other straws and the coin. Raise the horizontal straw gently and the whole thing should lift off the table. It does require a degree of dexterity so it's best not to ask the poor waitress whose turn it is to play Percy the Puffin to participate, especially if she's still wearing her flippers.

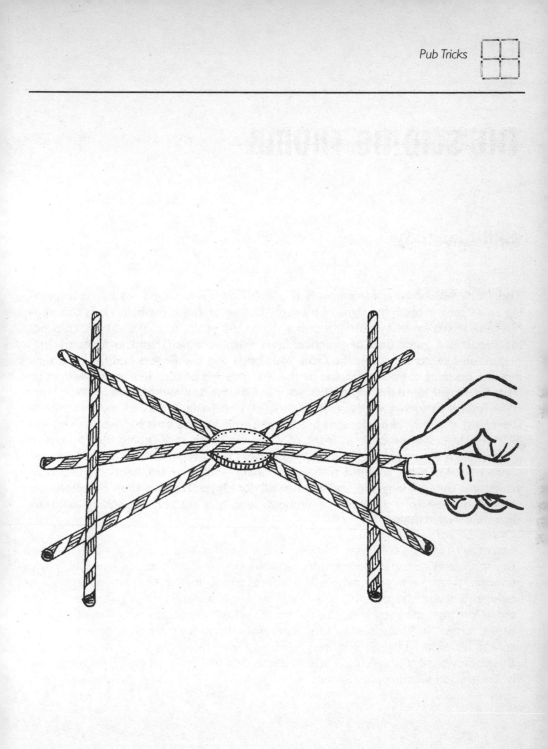

THE SLIDING THUMB

Skill Level: ⑨

There are several ways of removing the tip of your left thumb – such as inspecting an alligator's teeth for signs of plaque – but by far the most painless is this nimble trick much loved by pub illusionists down the years. To make it look convincing requires a great deal of practice. Start with your left hand in front of you, Napoleon-like, so that the palm faces your body and the fingers and thumb are all in a line pointing to your right. Cover the first knuckle of your left thumb with your right forefinger, bend the top part of your left thumb downwards and position your right thumb in such a way that its tip appears to replace that of the left thumb. Obviously this should be done as quickly and smoothly as possible, which is where all those hours of practice in front of a mirror come in. Keeping the thumbs in place, clench the remaining fingers of your right hand so that the audience can get a good view of what is about to happen. Finally hold your left hand still and slide your right thumb along the top of your left forefinger. You can then complete the return journey to a mixture of wonderment and horror, depending on how squeamish your friends are.

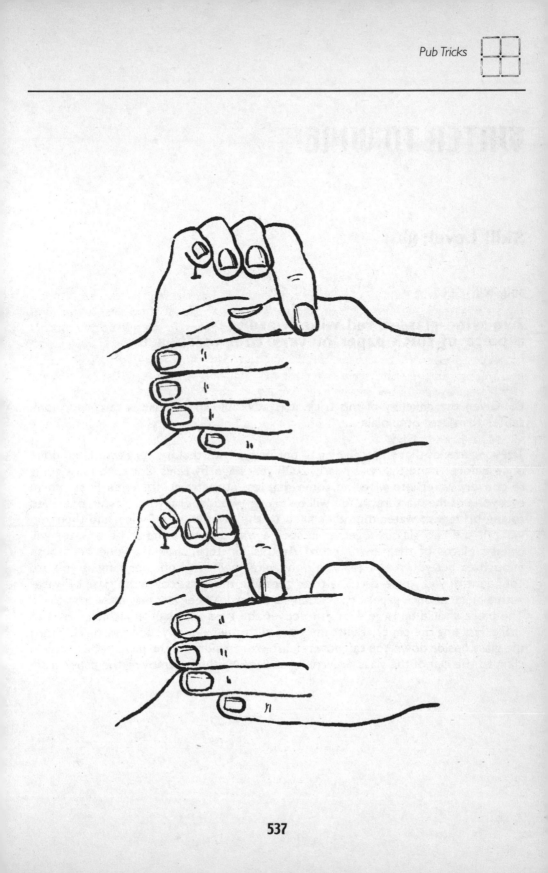

537

WATER TO WINE

Skill Level: ⑩

You will need:

**Two wine glasses, red wine, water,
a piece of thick paper or very thin cardboard**

P.S. Given the difficulty of this trick, it is advisable to practise with cheap plonk rather than best Beaujolais.

Tell your friends that you are going to perform a trick that has only ever been done once before… and that was nearly 2000 years ago, by Jesus Christ. You are going to convert water into wine and, somewhat less attractively, vice-versa. First inform everyone of the masterplan. You will be taking two identical wine glasses, one filled to the brim with water, the other filled to the brim with red wine, and then you will put the two glasses together in such a way that the wine and the water will change places of their own accord. At this juncture, should anyone be foolish enough to bet you that it can't be done, bite their hand off… as long as you are confident of your expertise. The trick goes like this. First cover the glass of water with a piece of thick paper or very thin cardboard. A beer mat may prove too thick. The piece should be large enough to cover the glass with half an inch all round to spare. Holding the paper against the glass with the palm of your hand, quickly turn the glass upside down. You can now release your hand from the paper which should cling to the rim of the glass, preventing spillage. Without removing the paper from the inverted glass, place that glass on top of the wine-filled glass in such a manner that the rim of the upper glass lines up precisely with the rim of the lower glass. With a steady hand (so perform this trick before you've drunk too much) slightly withdraw the paper from between the two glasses until there is a small space of not more than a quarter of an inch in width between the edge of the paper and the rims of the glasses. To the astonishment of your audience, the water will slowly descend through the opening you made by withdrawing the paper partition and will force the wine to rise through the same opening into the upper glass. This process will continue until all of the water has settled in the lower glass, previously occupied by the wine, and all of the wine has moved into the upper glass formerly occupied by the water. The problem of how to separate the two glasses after the trick has been completed without drenching everyone with water and wine should be for someone else to solve. You've earned a drink!

THE SNAPPING BAND

Skill Level: ⑨

You will need:

A long elastic band

This trick also requires considerable manual skill as you convince your friends that you have magically restored a broken elastic band. After showing everyone that there is nothing hidden in your hands, you grip the centre of the double band with your left hand and insert the thumb and forefinger of your right hand into the loop formed at either end. Stretch the band into a figure of eight with your left hand and move your right thumb and forefinger closer together, allowing the loop which was on your thumb to slide over on to your forefinger. Now put the remaining fingers on your right hand into the double loop and at the other side, do the same with your left hand, using your left thumb and forefinger to grip the loose knot which has been formed. The band should be stretched taut between your hands and, although double, should give the appearance of being single. Then remove your right forefinger from the loop and move the thumb and forefinger of both hands close together, still gripping the band tightly in its double loop. Pull your hands sharply apart and the band will make a snapping sound. As your hands separate to reveal the two ends of the double band, everyone will be convinced that it has broken. Ease your fingers from the band, enabling it to return to its single state, and cup it in both hands. Get someone to tap on your cupped hands with a pencil, beer mat or whatever happens to be around, and open them up to reveal a perfectly sound elastic band.

RAISE A GLASS

Skill Level: ⑩

You will need:

Two identical glasses, a small candle, a piece of paper

It's almost chucking out time. The bell has gone for last orders, the karaoke machine has been put away so you don't have to endure any more versions of 'White Christmas' sung by old Uncle Roy, and over in the corner a young man appears spell-bound by his girlfriend's eyes until you realize he is about to throw up over her top. But if you're in a pub or wine bar which has candles on the table, there is still one last trick you can perform before heading home. Put an empty glass tumbler on the table and challenge anyone to lift it off the table by magnetizing it with another tumbler. It's pretty difficult so, if you don't want to end up with a hefty bill for breakages, show them how it's done. Take a small piece of burning candle and place it in the bottom of the glass so that the flame doesn't extend beyond the rim. Then cover the glass with a piece of soggy paper and invert the second glass on top of the paper so that the rims of the two glasses are lined up precisely. As you lift the upper tumbler, the lower one should also rise from the table as if magnetized. If it doesn't work, you can always find another local, preferably one which doesn't have karaoke nights.

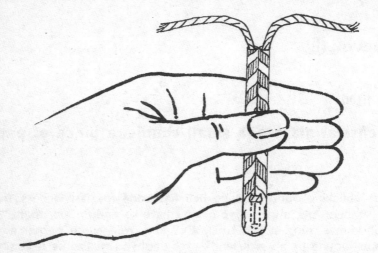

TRICKS WITH EVERYDAY OBJECTS

NAILED ON

Skill Level: ❶

You will need:

A box of coloured wax crayons

Sometimes a magician has to work overtime to make a trick appear convincing and only the brilliance of your patter will make this one seem anything other than a total con. The premise is promising enough – without looking, you are able to determine the colour of a chosen crayon – but the reality is mind-numbingly simple. You begin by putting a box of wax crayons on the table and, while your back is turned, ask someone to take one crayon from the box. Order the other crayons to be taken away and ask for the chosen one to be handed to you behind your back. At this stage, there is no way that you can have seen which crayon has been selected. Now for the chicanery. With the crayon behind your back, pretend that you are feeling it for inspiration (what rubbish magicians talk!), but instead dig the thumb nail of your right hand into the wax. Keeping the crayon out of sight behind your back, bring your right arm out in front of you and gesture to the person that he must really concentrate hard on the colour so that his thoughts can be transferred to you. With your arm before you, glance down at your thumb nail and the colour embedded there will be the colour of the crayon. As you put your hand back behind your back, craftily flick off the wax and name the colour. The only way this trick can fail is if you confidently shout 'red' before realizing you've got a blister on your thumb.

SYNCHRONIZED MATCHES

Skill Level: ❷

You will need:

A bowl of water, matches, a lump of sugar, a small piece of soap

Fortunately for the sake of our taste buds and our hygiene, most of us are able to tell the difference between a lump of sugar and a bar of soap. But if you do wake up one morning and suddenly realize that you are no longer able to differentiate between the two objects, here is a simple experiment to help you get through the day without foaming at the mouth every time you have a cup of coffee. Fill a bowl with clean water and carefully arrange a dozen or so matches in a circle on the surface so that it looks a bit like a clock face. For artistic reasons, the matches should be spaced apart equidistantly and should leave a clear circle of water in the centre. Now dip a lump of sugar into the centre circle and the matches should immediately move towards the sugar. Remove the sugar and replace it with a small piece of soap and the matches will instantly retreat back towards their original positions, the effect resembling a low-budget version of a Busby Berkeley musical. The reason for the erratic behaviour of the matches owes more to Tomorrow's World than Hollywood. When you put the sugar lump in the bowl, it absorbs some of the water and a small current of water flows towards the sugar, pulling the matches with it. The soap, on the other hand, weakens the surface tension in its immediate vicinity, allowing the stronger surface tension near the edges of the bowl to drag the matches outwards. So now you know.

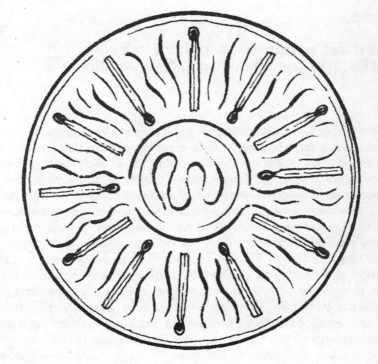

MAKE YOUR MARK

Skill Level: ❷

You will need:

Five identical envelopes, a pair of scissors, five chairs, five pieces of card, five pencils

By sheer magic (well, cheating actually), you can decipher the contents of a series of sealed envelopes as if blessed with X-ray vision. Beforehand, take five identical envelopes and make a tiny, almost undetectable, cut in each flap with a pair of scissors. The cuts should be in different positions along the flap – this is how you craftily work out which envelope belongs to which person. Ask your five friends (make sure you know their names) to sit in a line and, keeping the envelopes in order, hand one to each person so that whoever is sitting on the far right of the line receives the envelope with the cut on the far right and so on. Each cut must correspond to seating position. Then hand a pencil and a blank piece of card to each of the quintet and ask them to write down their name on the card and to seal it securely in their envelope. Ask someone to collect the envelopes and give them a good shuffle before handing them back to you. Of course, you can determine the owner of each envelope simply by looking at the cut and matching it to the chair position but, as with all the best tricks, you have to make it look much more difficult than it really is. Try gazing forlornly at the back of the envelope, praying for inspiration. You can even press the envelope to your forehead to imply that you are receiving extra-sensory messages. Finally call out a name and tear open the envelope to show that you have got it right. By the time you have done all five (although the last one is somewhat academic), there won't be a closed mouth in the house.

VERY DICEY

Skill Level: ❶

You will need:

Three dice, pencil and paper

Here is another opportunity to demonstrate your remarkable X-ray vision. Hand one of your friends three dice, a pencil and a piece of paper. Turn your back on him, and ask him to stack the dice in a pile and to add up the numbers on the five hidden faces (i.e., the bottom face of the top dice and the tops and bottoms of the other two dice). Tell him to write the total on the piece of paper and to put it in his pocket. You then turn around and, after nothing more than a quick glance at the dice, you are able to announce the figure on the piece of paper. It's easy really. The opposite faces of a dice always add up to seven and so the opposite faces of three dice add up to 21. All you need to do is look at the number on the upper face of the top dice and subtract it from 21. So if the top face shows six, the five hidden faces must total 15. If you need to remove shoes and socks to do this quick calculation, perhaps you should try a trick which doesn't involve any maths.

547

GET KNOTTED!

Skill Level: ❷

You will need:

An empty matchbox, a length of string

Take a piece of string and tie it in a single knot around a matchbox, the tray of which has been removed. You then push one end of the string back through the matchbox and also push the knot off the end of the box and into the empty cover. Hold the two ends of the string, pull it taut and the knot will magically disappear. This one requires a bit of practice because you must insert the string carefully and make sure the knot slides off the side of the box. It may not earn you your own TV series, but it's mildly impressive.

ASHES TO ASHES

Skill Level: ❷

You will need:

**Slips of paper, a pencil, a bowl,
an ashtray, a box of matches or a lighter**

This is a good trick to play when you've got a crowd of people – seven or eight at the very least. You get everyone present to call out the name of a football team and, as they do so, you appear to write each name on a separate slip of paper which you then fold over and put into a bowl or some other vessel. Next you ask one person to choose and take one of the slips without looking at it. Now you put the remaining slips into an ashtray and set fire to them (keep the soda syphon nearby in case the blaze gets out of hand). When all are burnt to a cinder, you study the ashes carefully for a minute or so before calling out the name of the team on the missing slip. The person unfolds the slip in his or her possession and shows it to everyone else to confirm that you have made the correct deduction. Far from being able to read ashes, your only power is that of deception. Instead of writing down all of the different team names on slips of paper, you simply wrote the same name on every piece. So you couldn't fail to get it right.

GUESS WHO?

Skill Level: ❷

This trick once more calls upon the services of a trusty assistant – a Robin to your Batman, a Laurel to your Hardy, a Renée to your Renata. While you are out of the room, the others choose one of their number to be identified on your return. And your boast is that you will be able to name that person. You enter the room again to be confronted with a sea of faces and no obvious clues, but, unbeknown to everyone else, one of those present is a mole whose task it is to pass on a hidden message. The clue is transmitted by the secret collaborator's stance – it will be exactly the same as that of the mystery person. Clearly if everybody speaks the same body language, you could be in trouble so you may have to wait until the chosen person makes a movement which can be mimicked by your assistant. Besides, you don't want to get it right too quickly, otherwise they will all know that it's just a trick.

SINKING SUGAR

Skill Level: ❷

You will need:

Four sugar lumps, a cup of tea or coffee

Stand three sugar lumps one on top of another in an empty cup. Carefully pour in sufficient lukewarm tea or coffee so that the top lump is just covered and the column remains undisturbed. If the beverage is too hot, the sugar will dissolve instantly and the column will crumble. Gather your friends around and tell them that you are going to make a lump of sugar float on the surface of your drink. Place it on top of the concealed pile of sugar lumps and there it will sit. With practice, you will even be able to command it to sink on cue as you correctly judge when the three supporting lumps do eventually dissolve.

DIRECTORY ENQUIRIES

Skill Level: ❸

You will need:

A telephone directory, pencil and paper

Only the most ardent trainspotter would dream of learning the telephone directory by heart, but after this trick your friends will be fully expecting to see you in bobble hat, tank top and anorak and armed with a copy of The History of Steam. In front of a captivated audience, take two minutes to flick through the local phone book and at the end declare that you have memorized the entire directory and are willing to be tested on it. In fact, you have only memorized one entry – the 10th name down in the left-hand column on page 89. Ask for a volunteer to test you, first confirming that no previous dialogue has passed between the two of you as to the contents of the directory. Say that he is going to do a simple sum to pick an entry at random. Hand him a pencil and paper and tell him to write down any three numbers. Ask him to reverse them and to subtract the smaller number from the larger one. If the answer to this is less than 100, tell him to add a zero to the front (such as 099). Next get him to reverse the new number and to add it to the previous number. As you know only too well, the answer will always be 1089.

For example:

$$764$$

$$- \quad 467$$

$$= \quad 297$$

$$+ \quad 792$$

$$= \quad 1089$$

OR

$$322$$

$$- \ 223$$

$$= \ 099$$

$$+ \ 990$$

$$= \ 1089$$

Tell him that the first two numbers in his answer refer to the number of entries down in the first column in a particular page and that the second two refer to the actual page number. Accordingly, he turns to page 89 and counts down 10 names in the first column. After a moment's meditation, you correctly state the name and address of that entry. Everyone will be mightily impressed... but hopefully not so impressed that they want to test you further.

THE AMAZING SUGAR LUMP

Skill Level: ❸

You will need:

A sugar lump, a soft pencil, a glass of water

Give one of your friends a soft pencil and ask him to write a number on a cube of sugar. Have the lump (the sugar not your friend) placed on a table with the number-side down so that you can't see what it is. Meanwhile pour some water into a glass, in the process dampening your right thumb. Pick up the sugar lump, still number side down, with your right forefinger at the top and your right thumb at the bottom. Press your moistened thumb firmly against the numbered base of the cube and the number should transfer on to your flesh. Drop the sugar into the glass number side down so that you still can't see it and, as it dissolves, ask your friend to reveal the number he wrote. Hold up your thumb to show the same number.

HIDDEN CASH

Skill Level: ❸

You will need:

An envelope, two identical sheets of paper, glue, a coin

Stick two identical sheets of paper together so that, to the naked eye, they look like one. If any edges are overlapping, trim them away. Fold each sheet an inch up from the bottom all the way along to create a flap. Leave the front flap empty, but slip a pound coin into the back flap before putting the paper into a suitable-sized envelope. Begin the trick by removing the paper from the envelope, taking care to show only the front side to the audience. Show them the inside of the envelope to convince them that nothing is lurking within and tip it upside down so that they know beyond doubt that the envelope is empty. Similarly, unfold the flap on the front side of the paper so that they can see that nothing is hidden. Fold the flap up again and replace the paper in the envelope. Now announce that by the miracles of modern science, you are going to conjure up a one pound coin. Take the paper from the envelope, this time showing only the back sheet to the audience, and open the flap to reveal the coin.

SIXTH SENSE

Skill Level: ❸

You will need:

Six everyday objects

This trick relies solely upon the art of deception and requires the services of an assistant. Arrange six everyday objects in a row on the table – say a comb, a pair of scissors, the remote control (if you can bear to be parted from it), a knife, a corkscrew and a potato peeler. As you are positioning them, announce which number refers to which object so that your assistant can make a mental note of each one. You then ask everybody present to concentrate really hard on one single object without telling you which one it is. In fact, so that you are unable to overhear their deliberations, you leave the room. On your return, all you need do is glance at your assistant who just happens to be leaning on the table. The number of fingers he has extended denotes the number of the chosen object. If his fist is clenched, the selected object is number six. You don't exactly have to be the Brain of Britain to work out the answer, although you could make life difficult for yourself by picking an assistant who recently lost three fingers in a bacon slicer.

SKIN DEEP

Skill Level: ❸

You will need:

An orange, an apple, a sharp knife, a large handkerchief

Some people can remember clearly what they were doing on the day Kennedy was assassinated – and, given that still nobody seems to know who was responsible, it's quite handy to have an alibi. Others are able to recall their precise whereabouts on the day England won the 1966 World Cup, or when Take That split up, or on the day when no furniture shop had a sale. Well, this trick is so awe-inspiring that it will have those who were privileged enough to witness it talking about it in the same breath as those other great historical events. They will proudly recall being there on the day you changed an orange into an apple! To make this stunning illusion work, you first need to use a sharp knife to peel the skin from an orange into four quarters. The orange must be peeled so that the skin remains joined at the top and when placed carefully on a table still looks intact from a distance. Take your orange and place it around an apple. Seeing it for the first time, your audience will think it is a perfectly ordinary orange because they won't be close enough to spot any cuts in the skin. Drape a large handkerchief over the orange and say that you'd rather have an apple. Grip the orange skin through the handkerchief, pull it away and slip the crumpled up handkerchief containing the orange skin into your pocket. All that is left on the table is the apple.

SUGAR TOSS

Skill Level: ❸

You will need:

Two lumps of sugar, an empty whisky glass

Ask one of your friends to hold an empty whisky glass in his hand with a lump of sugar wedged between his thumb and the side of the glass. Thumb and sugar should be approximately half-way down the side of the glass. Balance a second lump on top of the first one and bet him that, without using his other hand, he can't toss each lump into the glass, one at a time. It sounds easy enough and indeed it is at first, but it's the second lump which proves the downfall of so many. For, having tossed the first lump safely into the shallow glass, they find that it leaps out again when they try to repeat the feat with the second lump. After all of your friends have tried and failed, show them how the professionals do it. Toss the first lump into the air and catch it in the glass, but instead of tossing the second lump high, simply perform a minimal upward movement, release your thumb, allowing the sugar to fall, and bring the glass down to pouch the plummeting lump. Some may call it cheating and you can agree with them... over the drinks they've had to buy you.

THE SUSPENDED EGG

Skill Level: ❸

You will need:

An egg, a jug of water, salt

If you put an egg into a jug of water, it will sink to the bottom because it is denser than water, but if you add a quantity of salt to the water, stirring it until it dissolves, the egg will float to the surface because the salt has made the water denser than the egg. Better still, you can suspend the egg halfway up the jug. Remove the egg from the jug and pour away the brine until the jug is only half full, then fill it to the top with cold water. Lower the egg into the jug once more and it should sink through the water and float on the brine in the bottom half.

THE DATING GAME

Skill Level: ❸

You will need:

A calendar, pencil and paper

There are people who seem to go through their whole lives not knowing what day it is. They forget birthdays and anniversaries with monotonous regularity and even have to mark Christmas in their diary – that's if they can find their diary. If you have a box calendar (one in which each week of the month starts on a fresh line), there is a simple solution. Ask your forgetful friend to pick any month on the calendar and to draw a square around any four dates – two from one week and two from the next – without showing you. For, thanks to a cunning mathematical calculation, you are going to reveal precisely which four dates he has selected. First tell him to add up the four numbers and to tell you the result. Let us assume that he has chosen the 8th, 9th, 15th and 16th. Therefore his total will be 48. Now you divide by 4 (to leave 12) and then subtract 4 (to make 8). This will always be the lowest of the four chosen numbers. All you have to do now is add 1 for the next date (9) and add 7 to each of these first two dates (in this case 15 and 16). Unlike your friend's memory, it never fails.

THE UNSTOPPABLE EGG

Skill Level: ❸

You will need:

A raw egg, a plate

Here's another egg trick. Spin a raw egg on a plate and gently touch it with your finger to stop it. When the egg has stopped, remove your finger and, without any assistance from you, the egg will start spinning all over again. This is because when you put your finger on the egg, you stop the shell, but inertia keeps the white and the yolk spinning. So when you let go, the moving white and yolk make the egg start to spin again. This trick won't work with a hard-boiled egg because the contents are solid. It's none too effective with scrambled egg either…

THE TRICK ENVELOPE

Skill Level: ❹

You will need:

Five envelopes, five buttons, glue, a blindfold

From a set of five identical envelopes, take one and glue the inside of one corner. Then sort out five buttons, all the same size, but one a different colour from the other four. After leaving the glue to set, you can start the trick. Put the envelopes in a pile with the sticky one at the bottom. Hand the top four envelopes and the four identical buttons to four friends and ask each to drop a button in their envelope and to seal it. Allow them to examine the different button, assuring them that it is the same weight, shape and size as the others, and drop it into the trick envelope, sealing it. Shuffle the envelopes, keeping all the top edges together, and ask someone to blindfold you. To your stooges, it seems impossible to detect which contains the odd button, but all you have to do is hold each envelope in turn by the top edge and shake it from side to side. In four cases, movement will be unimpaired, but in the fifth the button will be unable to roll into the glued corner. This is the envelope containing the odd button. When you have found the trick envelope, declare that this is the one holding the different-coloured button, rip off your blindfold, tear open the envelope and parade the button in front of your fawning audience.

WELL, WELL

Skill Level: ❹

You will need:

A handkerchief, a pen

Form a circle with the thumb and forefinger of your left hand and drape a handkerchief over the top. Push a pen down into the circle to form a well in the handkerchief. Craftily open your thumb and forefinger slightly and this time push the pen down into the gap created at the side of the handkerchief next to the well. From your audience's viewpoint, it will look as if the pen is going into the well again. Pull the pen through from underneath and it will seem that the pen has gone right through the handkerchief. Then parade the intact handkerchief. It won't take everyone long to work out what you did, but you'll have enjoyed your moment of glory.

MAGIC GLASS

Skill Level: ❹

You will need:

A glass or see-through plastic cup, a handkerchief, a coin, two sheets of white paper, pencil, scissors, glue

Since this trick involves putting glue round the rim of a glass, you should avoid using the finest crystal and settle instead for a glass which came as a free gift from your local garage and which has been gathering dust in the loft along with promotional ashtrays, key-rings and pens that don't work. Alternatively, you could use a plastic cup provided it's transparent. Before meeting your public, you should place your glass upside down on a piece of white paper and draw a circle around the circumference of the glass. Cut out the circle and glue it to the mouth of the glass. It should fit precisely around the rim of the glass so, if there is any excess paper, you need to trim it off. Lay out another sheet of plain white paper on a table and place the glass on the paper. If your cutting has been up to scratch, the glass's paper lid will be undetectable. Now for the trick. Ask a friend to loan you a coin and boast that you have the ability to make it disappear and reappear at will, simply by using a magic glass. Put the coin on the sheet of white paper next to the glass. Produce a handkerchief, drape it over the glass and then lift the glass with the handkerchief and place it over the coin. Mutter a magic spell – like 'Liz Hurley's stripping off on the telly' (sounds magic to me) – and then remove the handkerchief. The coin seems to have disappeared although you know that it is lurking under the paper lid of the glass. If your friend looks crestfallen at having just lost 10p, assure him that there's no cause for alarm – you can magic it back just as easily. Drape the handkerchief over the glass again, say the magic words, lift the handkerchief and glass and, right on cue, the coin reappears. Your friend has kept his coin and you've kept a friend.

THE MYSTERY MATHEMATICIAN

Skill Level: ❹

You will need:

A small note pad with identical front and back covers, a pencil, a piece of paper

Take a small note pad, which has identical front and back covers, and on the back page write three three-digit numbers, such as 246, 759 and 333. Try to make the handwriting for each set of figures look different, suggesting that they were not written by the same person. Add the figures together (in this case 1338), write the answer on a piece of paper, seal it in an envelope and hand the envelope to someone for safe keeping. Then open the pad at the front page and ask three people each to write a three-digit number with the same pen you used. So far, so honest. Now comes the devious bit. Open the pad at the back page (where your numbers are), give it to someone completely different and ask him or her to add those numbers together. Finally ask the person with the envelope to open it and read out the number contained within. And, hey presto, they're exactly the same... because the numbers added up were the three that you wrote down originally.

THE MAGIC THIMBLE

Skill Level: ❹

You will need:

A thimble, a handkerchief

Put a thimble on the forefinger of your right hand and hold it up for all to see. Show everyone that your hand is otherwise empty. Keep your forefinger raised, but lower your remaining fingers. With your left hand, drape a handkerchief over your right, at the same time lowering your forefinger quickly and replacing it with your middle finger. Positioning your open left hand as a screen from the audience, poke your right forefinger under the edge of the handkerchief and, lowering your left palm slightly, grip the thimble in your palm and transfer it to the covered middle finger alongside. Swiftly bend the now thimble-free forefinger and sneak it back under the handkerchief. Move your left hand away and the audience will see one upright digit (your middle finger although they will still think it's your forefinger) covered by a handkerchief topped by a thimble. Unless they can find a more rational explanation, the thimble has penetrated the handkerchief. Let them examine handkerchief and thimble, both of which bear no indication of tampering. Reluctantly, they will have to conclude that you are a genius.

EGG AND BOTTLE

Skill Level: ❹

You will need:

An egg, a bottle, a piece of paper, a match or taper

First you need to find a bottle with a neck marginally narrower than a cooked egg from which the shell has been removed. An empty carafe is usually about right. Now you drop a crumpled up piece of paper into the bottom of the bottle and light it, either by dropping in a burning match or by using a taper. (It is important that you follow these instructions carefully and use a taper not a tapir, since trying to light a scrap of paper with a South American hoofed mammal only creates unnecessary difficulties.) Quickly, before the fire burns itself out, insert the shelled egg in an upright position so that it is wedged in the neck of the bottle. As the paper continues to burn, the egg should be sucked through the neck and into the bottle. It's all to do with the burning paper using up all the oxygen. With the egg acting as a sealant, the air pressure inside the jar is reduced and the egg sucked in. Whatever the reasons, it's a good stunt.

STEP INTO CHRISTMAS

Skill Level: ➍

You will need:

A Christmas or birthday card, a pencil, scissors

Of all the challenges likely to be thrown at you in life, stepping through a Christmas card isn't one of them. But it's always best to be prepared and so, mindful of that, here is how you can achieve the seemingly impossible. Take an ordinary greetings card (it doesn't have to be Christmas) and, keeping it closed, draw a dozen or so straight lines back and forth across the card. Line 1 should touch side A, but not side B; line 2 should touch side B, but not side A; line 3 should touch side A, but not side B; and so on with only alternate lines reaching the same edge of the card. Then carefully cut along the lines and open out the card. Now cut along the fold down the centre of the shredded card, taking care not to cut the strips of card at either end. Finally open the whole thing out and you should have created a circle of joined card large enough for you to step through.

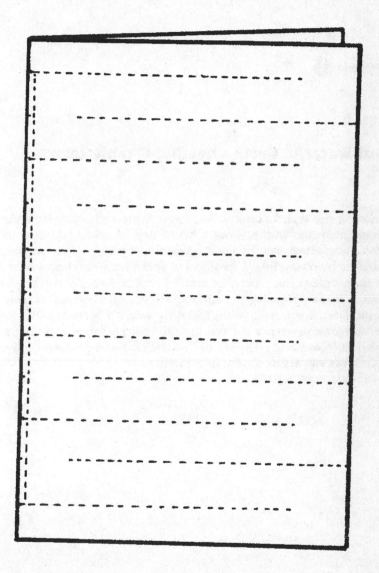

THE FLOATING NEEDLE

Skill Level: ④

You will need:

A bowl of water, a sewing needle, a table fork

This may not be the grandest magic feat ever witnessed – it is doubtful whether Houdini made his name with it – but a bit of dry ice and a roll of drums can do wonders for the most ordinary trick. Anyway making metal float on water is quite impressive in its own way. Take a small bowl and fill it with clean water. Then rest a sewing needle across the prongs of a table fork and very gently lower the fork onto the water, barely breaking the surface. As you take the fork slowly away, the needle should float. If you really want to know why, it's because, although the fork breaks the 'skin' on the water's surface, the skin quickly forms again under the needle to prevent it from sinking. The art of this trick is to be gentle with the fork. Any heavy-handedness will assuredly end in heartbreak.

THE MAGIC BOOK

Skill Level: ❹

You will need:

A hard-back book, eight 5p coins

For this trick, you need a hard-back book that has a little tunnel in the spine when you open it out flat. The tunnel must be wide enough to allow a 5p coin to slide in and out. When nobody is looking, slip a 5p coin into the tunnel. Place the book on a flat surface so that the coin doesn't fall out and count out another seven 5p coins to your audience. Make sure they can see that you have no other coins secreted about your person – under a thumb, up a sleeve, between fillings. Opening the book somewhere near the centre, ask your chosen stooge to place the seven coins in a row down the middle of the book. Close the book carefully, keeping it horizontal, and ask the stooge to hold his or her hands out. Then tip the coins into their waiting hands and watch for the look of amazement as the seven coins have turned into eight. Amid the avalanche of coins (rather like winning on a slot machine), nobody will notice that the extra coin has come from the spine of the book.

RAISE THE BOTTLE

Skill Level: ⑤

You will need:

A drinking straw, a bottle

The challenge here is to pick up an empty bottle without touching it, using nothing more than an ordinary drinking straw. The trick is to bend the straw back on itself at a point just over half the way up. Push the bent bit into the bottle and, with any luck, it will wedge itself against the side of the bottle, enabling you to lift it up gently. Position a couple of slip fielders, though, just in case it doesn't work.

THE DOUBLE BALLOON

Skill Level: ⑤

You will need:

Two different-coloured balloons, a pin

Stun your friends by changing the colour of a balloon before their very eyes. To carry off this amazing feat, you need to blow up two different-coloured balloons, one inside the other. Since you don't want anyone to know there is a second balloon, it makes sense to have a darker colour on the outside (red) with a paler colour (yellow) inside. Now announce that you are going to burst the balloon and make it change colour. Stick a pin in the outer red balloon, snatch the wizened remains, hide them in your hand and you are left with the still-inflated inner yellow balloon. The speed of the operation should be such that nobody spots the skin of the red balloon disappearing into your hand.

EVAPORATED MILK

Skill Level: ⑤

You will need:

A glass, white paper, cardboard, glue

The vanishing glass of milk always looks good on stage or on TV and therein lies its secret. For this is a trick which should not be attempted close-up, unless your audience are direct descendants of Mr Magoo. So position the table several feet away from the spectators and cover it with a tablecloth large enough to reach down to the floor at the back of the table, thus providing a screen. There are other things you need to do beforehand. First you must find an ordinary glass tumbler or indeed a plastic one, as long as it is transparent. Take a rectangular piece of cardboard and roll it into a tube so that it not only fits neatly over the glass, but is also slightly taller than it. Glue the edges of the tube together for that professional look. Next find a sheet of white paper and roll this into a tube which fits perfectly inside the glass. It should be an inch or two shorter than the glass and must reach right down to the bottom. Since this white paper is going to play the part of the non-existent milk, make sure you keep the join away from the audience's view. When you have completed your preparations, it's showtime. Stand the glass with the white paper inside it on the table. Don't move the glass around or some bright spark will cotton on to the fact that the milk is solidified. Show the cardboard tube to everyone so that they can see there's nothing hidden inside and place it over the glass of 'milk'. Now announce that you are going to make the milk disappear. Utter a few magic words and lift the cardboard tube up from the glass, at the same time using your fingers to pull the white paper clear too. As everyone reacts in astonishment, momentarily rest the cardboard tube on the back edge of the table, allowing the paper to fall to the floor (its descent hidden from the audience by the tablecloth). Keeping hold of the cardboard tube, pull it towards you and pass it and the glass around so that everyone can check that there is nothing untoward about either item. If only they knew…

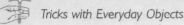

THE SWINGING VASE

Skill Level: ⑤

You will need:

A small, narrow-necked vase, a length of rope, a small rubber ball or rubber eraser

Warning: This trick could be dangerous. Take care!

No matter how enthusiastic you are about certain tricks, it is hardly worth destroying family heirlooms to perform them. Just as you wouldn't play noughts and crosses on a Rembrandt or make a doorstop out of a Chippendale, so you shouldn't use a half-decent vase for this trick. So put the Ming away and opt instead for some ghastly ornament which is destined for the next car boot sale. You also need a small rubber ball or a rubber eraser, the size of which is solely dependent on that of the neck of the vase. For the ball or eraser must be large enough to wedge itself in the neck of the vase, but small enough to pass through the neck with a gentle shove. In general terms, the smaller the vase the better. To prepare for the trick, push the ball or eraser through the neck into the bottom of the vase. Since the rubber item must not be seen by the audience, don't choose a cut glass vase. Explain that you are going to perform the amazing Swinging Vase trick whereby an ordinary vase will be suspended in mid-air by an ordinary length of rope.

Show everyone the piece of rope, which should be about 1ft long, so that they can see that there's no Blu-tack or chewing gum stuck to the end and then lower part of the rope into the vase. Next turn the vase upside down. Do this quickly so that nobody can hear the ball or eraser rattling around inside. If all goes well, the hidden ball should roll into the neck and wedge the rope firmly in place so that when you let go of the rope, it will hang from the neck of the vase. Just to make sure, tug the rope towards you a little. This should pull the ball further into the neck. Now for the moment of truth. Turn the vase the right way up again, let go of the vase entirely and only hold on to the end of the rope. You should now be able to use the rope to swing the vase back and forth. Everyone will be mightily impressed, but you still need to conclude matters without giving the game away. So as you pull the rope out, cup your hand over the mouth of the vase and allow the ball to drop into your palm. Keep the rubber ball hidden in your fist and then slip it into your pocket while allowing your fans to inspect the vase and rope.

BALLOON SWITCH

Skill Level: ⑤

You will need:

Four balloons (two of each colour), two paper bags, a pencil

Here is another balloon baffler. Prepare for it by acquiring four balloons, two of each colour (say purple and green) and, using something like the blunt end of a pencil, push one purple balloon inside one of the green balloons and vice-versa. Don't inflate the balloons and make sure that in both cases you leave the tip of the inner balloon protruding. Now take two ordinary brown paper bags and on the outside of one bag write 'purple' and on the other write 'green'. Hold the balloons by the neck so that the protruding tips of the inner balloons are concealed from the audience. All they can see is one deflated purple balloon and one deflated green balloon. Allow everyone to inspect the bags for booby traps and then, still keeping the necks hidden, drop the purple balloon into the bag marked 'purple' and the green balloon into the bag marked 'green'. To gasps of disbelief, declare that you are about to make the purple balloon jump into the green bag and the green balloon perform similar somersaults into the purple bag. Blow on the purple bag and, gripping it by the sides so that you have a firm hold on the balloon, pull out the inner green balloon by its neck. Wave it aloft to the audience, quickly crumpling the bag and the purple balloon contained within. Repeat the procedure with the green bag, pulling out the purple balloon to prove that the two balloons have swapped bags just as you promised.

RECYCLED PAPER

Skill Level: ⑤

You will need:

Two paper tissues, a box of matches, an ashtray

In these days of conservation and green issues, recycling is an important issue. And nothing makes you think 'green' more than a paper tissue, particularly if it's been used a lot. With this trick, you achieve every Amazon Rain Forest PR man's dream by appearing to make a burnt-out tissue rise from the ashes and become new again. If only it were that simple. For sad to say there is no simple solution – the trick relies upon the use of a second hidden tissue masquerading as the original. The audience see you hold up a perfectly ordinary tissue. On the table are an ashtray and a half-open matchbox, containing, not unreasonably, a few matches. But only you know that the box is half open for a very good reason because secreted in the sleeve of the box behind the tray is the second paper tissue. Next you crumple the first tissue and put it in the ashtray. Placing the palm of your right hand at the rear of the matchbox, you pluck out a match with your left hand and strike it against the side of the box. Everybody's eyes will be on the lit match which means that they probably won't pay much attention to you shutting the box, a movement which pushes the second tissue into your right hand. As soon as this happens, you clench your right fist and then set fire to the first tissue in the ashtray. After that tissue has been reduced to a cinder, you reach your right hand into the charred remains, rummage around and open your hand to reveal a perfectly recycled tissue.

THE KNOTTED HANDKERCHIEF

Skill Level: ⑤

You will need:

A handkerchief

When worn on the head, the knotted handkerchief is one of the great fashion accessories of the British seaside holidaymaker. You can see them every heatwave on promenades from Blackpool to Bognor, as much a part of the scenery as donkey rides, kiss-me-quick hats and dodgy hamburgers. The knotted handkerchief is also the end product of this trick as you challenge all-comers that they won't be able to tie a knot in an ordinary handkerchief without letting go of the ends. The theory is straightforward enough. You fold one corner of the handkerchief across to the opposite corner and then fold your arms in front of you. Keep your hands in this position and pick up the ends of the handkerchief. Maintaining your grip on the ends of the handkerchief, unfold your arms and you should finish up with a knot in the middle of the handkerchief. But don't bet your mortgage on it until you've practised it a few times.

ROLLING PIN

Skill Level: ⑤

You will need:

A safety pin, a handkerchief,

Spread a handkerchief out on a table and fasten a safety pin near the edge of the handkerchief which is closest to you. Roll the safety pin over to the left three times, the result being that the handkerchief also rolls over. Press your left hand firmly on the handkerchief to keep it in place and hold the protruding end of the pin between the thumb and forefinger of your right hand. Now pull down sharply and the pin comes away without tearing the handkerchief even though it is still closed. You may need to practise this, though.

CHANGING THE CUTLERY

Skill Level: 8

You will need:

A spoon, a fork, a table napkin, a tablecloth

Cover the table with a cloth and place a spoon on the cloth. Lay out a table napkin in a diamond shape so that the centre of the napkin covers the spoon. On top of the napkin and directly above the spoon, put a fork. Fold the corner nearest you (corner A) over to the opposite corner (corner B), leaving it an inch or so short. Attribute this to carelessness rather any pre-conceived plan, but the shortfall ensures that the spoon remains hidden beneath the napkin. Hold the two concealed items of cutlery through the napkin with both hands and roll the napkin back towards you (the tablecloth will muffle the sound of the spoon) until corner A has made one complete rotation of the tightened roll. Both corners will now protrude from the roll. Placing one finger firmly on corner A, pull corner B sharply towards you and, by magic, the fork has changed into a spoon. Gather up the evidence before anyone realizes that the fork is now beneath the rolled-up napkin.

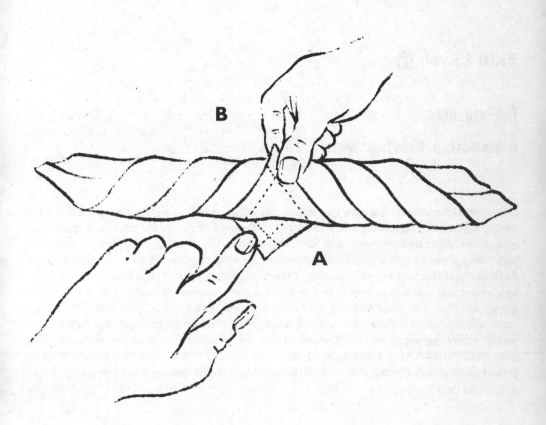

THE SLIDING PENCIL

Skill Level: ⑤

You will need:

A pencil, a scarf, a jacket

You need to wrap up for this game, not only because there'll be a chill in the air if you get it wrong, but because a jacket is a definite requirement. Hold a pencil up and allow everyone to inspect it for authenticity. Once they are satisfied that it is definitely an ordinary pencil and not some cunning disguise like an HB stick insect, hold the pencil in your right hand and cover it with a scarf. Magicians usually favour brightly coloured silk scarves, but if all you can lay your hands on is a Mansfield Town scarf or the Rupert Bear one that Granny Vera knitted you last Christmas, that will have to do. With the scarf draped over pencil and hand, thrust your forefinger stiffly skywards so that the audience will assume that it is the pencil poking into the material. At the same time, allow the pencil to slide into the sleeve of your jacket. Remove the scarf and, would you believe it, the pencil has vanished.

CATCH A FALLING KEY

Skill Level: ⑤

You will need:

A key, a tea towel

The most important item of equipment for this trick is not listed above because it's the services of a willing assistant who has been primed beforehand as to what to do. Make sure your friends are sitting around a table. Take a single key and a tea towel and drape the tea towel over the key. Pick up the key through the tea towel and hold it up for all to see. Grip the key at either end so that its presence is clearly reflected in the position of your fingers. Now lower the towel over the lap of one of your friends and ask her to feel under the towel and confirm that the key is still there. Do the same with a second person. Both will verify that the key remains under the towel. Then select, apparently at random, a third volunteer, but this time it is your clandestine accomplice. Once again hold the towel over her lap, but make sure that the sides of the towel reach down to her legs so that a screen is formed. As she reaches underneath, she gently removes the key and hides it in her lap. For their part, your fingers, which were holding the key, stay in the same position, implying that the key is still beneath the towel. After your accomplice has confirmed that the key is still there, you suddenly whip the towel into the air and reveal that the key has vanished. But that's only part of the trick. For now you promise to make the key return. Position your fingers as before over the towel as if the key is underneath and return to your assistant. Once again hold the towel over her lap so that the sides act as a screen and ask her to feel whether the key has reappeared. As she reaches under the towel, she simply replaces the key and exclaims her astonishment. You then pull away the tea towel to show that the key has materialized again, just as you promised it would.

587

MAGAZINE MAGIC

Skill Level: ⑥

You will need:

Nine magazines, pencil and paper

This is one of the more expensive tricks in this book because you need nine magazines. You might be able to borrow three from the doctor's waiting room (if you don't mind a pre-decimalization issue of Woman's Realm extolling the virtues of Oxydol and Tide), but the remaining six must be three pairs of duplicates so you will probably need to buy those. If possible, the six different magazines should each have highly distinctive covers so that they are easily recognizable. To prepare for this mind-reading extravaganza, you need to remove the covers from the three duplicate magazines and replace them with the covers from three of the different ones so that you are left with six magazines, all with different covers, but the copy inside three of them is identical with that of the other three! Make a mental note of which pairs of covers contain the same material. Now that your preparation is complete, you can display your mind-reading prowess. Hold up the six magazines and point out that they are all different which, of course, the audience can see for themselves by the covers. But don't let them inspect the magazines or they might become a shade suspicious to find that a cover of Philately Monthly contains a copy of Loaded! Even an explanation that it is a special edition of Philately Monthly in which stamp collectors nominated their favourite sexual fantasies is unlikely to convince. Ask one of your friends to pick any of the magazines and to think of a two-digit number, and tell it to you. This, you explain, will denote the page number, line and word. So if he chooses 26, this will be the sixth word on the second line of page 26. To underline this, casually pick up the magazine which you know to be identical to the one which your friend has selected. As you explain how it works, you turn to page 26 of this duplicate magazine and silently remember the sixth word on the second line, emphasizing that this demonstration is merely to reiterate the rules of engagement. When you have done that, put down the magazine and ask your friend to concentrate hard on the word. Say that when your friend's thoughts are transferred in your direction, you will write down the word. Duly write down the word you remembered from the duplicate and fold the slip of paper. Then ask him to name the word, at which you open out the paper and reveal the very same word. Uncanny.

PENETRATION

Skill Level: ⑥

You will need:

Three polystyrene cups, two paper pellets

By the simple act of tapping your finger, you will appear to make a small paper pellet pass through an ordinary polystyrene cup to the table below. The catch is that one of the cups already contains a hidden paper pellet. Begin by finding a colourful page in a magazine and tear off sufficient to make two paper pellets. These should be of the same size and colour. Take three polystyrene cups and put one of the paper pellets inside one of the cups. Stack the three cups on the table, mouth side up, ensuring that the one with the hidden pellet is in the middle. So to the performance. After explaining your intentions, show the audience the base of each cup so that they can see there are no holes. Then invert each of the cups in turn and line them up on the table. This should be done smoothly and swiftly so that nobody is able to see the hidden pellet. The cup containing the pellet should be in the middle of the row of three. As a result of the inversion, the pellet is now, of course, underneath the cup. Pick up the other paper pellet and put it on top of that centre cup before stacking the remaining two cups on top. So you now have a stack of three polystyrene cups and all the audience know is that there is a paper pellet on top of the bottom one. Tap your finger on the top cup and announce that you will make that pellet force its way through to the table. Lift off all three cups and there indeed is the pellet on the table beneath the bottom cup.

UPRIGHT CORKS

Skill Level: ⑥

You will need:

Six corks, a bowl of water

When dropped in water, corks naturally tend to float on their side so the trick here is to get six corks to float upright. The secret is to hold all six corks together in an upright cluster. Dip them in the bowl of water and hold them submerged for two minutes so that they are thoroughly soaked. If you then raise them gently to the surface, they should stay upright.

POLO

Skill Level: ⑥

You will need:

Two Polo mints, a piece of string, a pencil, a handkerchief

With a Polo mint hidden in your right hand, give one of your friends another Polo mint and a length of string and ask him to pass the string through the mint and then to hold the two ends of the string. Now that the Polo is perched astride the string, challenge anyone to remove the mint from the string without cutting the string or letting go of the ends. Of course, nobody will be able to manage it, but you insist that the solution rests with a handkerchief and a pencil. Let the spectators see that both items are perfectly ordinary and then drape the handkerchief over the mint on the string. Slide both hands under the handkerchief and place the second mint (the one hidden in your right hand) on the string and insert the pencil between it and the string. The presence of the pencil causes the mint to be held in place even though it is not attached to the string. Then put one hand over the first mint, drag it along to the end of the string and take both ends from the volunteer. As you do so, conceal the mint in your hand. Holding both ends of the string, you claim that if your volunteer were now to remove the handkerchief and the pencil, the mint would be released from the string... and that is precisely what happens. Everyone looks puzzled and you eat the evidence.

THE WORD

Skill Level: ⑥

You will need:

A thick paperback book, a business card

This is another impressive exhibition of mind-reading, performed with a thick paperback book and a business card. Show the book to one of your friends and ask him to flick through it to verify that it is the genuine article and has not been tampered with in any way. Underline the fact that there are a couple of hundred pages and a few hundred words on each page. This will make your eventual revelation seem all the more incredible. Ask your volunteer to scan the book, to choose any page and to insert a business card at that page. Before he hands the book back to you, tell him to remember the page number and also the last word on that page. By sheer concentration, you will name both the chosen page number and the last word on it. Holding the book in your hand, flick through the pages as if you are innocently emphasizing just how many pages and words there are. The presence of the business card will cause your thumb to jump at that page, allowing you a split second to make a mental note of the page number and the last word before you continue apace through the rest of the book. Obviously you need to practise this action so that it looks smooth and undetectable. If you pause for an eternity at the chosen page or have to put glasses on, it rather detracts from the element of surprise. When you have finished leafing through the pages, ask your volunteer to concentrate hard on the page number and final word. After appearing to struggle for a few moments (a hint of fallibility always makes the performance seem more genuine), rejoice in the news that your volunteer's thoughts have been successfully transferred to you and reveal the answers. While you're at it, you could mention that you've picked up on another of his thoughts. Does his girlfriend know that he fancies the barmaid at the Nag's Head?

THE TORN TISSUE

Skill Level: ⑥

You will need:

Two paper tissues

Prepare for this trick by folding a paper tissue six times until you are left with just one-64th of the original surface area. Press the squashed tissue against one corner of another ordinary tissue and grip it firmly in place between the thumb and forefinger of your left hand. Hold the unfolded tissue aloft, keeping the folded one hidden at the back, and announce that you are going to rip the paper tissue into strips and then magically restore it. Keeping the folded tissue in place with your left hand, start tearing the other tissue into strips with your right hand. When you have torn everything except the corner where the folded tissue is hidden, gather all the pieces in your left hand and blow on it as magicians are wont to do. Then with your right hand, reach into the torn pieces and pull out the folded tissue, allowing it to open up in your hand. At the same time keep the torn strips hidden in your left hand. To those who are easily pleased, it will look as if you have restored the torn tissue.

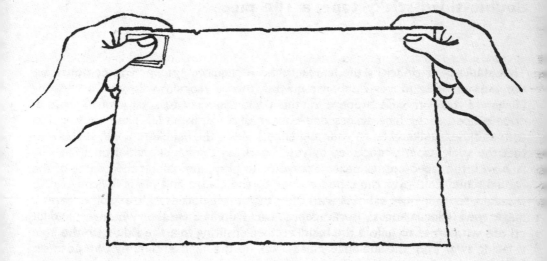

THE VANISHING COIN

Skill Level: ⑥

You will need:

A handkerchief, a small piece of double-sided sticky tape, a 10p piece

That staple of magic tricks, the handkerchief, is required again as you demonstrate the art of making money disappear quicker than a vengeful wife with a cheating husband's credit card. To prepare for this trick, you need to stick a small piece of double-sided sticky tape across one corner of a handkerchief. Then show a 10p coin and the handkerchief to your audience, holding the handkerchief in such a way that the sticky tape is concealed by your hand. Lay the handkerchief on a flat surface with the taped corner nearest to you and place the coin in the centre of the handkerchief. Fold over the taped corner to the centre and press it firmly on to the coin, repeating the process with the other three corners. Utter some form of magic spell ('Hocus Pocus', 'Abracadabra', 'Una Paloma Blanca' or whatever) and lift up the last corner to unfold the handkerchief, ensuring that the side with the coin is facing away from the audience. Finally pick up the handkerchief by two corners, including the one with the coin now stuck there, to reveal that the coin has vanished completely… because your finger and thumb are covering the coin.

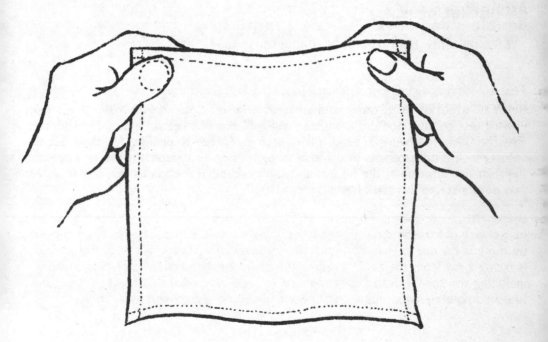

SWING THE BUCKET

Skill Level: ⑥

You will need:

A bucket of water

Warning: This trick could be dangerous. Take care!

Half fill a bucket with water and swing it in a full circle. If you make the bucket swing fast enough, none of the water will spill out. The reason is suitably scientific. As the bucket is swung around, it is constantly forced to change direction, but the water inside still attempts to travel in straight lines. As a result, the water is pressed against the interior of the bucket and can't escape. For obvious reasons, it is best to demonstrate this trick in the garden.

HEMMED IN

Skill Level: ⑥

You will need:

A small coin, a large handkerchief

Before performing this vanishing coin routine, you need to slip a small coin – something like a 5p piece – into the hem of a large handkerchief. Then ask to borrow another coin of the same denomination from one of your friends. Holding the handkerchief in your right hand and the borrowed coin in your left, give the impression that you are wrapping the coin somewhere in the middle of the handkerchief, but instead palm it in your left hand at the fleshy bit between the base of your thumb and forefinger. With the handkerchief still folded over, hand it to your volunteer so that he can feel the coin tucked in the hem. Not unreasonably, he will assume it is the coin which he has just given you. Once he has assured everyone that the coin is still wrapped in the handkerchief, you announce that you will make the 5p disappear. Whip one corner of the handkerchief through the air in your most theatrical manner and hold up both sides for all to see. It will seem that the coin has vanished although, unless your handkerchief has got loose stitching, it will still be tucked safely in the hem.

WITH THIS RING

Skill Level: ⑦

You will need:

A small ring, a piece of string, a large handkerchief

Take a piece of string, about a metre and a half (5ft) long, and show it to the assembled throng. Then produce a wedding ring or, if you don't want to risk losing the ring, a metal washer – unless of course you bought the ring from a market stall, in which case the washer is probably more valuable. Fold the string in half and push the loop through the ring. Push the two ends of the string through the loop and pull them tight. Holding the ring in one hand, ask a volunteer to clasp the two ends of the string. Pick up a handkerchief and drop it over the hand holding the ring. Put your free hand under the handkerchief, in such a way that the ring remains hidden from view, loosen the string a little and slide the loop over the ring, thus freeing ring from string. Finally ask your volunteer to pull the string and, as he or she does so, the empty string emerges from beneath the handkerchief and you are left holding the ring.

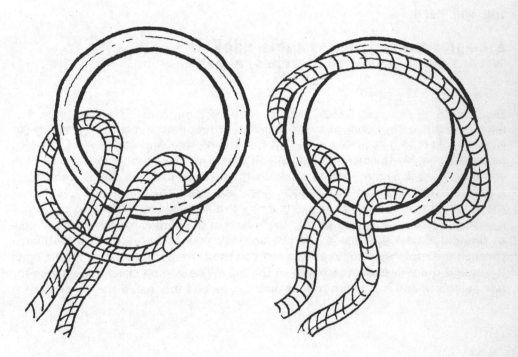

THE UNBROKEN MATCH

Skill Level: ⑥

You will need:

A large handkerchief or table napkin with a hem, a box of matches, a pen

To set up this trick, you need to slip a match unseen into the hem of a napkin (or large handkerchief) and make sure that it stays in place. And don't forget in which part of the napkin the match is hidden. You then produce a box of matches and ask someone to pick a match and to mark it with a pen so that it is clearly identifiable. Open out the napkin so that everybody can see that it is empty and fold it over the selected match. Now you need to bring the first hidden match into play, casually manoeuvring the napkin so that the match in the hem is roughly in the middle of the folded napkin. When it is in position, ask your volunteer to feel the match through the napkin and to break it in half. You then shake the napkin in the air, open it out and the unbroken match falls to the floor. The person checks the match for her pen mark and is stunned to find that it is indeed the match she chose earlier.

HIGH AND DRY

Skill Level: ❼

You will need:

A saucer of water, a coin, a glass, paper, a match

Place a small coin – something like a 1p piece – on a saucer and cover it with water. Bet your friends that you can remove the coin from the saucer with your fingers, but without getting them wet. Tipping up the saucer or sucking the water through a straw are not permitted although both methods are considerably easier than the one which follows. Drop a piece of paper into an empty glass and set fire to the paper. Then invert the glass on the saucer alongside the coin, positioning the glass so that there is a small gap at the bottom between it and the saucer. The flame quickly burns up all the oxygen inside the glass to form a partial vacuum, as a result of which the water is sucked into the glass, leaving the coin high and dry on the saucer. Simply pick up the coin to win the bet.

MONEY TO BURN

Skill Level: ⑦

You will need:

**An envelope, a banknote, a
box of matches, an ashtray, a pen**

If you are blessed with a sadistic streak, you'll love this trick where you watch an innocent volunteer squirm with discomfort at the thought that you have destroyed his hard-earned cash. Maybe in the hands of Paul Daniels or Wayne Dobson, he would be confident that the note would somehow reappear intact, but with a novice like you he's not so sure. His fears may not be groundless, so practise this a few times with a slip of paper instead of a banknote until you get the hang of it. To prepare for the trick, you need to make a small slit, about an inch and a half long, in the address side of an ordinary white envelope. Place the envelope flap side up on the table so that the slit is hidden from view. Arrange an ashtray adjacent to the envelope. Also put a box of matches in your left trouser pocket. Start proceedings by borrowing a banknote (the higher the denomination the better) from a reluctant volunteer and ask him to sign it clearly with a pen for future identification. Show the note to the audience so that everyone can see the telltale mark. Fold the note in half three times so that you end up with a small packet. Pick up the envelope with your left hand in such a way that your fingers cover the slit and with your right hand, pull back the flap and push in the banknote so that part of it passes through the slit to the outside of the envelope. Making sure that the protruding note and the slit are still concealed by your fingers, seal the envelope. Next transfer the envelope from your left hand to your right, using the fingers of your left hand to drag the protruding note into the palm of your hand where it must remain hidden. With your right hand, place the envelope flap side up on the table once again. Meanwhile reach your left hand into your trouser pocket, deposit the banknote there and pull out the box of matches. Hold the envelope over the ash-

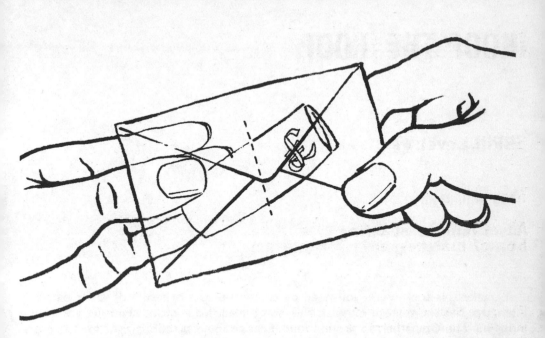

tray, showing the flap side to the audience, and set fire to it with a match. When the envelope has been reduced to a pile of cinders, rummage through the debris with a horrified look which strongly implies that the banknote has not survived its ordeal. Offer profuse apologies, promising to get it right next time, and ask your volunteer whether there is anything he would like by way of recompense – maybe the signed photo of Anne Robinson from your collection of celebrity winkers. Now that he is almost certainly incandescent with rage, agree that you'll have to reimburse him financially. Retrieve the banknote from your pocket, open it out and hand it to him. As he takes it, point out the signature. While he stands mouth ajar at the realization that it is his note, hold it up so that everyone else can see what a clever boy you are.

LOOP THE LOOP

Skill Level: ⑦

You will need:

Two lengths of string

To make this trick work, you need to cut two pieces of string of vastly differing lengths. The short piece must be able to fit inside your mouth without you looking like The Godfather, so around four inches should be about right for the average-sized orifice. The other piece can be three or four times longer. Before confronting your audience, you need to loop the short piece and the long piece together and cover the loop with your thumb. The first thing the audience will see is you holding in your right hand what appear to be two parallel pieces of string of the same length. What they don't know is that your thumb is concealing the loop linking the two pieces and that consequently the two top ends belong to one piece of string and the two bottom ends to the other piece. Tell the audience that you are going to make the two lengths join into one and that the only way to do that is to apply a touch of magic spit (this will have the added advantage of making some people turn away in disgust, rendering them unable to witness your sleight of mouth). Suck on the two top ends and bring your right hand up to your mouth so that it not only hides the loop, but also the fact that you are about to put the whole of the shorter piece into your mouth. With the loop broken, you pull the long piece free and, in the eyes of the audience, the two lengths have joined up. The shorter piece meanwhile remains in your mouth while you pray that nobody asks you to make a victory speech.

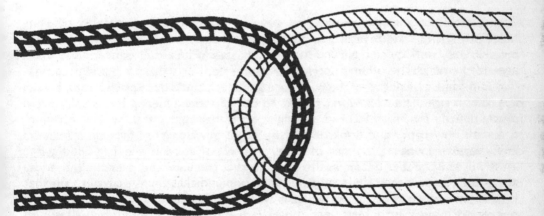

THE TABLECLOTH TRICK

Skill Level: ⑦

You will need:

A sheet of paper, a polystyrene cup, water

At one time or another, most of us have probably tried some form of The Tablecloth Trick… and have had to pay for the broken crockery afterwards. It all looks so easy on TV. The table is laden with glasses, plates, cups, saucers and bottles and the magician saunters up, gives the tablecloth one sharp tug and it comes away in his hand, leaving all of the glassware and china standing in place. Not a crack or a chip in sight. The trick works thanks to our old friend inertia, but is still notoriously difficult for an amateur to get right. So rather than risk a future of having to eat off newspaper and drink out of the dog's bowl, practise first on a scaled-down version involving a sheet of paper and a polystyrene cup half-filled with water. Put the sheet of paper on the table so that the very end overlaps the edge of the table and place the cup on top of the paper, making sure that the paper is completely dry. If any of the water spills from the cup on to the paper, the trick won't work. Now for the tug. It must be swift and sharp – any hesitation will prove fatal. At the moment you pull, the paper must also be kept flat and not raised, which is why it is a good idea to position it so that it overlaps the table. If you manage to perfect it, you can move on to more ambitious projects, but resist the temptation to try The Tablecloth Trick in a posh restaurant. Successful or not, the waiter is unlikely to see the funny side.

A TALE OF TWO BAGS

Skill Level: ⑦

You will need:

**Two identical paper bags,
a paper tissue, confetti, scissors, glue**

Find two paper bags of the same size and colour. Trim a strip all the way around the top of one bag and make a few holes in the bottom. Leave the second bag intact and sprinkle some confetti inside it. Put the first bag inside the second and glue the outer top edge of the first bag to the inner top edge of the second so that the two bags are stuck together. Show the audience the result of your hard work – what appears to be an ordinary paper bag. Tip it upside down so that they can see it is empty and pop in a paper tissue. Tell everyone that you are going to make the tissue undergo a remarkable transformation. Using all the strength you can muster, blow up the bag and burst it. As a result of the holes in the first bag, only the second outer bag will burst, allowing the confetti to fall to the floor. With you hiding the crumpled bags and the tissue in your hand, it will look as if the plain white tissue has turned to coloured confetti.

THE MADNESS OF KING EDWARD

Skill Level: ❼

You will need:

A small potato, a cocktail stick, two forks, a length of string

Here is an unbelievable opportunity to re-enact the career of Blondin, the famous French tightrope walker, using a potato. Simply stretch a piece of string between two chair legs so that it is taut like a tightrope and instruct your potato (the smaller the better) to go out there and balance on the string. No potato in its right mind would attempt such a feat, but with the aid of two forks and a cocktail stick it can be done. And, in the immortal words of Jimmy Young, this is what you do. Press the cocktail stick into the potato and make a notch in the other end of the stick so that it can stand upright on the string. Holding it in place, stick the prongs of the forks into the potato (one on each side) with the handles hanging down and you will find that the contraption balances because its centre of gravity is below the string.

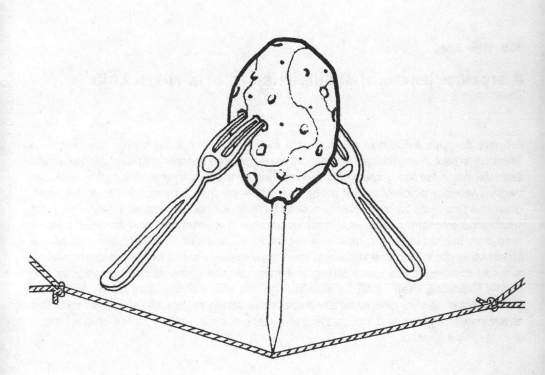

THE SECRET SLIT

Skill Level: 7

You will need:

A straw, a length of string, scissors or a sharp knife

Prepare for this exhibition by making a two-inch vertical cut along one side of a drinking straw. The incision should be made approximately halfway up the straw and will be invisible to spectators. When everyone is sitting comfortably, you can begin. Thread a piece of string along the straw so that it protrudes at either end. Give it a little tug so that they can see there is just one piece of string. Put your right hand over the centre of the straw and bend it sharply in half at the slit. Make sure that the slit is on the inside of the bend. Gently pull on the lower end of the string to force it into the slit. Keep the straw tightly folded in half so that nobody can see the slit or the loose string and then cut the straw at the bend above the string. Everyone should still be able to see the string protruding from either end of the straw so they will naturally expect the string to have been cut in two. But when you straighten out the straw and blow on it magically, you are able to brandish the string intact.

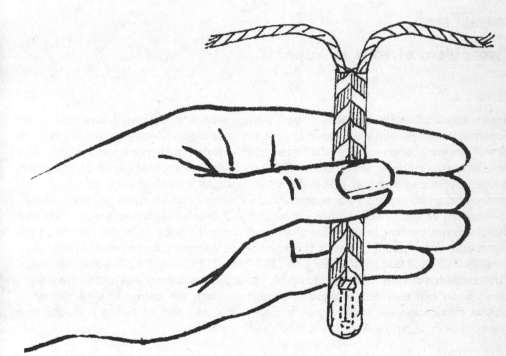

A KNOTTY PROBLEM

Skill Level: ⑦

You will need:

Two pieces of cord or rope

This trick requires the services of two friends who are perfectly happy to be tied together until you work out how to free them. You begin with two pieces of cord or rope, each about one and a half metres (5ft) long. Tie the two ends of the rope in knots around the wrists of the first person. Take the second length of rope, pass it over and under the first piece and tie it in knots around the wrists of the second person, leaving the two people suitably entwined. Tell them to try and free themselves without undoing any knots. This will prove spectacularly impossible so put them out of their misery and show them how it's done. Take the centre of the first person's rope and thread it through the noose around the wrist of the other person, the first rope passing between the knot of the second rope and the wrist. Pull the first rope to make the loop bigger and pass it over the second person's hand. Then pull the loop along and pass it through the other side of the wrist noose. Finally pull the rope right through the noose and, all being well, the two ropes should separate. And if not, there's always tomorrow…

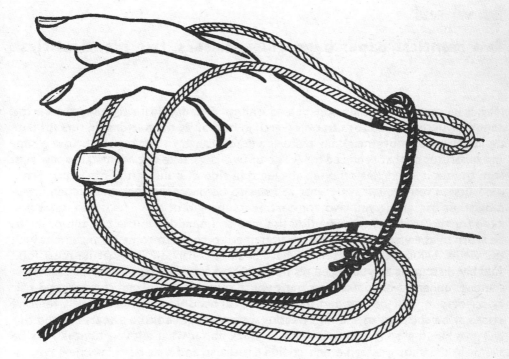

THE CUT TIE

Skill Level: ❼

You will need:

Two identical paper bags, glue, scissors, two identical ties

Magicians thrive on humiliation. Indeed one of their favourite tricks is the cut tie routine where a spectator can only watch in horror as the performer cuts his best tie into pieces before magically restoring it. You can try this yourself by using similar apparatus to that required for A Tale of Two Bags. Take two identical paper bags, trim the top two inches off one and glue one side of it inside the other bag. From the outside you are left with what appears to be one paper bag, but hidden inside is another bag, giving you two compartments instead of one. The other items you need for this trick are two identical ties, one to be hidden in the bag, the other to be worn by the victim. Consequently you need to come to some arrangement with the victim beforehand, explaining what is going to happen and that he must look suitably distraught as you shred his new tie. So your starting position is one tie in the bag (under no circumstances must you allow anyone to inspect the bag), a pair of scissors in your pocket and the other tie around your friend's neck. Everyone else may be shocked to see him wearing a tie as opposed to a sweatshirt and this will give him the opportunity to lay it on thick about what a lovely tie it is, how he saw it in the shop yesterday and couldn't resist it, and that he thinks he'll wear it for ever more, even in bed. This will make its destruction all the more poignant in the eyes of the rest of your entourage. After he has waxed lyrical about his neckwear, you quietly produce the scissors from your pocket and, with an assassin-like iciness, cut his tie into pieces. Everyone, your victim included, will look aghast. What could have prompted such action? Was it because he beat you at Snakes and Ladders the other night or because he stole your last Rolo? You refuse to comment, silently placing the pieces of tie into the bag in the compartment next to the whole tie. As your friends plead with you to be reasonable about this feud, you finally relent and promise to get him a new tie. It won't take a second, you say. Close the bag, pronounce a magic spell and pull out the intact tie from its compartment, leaving the cut one inside the bag. You then hand him the restored tie against a backdrop of stunned silence.

THE INVISIBLE TEAR

Skill Level: ⑧

You will need:

A handkerchief, a large safety pin

It may not exactly have been your life's ambition to slide a safety pin along a handkerchief without ripping it to shreds, but it is nevertheless quite an achievement. Fold the handkerchief in half and ask someone to hold one end of the fold firmly while you grip the other. Keeping the handkerchief as taut as possible, put a safety pin (the bigger the better) through both layers just below the fold. Make sure that the non-opening bar of the safety pin is to your left. Close the pin and, with your other hand, hold the base tightly and pull the whole pin sharply down and along to the right. This has the effect of pushing the cloth up and around the point inside the cap. Slide the safety pin a little way along the handkerchief and then suddenly force the point up through the cloth again. Despite the unnerving sound of tearing, the closed safety pin has travelled along the fold without ripping the handkerchief. This trick will only work if your actions are swift and decisive. If you are too slow pulling the pin down or pushing it up again, you will end up with nothing more than a ruined handkerchief.

HOLDING YOUR DRINK

Skill Level: 8

You will need:

A glass of water, a postcard

Whilst this is a relatively straightforward trick in that there is no complicated procedure, it is by no means an easy one to perfect. You need a smooth-rimmed glass and a piece of smooth card – ideally a postcard. Fill the glass to the top with water and wet the rim slightly. Then place the card on top of the glass. Holding the card firmly in place, turn the glass over and take your hand away from the card. By the laws of science, the water should stay in the glass because the pushing power of air against the card is greater than the downward force of the water. But even science has its off days so, to be on the safe side, perform the trick over a sink or a bath.

JUMPING PAPERCLIPS

Skill Level: ❽

You will need:

A banknote, two paperclips

This one will drive you to distraction. By the time you have perfected it, Boyzone will have bus passes, Coronation Street will have become a multi-storey car park and Manchester City will have won the Premiership. In principle, it's easy enough. You take a banknote and bend it into an S-shape, linking the first and second layers with one paper clip and the second and third layers with the other clip. When in place, the clips should be just over an inch apart. In one rapid movement, pull the two ends of the banknote and the clips should link together. But don't bet on it...

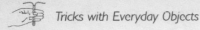

RESTORED ROPE

Skill Level: ⑨

You will need:

A length of string or rope, scissors

As illusions go, this may not exactly be on a par with making the Statue of Liberty disappear, but the effect by which a cut piece of string appears to be magically restored is impressive enough. It also has the advantage of being one of those rare classic illusions which you can perform in your own home without having to demolish most of the lounge. Another plus factor is that no preparation is required so the whole routine can be acted out in front of your eagle-eyed friends. When professional magicians perform this trick, they use a length of rope, but for your purposes, string will do nicely. Take a piece of string, about 3ft long, and tie the ends together in a knot. Take the two ends of the resultant loop in your hands, draping the string between your respective thumbs and forefingers and keeping your palms face upwards. Position the knot so that is an inch below your left forefinger. Twist your right hand, still holding one loop, over towards your body and bring your left hand (still holding the other loop) in front of your right hand. As you do so, turn your left hand so that the two palms are facing each other and slip the loop held by your right hand over the fingers of your left hand. All the string is now in your left hand and has formed a double loop (see illustration). Close your left hand over the string and, with your right hand, move the string until between your left thumb and forefinger you are able to feel the twist in the string which creates the double loop. Hold that twist in position with your left thumb and forefinger, keeping it con-cealed from the audience, and keeping the knot just below your left forefinger. Ask one of your friends to cut the two strands about an inch above your left thumb and show everyone the two ends of each piece to prove that the string has indeed been cut. In fact, however, because the strands are cut just above the twist and knot, the string is not cut in half at all. All that is being cut is one small section of the loop, with the knot in – the rest of the string remains intact. Next tie togeth-er the two ends of the short section, held between your left thumb and forefinger, and demonstrate the knot. Hand your volunteer the length of string containing the original knot and ask him to grip it tightly. Take the other end of the string in your left hand and hold the string taut. Now tell everyone that you are going to restore the string in such a way that nobody will be able to see where it had been cut in two. Cover the second knot with your right hand, rub a little and suddenly slide your hand off the string, taking the knot, which should remain hidden under your hand, with you. Since the knot is, in effect, a separate piece of string, it will slide readily off the longer piece. Ask your volunteer to untie the other knot and, while all eyes are on him, you can slip the fake knot into your pocket. With the knot untied, you are able to present a fully restored length of string and with no evidence of any cut.

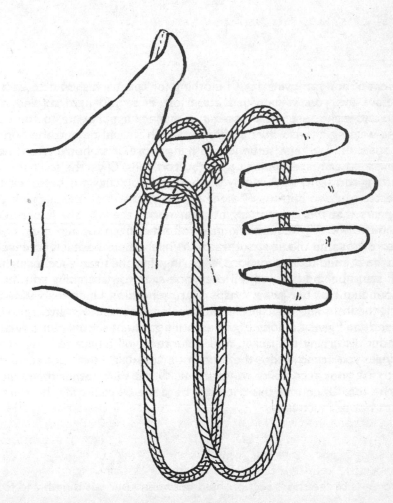

STRIP SHOW

Skill Level: ⑨

You will need:

A chair

The prospect of you removing a girl's clothing for this trick should at least ensure that you have everyone's undivided attention. First you have to find a willing accomplice and make sure she dresses in a manner appropriate to the occasion. This means wearing a loose shirt or blouse which should be buttoned up around the neck, but should otherwise be left to hang loose. She shouldn't put her arms in the sleeves either, merely doing up the button cuffs. Over the shirt she wears a jacket (nothing too tight) so that only the buttoned-up cuffs, the buttoned-up neck and maybe the top two buttons of the shirt are visible underneath. From the outside, it appears that there is nothing peculiar about the way she is dressed. Now for the moment of truth. Request a female volunteer from the audience, saying that you plan to take some of their clothes off. While others hesitate, your volunteer will have been primed to leap forward, declaring that she's game for a laugh. Sit her on a chair, stand behind her and tell everyone that you are going to remove her shirt without taking off her jacket. Gasps of apprehension. Undo the visible buttons at the neck, the front and the cuffs. As the tension reaches fever pitch, grip the collar of the shirt and give it a hefty tug. The entire garment should come away in one piece without disturbing the jacket. Your volunteer will be left to shiver for a few seconds while you acknowledge the rapturous applause. In case of accidents, it is advisable to ask your accomplice to wear a fairly old shirt, rather than risk ripping her favourite top. Of course, this trick can be done by removing the shirt from a man, but it's not as much fun.

POP THE CORK

Skill Level: ⑨

You will need:

A cork, a bottle, a handkerchief

At one time or another, most of us have encountered wine bottle corks which either steadfastly refuse to budge or crumble into tiny fragments. In the latter case, you often have to resort to pushing the cork through the neck and into the actual bottle before draining the precious wine. This trick shows you how to get a cork out from the inside of an empty bottle without smashing the bottle. Unless you're an avid collector of corks, it's a situation which is unlikely to arise, but it's fun anyway. Push the cork through the neck and into the bottle. Then push one end of a handkerchief through the neck (keeping hold of the other end) and toss the contents around until the cork is resting on the handkerchief. Now slowly, but surely, pull the handkerchief out.

In theory, the handkerchief should pull the cork out with it. Then again...

LEVITATION FOR BEGINNERS

Skill Level: ⑩

You will need:

Two identical pairs of shoes or trainers, two sticks, a low table or bench, a sheet

Are magicians taking the rise when they perform acts of levitation on TV? Certainly they appear phoney, but how on earth do they do it? Well now you can levitate your own friends with this splendid con trick. They might not end up floating around the ceiling, but they will seem to rise a couple of feet off the ground. The key to the trick is acquiring two pairs of identical footwear. This is no easy matter since most discerning folk change their wardrobe from time to time, but you may strike lucky and find a friend with similar taste. If all else fails, there is nothing to stop you using two pairs of identically coloured Wellington boots of similar sizes. There's bound to be a pair in the garden shed tucked under the wheelbarrow and another pair in the garage under a heap of crumpled up paper. The only drawback is that when everyone sees you wearing Wellington boots in your lounge, they'll suspect there's something afoot. Anyway, let's assume you've managed to unearth two pairs of matching trainers. The first thing you need to do is enlist the services of three assistants and let them in on the trick. Bring in an ordinary low table (you can allow people to inspect it if they so desire) which must not only be strong enough to take a person's weight, but must be narrow enough for them to be able to straddle it. The ideal item of equipment is a small bench, but not too many homes possess such a thing. Produce a sheet and instruct two of your assistants to hold it up so that it screens the audience from the table. Get your third helper to lie on the table so that his head is visible at one side of the sheet. At the other side of the sheet, the audience will see what appear to be his shoes sticking out, but in fact they are the matching pair of shoes tied to two long sticks which are resting on the table. For although he is lying down, his knees are bent and his own feet are touching the floor. He is holding the ends of the sticks in his hands. With everything in place, you can start your magic words of levitation, at which the person behind the screen will slowly rise to his feet. He must keep his head back so that it looks as if he is still lying in a horizontal position and, of course, he must remember to raise the dummy shoes in time with his head. As if that isn't enough to remember, he must also keep the sticks level. It's good fun if you can carry it off, but it does need a fair amount of practice, so have a few dummy runs before you go public.

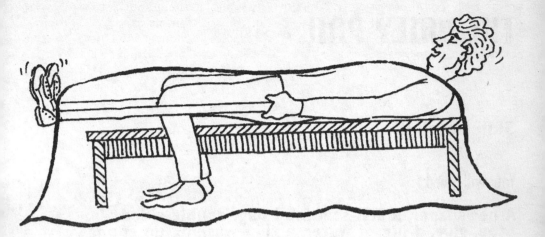

THE DAILY PAIL

Skill Level: ⑩

You will need:

A newspaper, a self-seal food bag, double-sided tape, glue, a jug of water, a thin washing-up sponge

This is a trick for the more ambitious performer, someone just the wave of a wand away from sawing acquaintances in half. We've all seen it demonstrated on TV, usually just after the Nigel Lythgoe Dancers and immediately before the scouse comic on one of those summer entertainment shows they used to put out from places like Minehead, Skegness and Bognor Regis, but nevertheless its ability to astound remains undiminished. The trick involves a fair amount of preparation so allow yourself plenty of time. First take a newspaper and glue the pages together along its spine. Open the paper towards the back and, using double-sided tape, fix a self-seal food bag (the sort you keep freezer food in) on to one half of the double-page spread so that the top edge of the bag is in line with the top edge of the page. Stick another piece of tape on the opposite side of the bag, glue along the side and bottom of the page and close the paper so that it is firmly stuck together on every side except the top. Finally open the concealed bag and insert a thin washing-up sponge. With the preparation complete, it is time for the serious business. Show the paper to your audience by opening it at the centre pages and then roll the paper into the shape of a cone. Next put your hand inside the cone and open the top of the bag before slowly pouring in a small jug of water (about 100ml). Your audience (poor gullible fools) think the water is going straight into the newspaper, but you know that it is being poured into the hidden plastic bag where it is soaked up by the sponge. When you have finished pouring the water, unroll the paper from its cone shape and fold it in half again, taking care to close the bag at the same time by running your finger along the top of the page. The deception complete, it is time to open the paper once more at the centre pages to reveal that all the water has vanished. And that's magic…

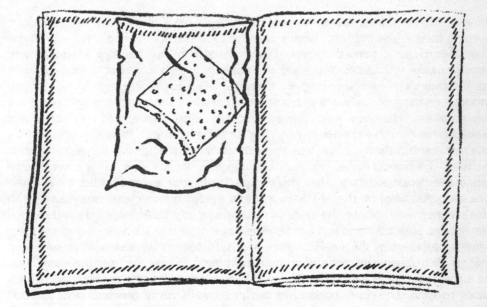

ESCAPOLOGY

Skill Level: ⑨

You will need:

A length of rope, a large handkerchief, a towel

There are some things you simply can't escape – like Cliff Richard at Christmas, hosepipe bans at the first hint of summer and Otis the Aardvark all the year round – but this trick is something you can escape from, as budding Houdinis and bondage freaks will testify. You need someone to tie your wrists tightly together with a handkerchief large enough to cater for Cyrano de Bergerac's nose. If you can't find anything of adequate size, a scarf will do. As your wrists are tied, you must keep your fists clenched. Ask your assistant to wind a length of rope over and under the handkerchief and between your wrists and to pull the ends tight. At this point you explain that you will free yourself from the shackles of the rope without removing the handkerchief which is binding your wrists. Ask for a towel to be draped over your wrists so that you can perform your escape without giving the game away. An air of mystique always makes a performance more impressive. With your assistant still holding the ends of the rope tightly, open your fists and extend your fingers. Step back and pull hard on the rope until you are able to trap the loop in the rope between the heels of your hands. Rub your wrists together and step forward to slacken the rope. Continue rubbing your wrists together until you make the loop large enough to slip the fingers of one hand through. Step back quickly to stiffen the rope, manoeuvre the loop over your fingers and wrist and pull it from under the handkerchief. A quick tug and you are free from the rope. Ask for the towel covering your hands to be removed and everyone will see that your wrists are still constrained by the handkerchief.

DRINKING GAMES

There's nothing that livens up an evening out (or indeed 'in') with friends quicker than a good old-fashioned drinking game. Using the random nature of spinning coins, or tumbled dice, or even bringing in tongue-twisters and word games, you can quickly turn an innocent night's beer-swilling into a fiercely competitive booze-a-thon where the first stop on your mazy ride is Hazy Central and nobody is allowed to get off.

INTRODUCTION

Or how to get drunk cleverly

A selection of welcoming words and a smattering of rules and regulations to ensure fun for all

Included here are games that range from the simple (**The One Coin Game**); to the daunting (**Anchorman**) and the terrifying (**Drink Don't Think**). Games that require skill and strategy (**Penny Rugby**); games that demand mental agility (**Fizz Buzz**); and games that necessitate an over-generous chunk of blind luck (see any dice game). Everything you could possibly want to know about drinking games is revealed in the following pages. You'll be amazed at the number of games you can play with the change in your pocket, or with a few dice. And once you've started, you'll find it difficult to stop. The addictiveness of these games is sky-high and when you've found the game that's right for you, it's difficult to have a 'normal' drink again. So, read on, read on ...

Important Note: while the drinking games presented in this book are designed to enhance the enjoyment of a night's social drinking, the publishers and the creators of this book would like to point out that, while they do enjoy hearty boozing, they do NOT, in any way, condone drinking and driving. Or for that matter, drinking and cycling, drinking and vandalism, drinking and operating heavy construction machinery, etc. The games in this book are meant to be fun, and a certain degree of planning must take place before embarking on any one of them. (1) Do NOT drive under any circumstances. The very nature of the drinking games here means that you and sobriety will not be friends come the end of the night. (2) Take enough money to be able to buy your share of the drink, and to get yourself a cab home when the hilarity winds up. (3) Carry a matchbox, some assorted coinage and a set of five six-sided dice - just in case. (4) Stronger drinkers may want to carry a chess set or a small table with them in addition.

* It is illegal to consume beer and alcohol if you are under the age of 18. So DON'T do it.

SOME BASIC RULES

To enable you and your friends to enjoy an argument-free night of heavy drinking, there are a few simple rules that you should bear in mind:

RULE (1) Each game in this book has been carefully categorized and broken down into five separate chunks: **the title;** what **you will need** to play it; the **danger factor** which tells you how easy the game is to play; the **'drunken factor'** which gives you an indication of how drunk you should be before you start to play it; and the **main description.** A sample layout will look as follows:

- ### 'The Pub Crawl'
- ### You will need
  A large amount of pubs, in a very small area. Money.

- ### Danger factor/Ease-of-play
  A game as old as recorded time. Which is pretty damned old.

- ### Drunken factor

- ### Hints and tips
  Helpful advice, unsurprisingly.

RULE (2) Beer, lager or cider must be drunk from a pint glass or from the original bottles that the drink came in.

RULE (3) Cocktails or spirits must be drunk from a half-pint glass.

RULE (4) The definition of a pint is eight fingers. One or two finger drink penalties can be measured by placing your first two fingers side-by-side on the glass, the first finger at the level of the alcohol remaining. The player must drink enough beer so that the level of the drink drops to below the second finger.

RULE (5) The 'gulp', 'sip' or 'swig' is a bit of a grey area, ranging from a small sip to a big mouthful. Decide which you'll use before you play.

RULE (6) The majority of the games here (unless otherwise specified) are designed to be played with pints of beer. Fines can be halved for those players drinking spirits.

RULE (7) If any player is required to 'down a pint', the drink must be drained completely within 60 seconds.

MONEY GAMES

Even if you can't lay your hands on a pack of playing cards, all you really need to explore some very fine drinking games is a pocket of loose change and very few inhibitions. Reading through the 14 choice diversions gathered here, you'll be amazed how a pile of coins (pennies, 2-pences, 5-pences and 10-pences), can be used to enhance the late-night alcohol experience. In the games below, for example, you'll discover how to play football with 4p and rugby with 2p; how to 'shuffle' a stack of 1p pieces; and which coins have the best aerodynamics and bounceability. In our experience, the answer to this last question is the tiny 5-pence piece, a triumph of lightweight construction that seems to take brilliantly to the group of 'chucking-coins-at-tables' games. So, be popular, liven up a dull night out at your local watering hole with a few bouts of **Anchorman, Chandeliers** or **Taps.** All of them are drinking games beyond compare.

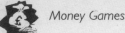

THE ONE COIN GAME

 Simple yet deadly. Especially if you play it for more than two hours. And are unlucky.

You will need:

A coin. A table. Beer.

Simple but deadly if played for more than an hour, **The One Coin Game** involves gathering a group of friends around a table and nominating an honorary coin-flipper. The game unfolds thus: the designated money-chucker spins the coin into the air, while the player to the left of the flipper has to guess whether it will land on heads or tails. If they manage to get it right, they become the coin-flipper for the player to the left of them. If they get it wrong, they must rush a two-finger/sip fine and are forced to face another 'heads' or 'tails' flip. Only when the player guesses the upturned face of the coin correctly, do the coin-flipping duties move onwards and he/she is saved from further penalty guzzling.

 Hints & Tips
Remember to keep a good supply of coins as you'll probably lose quite a few behind benches and down cleavages.

Drunken factor...

MULTIPLE COIN SPIN

⚠ **The tabletop equivalent of spinning plates on sticks. But without the plates and the sticks.**

You will need:

A stack of coins. A table. Beer.

A simple game, enhanced by the sneaky addition of increasingly higher alcoholic stakes. Make sure you have a big stack of coinage and a clear table, for the aim of this game is simply this: how many coins can you spin simultaneously on a tabletop? Four? Five? Player one, for example, might bet that he/she can spin three coins at the same time. If successful, the stakes can then be raised higher. But if he/she fails in spinning the number of coins bet, the unfortunate change-spinner has to drink X fingers/sips of beer (where X is the number of coins that the player tried to spin). The betting moves clockwise around the table, anybody unwilling to take the challenge must drink the current penalty. This goes on until somebody foolishly tries to spin 14 coins at once and is forced to drink 14 fingers/sips of beer as a punishment. How high can you take it? How many coins can YOU spin?

Hints & Tips

Practice this at home and see how many you can do. 'A man's gotta know his limitations,' as Clint Eastwood said.

Drunken factor...

🍾🍾🍾🍾🍾🍾🍾

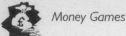

THE TWO COIN GAME

⚠ **A game of coin-flicking superskills and tremendous drinking stamina.**

You will need:

Two identical coins. A matchbox. A table. Beer.

An easy game to play if you're out in the pub (and an obvious sequel to **The One Coin Game**). Simply rifle your pockets for two identical coins – a couple of 10-pence pieces or some 2-pence pieces seem to work the best. Players then gather around a table and take it in turns to flick the two coins from BELOW the level of the table onto the top of the table (pile the two coins together on your thumb and forefinger to get a truly random result). When the coins clatter to a standstill on the table, consult the following drink-related rules and pay the appropriate consequences:

(1) If one coin lands on **'heads'** and the other on **'tails',** the current coin-flicker suffers no penalty and the matchbox (merely a symbol of whose turn it is, rather than an integral part of the whole proceedings) is passed on to the next player in the circle.

(2) If **both** coins land on **'tails',** however, the unfortunate player is forced to down two fingers/sips of beer.

(3) Conversely, if **both** coins land on **'heads',** the coin-flicker is allowed to make up an additional rule to spice the game up (the sillier, the better).

Hints & Tips
Make sure to use any new rule to your advantage.
If you're well coordinated, make everyone flip
from a metre away, for instance.

(4) If either of the two coins land on the floor, the player who flicked them so inexpertly must suffer a four-finger/sip fine.

Variants:

Ever heard of **The Three Coin Game?** Or **The Four Coin Game?** Obviously, once you can play this simple drinking game with two coins, the rules for these two variants pretty much explain themselves.

Drunken factor...

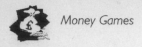
PENNIES

⚠ **Requires good hand/eye coordination. Psychic ability an advantage.**

You will need:

11 pennies (1-pence pieces). A table. Beer.

Known as **Dimes** in America, the coin game **Pennies** plays much like a traditional card game (it also works equally as well with distinctively designed beer mats, which may be easier to come by). Best played with five players or fewer, every player gets a chance to **'deal'** the coins. The dealer simply gathers all eleven pennies in his/her hand, shakes them about a bit, and then forms a neat little stack which is then placed on top of the table. Now it's a test of nerve and blind luck – the player to the left of the dealer must guess whether the next coin will be **'heads'** or **'tails'**. The top coin is then removed – if the player is correct, he/she then moves swiftly on to try and guess the orientation of the next coin. If wrong, the player simply drinks a two-finger/sip fine and continues to the next coin. When the player has worked through all of the remaining coins, drinking or surviving (depending on how lucky they are), the coins then move on to the next player who becomes the dealer, 'shuffles' the coins and then stacks them up as before.

Variants: More coins equals more chances to drink. Similar to the card-based **Landmine** game.

 **Hints & Tips**
Obviously anyone clumsy enough to knock the coins over has to drink a penalty. Eleven fingers should be a deterrent.

Drunken factor...

SPIN THE PENNY

⚠ **A game of no skill whatsoever. But then they're usually the most effective...**

You will need:

A coin (usually a penny). A table. Beer.

Another effective, remarkably simple drinking game that's short on rules and big on drunken hilarity. Here's the gist: one player flips a coin, the player to the coin-flipper's immediate left guesses whether it will land on **'heads'** or **'tails'**. If the player manages to guess the result correctly, then he/she takes the coin from the first flipper and tosses it expertly for the player next to them (and so on around the group). If, however, somebody gets the guess wrong, then the player who chucked the coin spins it on the table and the unlucky player has to drink from his/her glass for as long as the coin keeps spinning. Then, just before it starts to settle, someone quickly smacks the spinning coin down on the table underneath their hand, and asks the bad-guesser to plump for heads or tails again. If he/she gets it right this time, the coin is passed on. But if he/she gets it wrong again, the coin is spun yet again and the same drinking penalty applies. Repeat until they get it right.

Hints & Tips

Be careful of your glasses when arresting the motion of the spinning coin. A separate table is recommended for the beer.

Drunken factor...

ANCHORMAN

⚠ **A team game for backstabbing individuals everywhere.**

You will need:

One coin per player. A table (with at least 2 feet of clearance). A large jug of beer.

Anchorman is a simple team game (of some considerable skill) that can not only create a fierce rivalry between the people playing against each other, but amongst players on the same team. The game requires that at least eight people take part, or failing that, there must be an even number of potential coin-flickers and drinkers. Obviously, the more players you have in your drunken throng, the more dangerous it gets.

Here's how things work: two teams (of equal numbers) sit on opposite sides of a table and attempt, by flicking their coins, to get them into the large jug of beer. Each team member takes it in turn to shoot their coin towards the Jug-O-Beer, trying to make it land with a satisfying 'splunk' in the middle. Each player only shoots once per turn (even if they are successful in looping their coinage into the jug). When everyone on the team has flicked, the second team tries their luck with their own coins.

This continues until one team manages to get all of its complement of coins into the jug. The losing team then has to drink the jug of beer between them.

Hints & Tips
If you get a draw (0-0 can become common at the end of the night) play again without drinking – you obviously all need to sober up a bit.

But here's the twist – before the losers drink, the winning team must choose someone to be the **Anchorman.** It's the **Anchorman's** job to drink last and to finish any remaining beer. Therefore the **Anchorman's** teammates can be as kind (everybody drinks in equal measures) or as nasty (everyone else takes a few mouthfuls and cruelly leaves the anchor to drain the rest) as they wish. While drinking the contents of the jug, the **Anchorman's** team-mates cannot take their lips off it. If they do, even for a moment, they must pass the jug onto the next player. When the jug reaches the **Anchorman,** he/she has two minutes to drink the rest of the beer. When it's empty, simply refill the legendary Jug-O-Beer and begin anew.

Drunken factor...

CHEERS!

PENNY RUGBY

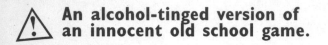 **An alcohol-tinged version of an innocent old school game.**

You will need:

A coin. A table. Beer. 2 players.

A classic, easy game of some skill with a fresh, slightly dangerous beer-related twist, **Penny Rugby** takes most of the pain out of its more physical namesake and replaces it with liberal doses of liquid anaesthesia.

Here's how it works: the two players sit opposite each other at a table. Using the width of a table, place a suitable coin (a 2-pence piece seems to work the best) on the edge so that it hangs half-over the lip of the table. Then, kick off this metal 'ball' by hitting the coin with your flattened palm so that it skids across the table. The idea behind the game is to then nudge the coin with your forefinger so that it skids further across the table and onto the opposite edge. You get three nudges after the initial kick-off, with the ultimate objective being to nudge the coin so it hangs precariously over the other lip of the table.

If after three nudges the coin is (a) still on the table because you haven't nudged it hard enough, or (b) somewhere on the floor because you've nudged it too hard, player two gets to have his/her turn, kicking off as before. If during your three nudges, you manage to manoeuvre the coin onto the opposite edge of the table, you can then attempt to score. To score a **try,** reach under the hanging coin with

Hints & Tips

If you find you drink faster when NOT playing this game, just add some penalties for not getting into a try-scoring position after three nudges.

your forefinger and flip it into the air, attempting to catch it with the other hand. If you succeed, you score five points and can go for the conversion. If not, you fumble the ball at the last minute, score nothing and drink a forfeit for your sheer cack-handedness. For the **conversion,** the opposing player forms a makeshift set of goalposts by pressing his/her two forefingers on the table, joining the thumbs together and raising them up like a set of posts. All the conversion-taker has to do is spin the coin on the table and catch it between his/her two thumbs. If caught successfully, the coin can then be flicked (still between the two thumbs) over player two's hand-made goalposts. Each time you score, the opposing player drinks. And vice versa.

Drunken factor...

647

PENNY FOOTBALL

⚠️ **An alcohol-tinged version of another innocent old school game.**

You will need:

Three coins (two 2-pence pieces and a 1-pence piece). A table. Beer. 2 players.

Like **Penny Rugby** on the previous page, **Penny Football** involves skidding coins around on a tabletop. This time in a rudimentary simulation of England's greatest contribution to the culture and civilization of our planet.

Here's how it works: Once again, the two players sit opposite each other at a table. Using the width of a table, place the three coins on the edge so that one of the 2-pence pieces overhangs the table and the two remaining coins sit in front of it, each one touching the precariously-placed 2-pence (the three coins should form an inverted triangle shape).

Then, kick off this metallic trio by hitting the overhanging coin with your flattened palm so that the three coins fan out and skid across the table. Meanwhile, the second player closes his fist and extends both the forefinger and the little finger to make a goal (this is then placed on the table, two fingers on top, knuckles of the clenched fist resting against the edge).

What the attacking player has to do is to manoeuvre the 1-pence piece (the ball), by nudging it through the gap between the two 2-pence pieces (the players), into a

Hints & Tips

If you want to drink more, try giving each player three turns and then having a penalty shoot-out if there's a draw.

position where it can be nudged (again this must be through the two 2-pence pieces) into the opposing goal. Drink whenever the other player scores against you. The coins eventually pass to the opposing player when (a) a goal has been scored, (b) if the attacking player fails to move the 1-pence through the two 2-pence pieces, or (c) if the attacking players shot misses the goal. And no, you can't score with a 2-pence piece.

Drunken factor...

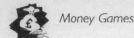
BASEBALL

⚠ **They say that playing sport is good for you. But not this version of Baseball...**

You will need:

Four shot glasses. Beer. A coin. Some matchsticks. Two teams of people.

Although you might expect to see shot glasses arranged in a typical baseball diamond for this game, **Baseball** merely uses the idea of the popular US sport for shallow, alcoholic ends. Something to be heartily condoned, you'll surely agree.

In short: The four glasses are set up in a row moving away from the player. The nearest glass is the 'home base', the second is the 'first' and so on. One by one, each player in the team must step up to 'bat', i.e. they must attempt to flick a coin into any of the four shot glasses. Like baseball, the farther you can flick the coin, the better.

The first glass represents a single dash, the second a double, the third a triple, and the last a crowd-pleasing home run. Three strikes (if you manage to miss all four shot glasses) and you're out. Three outs by people on your team, and your innings is over and the other team steps up to bat.

The game runs along similar lines to baseball (or rounders if you can remember the rules from your schooldays) and runs are scored in the same way. If, for example, a player manages to flick a coin into the second shot glass, then their go ends and a matchstick is placed next to the glass denoting how far that player has managed to 'run' around the four bases. The player must then drink the contents of every shot glass up to and including the glass that his/her coin landed in (in this case, the

Hints & Tips

Patience is the key to this game. Aim low and keep the matchsticks moving. You won't drink too much, and your opponents will.

player would drink the home and the first base glasses. The glasses are then refilled and the next player steps up to flick a coin. If that player manages to flick it into the third glass, the matchstick on second base moves to the fourth glass, another one is placed on third, and the player drinks three shots.

Every time a matchstick manages to move onwards from the last glass, the batting team scores a **run** and the opposing team must take a drink. Anybody who **strikes out** (i.e. misses the glasses with their three attempts) must drink the contents of all four shot glasses.

Drunken factor...

TAPS

⚠ **It may sound simple. But Taps requires concentration, focus and good coordination.**

You will need:

A coin each. A table. Some beer.

A simple game with the bare minimum of verbal communication between players, **Taps** is less a game about shiny bathroom fittings, more a game of skill and dexterity that involves banging a coin on a table.

In this unspoken, fast-paced game, one player starts by tapping his/her coin once. The person sat immediately to the coin-tapper's left then taps his/her coin once and the process continues around the table. Tapping the coin once on the table maintains the current direction of the play. Tapping the coin twice reverses the direction (i.e. from left-to-right, from right-to-left), while tapping the coin quickly three times skips the next player. Play this game as quickly as possible. Anybody who misses a tap, or gets a tap wrong (banging the table when the direction of play has, in fact, been reversed; or tapping without realizing that the player next to them has tapped three times, for instance), must drink the usual beer-related penalty.

Hints & Tips

Watch your grandad's antique coffee table when you're playing this one; there'll be marks left.

Drunken factor...

SPOOF

⚠ **The classic coin game. Passport to drunkenness and spoons of lime pickle.**

You will need:

Three coins each. A curry house location. Beer. (Optional: lime pickle.)

Let's hear it for the traditional curry house party game – a game of skill, of extreme backstabbing, cunning, and of large drunkenness coupled with compulsory swallowing of lime pickle. Simply pick your favourite curry location, stock up with beer and make sure that each player has three coins with which to play the game. **It works thus:** each player puts their hands underneath the table and secretly puts either three, two, one or no coins at all into one hand. This clenched hand is then held over the table and the participating players take it in turns to guess the total number of coins held by all the players (if six people play, that's a maximum of 18 coins and a minimum of zero). When all of the guesses have been made, the players open their hands to reveal the coins inside. All the coins are totalled up and any player that has guessed the total correctly, wins the round and gets to sit out the remainder of the game. With the numbers whittled down a notch, the coin-hiding process begins again. Whichever player is left at the end of the game, having guessed each coin total incorrectly, has to drink a pint in one go and eat a generous spoonful of lime pickle.

Hints & Tips

You can also play this game in any bar to settle who has to pay to get the next round in. And fetch them. And buy nuts.

Drunken factor...

BOUNCE 'EM

 **The quintessential drinking game. Portable. Easy. Deadly.**

You will need:

A coin. A cup/glass. A table. Beer.

On the one hand, **Bounce 'Em** is a game involving skill and luck, not to mention some keen dexterity, a touch of physics and an appreciation of the relationship between velocity and angles. And on the other, it's a game about throwing a coin against a table and bouncing it into a cup. Whichever you prefer.

Gather a group of friends around a table (six players is a good number) and decide who will go first – an easy way to do this is to spin the coin you'll be bouncing, say a light 5-pence piece, and whoever the Queen's nose points at (or the thistle's crown) gets to start the game. The aim of **Bounce 'Em** is simple and rather obvious – each player attempts to bounce a coin off of the table and into a glass or cup of beer. If the coin misses, the next player steps up to try his/her luck. But if it makes it in, the successful bouncer can pick one of the other players to drink a beer forfeit. Shoot successfully three times and you can then make up your own foolhardy rules.

Variants:

Bounce 'Em, Drink 'Em: How about this? The glass that you bounce the coin into is also the glass that contains the beer forfeit. The extra element of danger is trying to drink the beer without swallowing the coin that's swishing around in the bottom of the glass. Players who bounce hopeful coins which hit the rim of the

Hints & Tips

We've found that aiming the coin vertically at the table is the most effective method of getting a decent height on your bounce.

glass ('oooh') and narrowly miss going in ('awww'), get another go for free. If a player misses, but he feels confident that he/she will get the coin in 'the next time', the other players can encourage the player to 'chance their arm'. This means that the player is allowed one free attempt and, if the go succeeds the game continues as normal. If the chancy attempt fails, however, the unfortunate coin-shooter must drink all of the beer in the forfeit glass.

Ice Cube Bounce 'Em: In short, instead of a cup, **Ice Cube Bounce 'Em** makes use of an ice cube tray, preferably one with two distinct sides. Play obviously continues as in the original **Bounce 'Em** game, only this time the coin is aimed at the empty tray. One half of the tray is designated the 'give' side (where drinking forfeits are dished out to the other participating players), while the other is the 'take' side (the shooter must drain the beer themselves like a L-O-S-E-R). Make it more interesting by shooting your coins from further away each time. Or how about trying to bounce the coins off of two tables...?

Speed Bounce 'Em: Said to be more fun than the original game, **Speed Bounce 'Em** is played at three, four, even five times the pace of your basic **Bounce 'Em** contest. That means no concentrating, no calculating flight paths, no thinking, no abortive attempts, just simply aim, fire, and miss. If you hesitate, you drink. It's as simple as that.

Drunken factor...

Bounce 'Em 2: Sit everybody in a circle. Give a coin each to two people sitting opposite each other. Then, quite obviously, each player attempts to bounce their coin into the same glass (this time it's an empty one). The players get as many attempts as they want and, when one of the players does finally get a coin to clink into the glass, the successful person retrieves said coin and passes it on to the person sitting on their left. This process continues until somebody in the circle gets passed a coin when they already have a coin that they're trying to launch into the glass. This person is then mocked mercilessly and forced to drink an entire pint. Very, very quickly.

DROP THE PENNY

⚠ **Think Jenga, Buckaroo, Kerplunk or card pyramids. But with a napkin and a cigarette.**

You will need:

A cigarette. A glass. A paper napkin. A coin. Beer.

Remember the old kids game **Jaws**? A game where you had to hook plastic debris out of a big shark's mouth before it snapped shut...? Or how about **Kerplunk**? The old family favourite involving a clear plastic cylinder, straws and a bag of marbles...? Well, **Drop The Penny** is similar to both of them. Only it involves burning away a napkin with an unhealthy cigarette.

To play, get a paper napkin, place it across a glass and place a light coin on top of it – say a 5-pence piece. The aim is a simple one: how much of the napkin can you burn away (taking turns, each player MUST make a discernible hole) without causing the structural integrity of the napkin to fail and the coin to drop? Whoever burns too much of the napkin away, and makes the coin drop into the glass, is announced as the loser and must drink a whole pint of beer as a punishment and get the next round in.

 **Hints & Tips**

In the early stages of the game it can be a good idea to burn big holes, speeding the game up considerably.

Drunken factor...

🍾🍾🍾🍾🍾🍾

CHANDELIERS

⚠️ **A game like Bounce 'Em. Nothing to do with ornate lighting fixtures.**

You will need:

Coins. A large glass or jug. Some smaller glasses. A table.

This is a game that's quite a lot like **Bounce 'Em** (see page 654), but **Chandeliers** differs in several key areas. For starters, it moves a lot faster and this is mainly due to the fact that there are more targets to hit – specifically a large glass of beer in the middle of the table and a ring of smaller glasses surrounding it.

Here's how it works: A large glass (say, a pint glass) is topped up with beer and placed in the middle of the table. Some smaller glasses (half-pint tumblers, enough of them for each player) are also filled with alcohol, probably some sort of appropriate short, and these are then positioned around the large centre glass in front of the other players in the circle.

One by one, the players try to bounce their coins at the glasses as before, hoping to hit either the small glasses or the big pint glass. If the coin lands in one of the smaller glasses, the player sitting nearest the glass must drink the contents and refill the glass with beer.

If the coin lands in the large glass, all of the players around the table have to drink the booze in the glasses next to them. The last player to slam their empty glass down on the table is deemed the **'loser'** and must subsequently drink the beer in

Hints & Tips
You can stand where you like when bouncing the coin, so don't throw on the side with your glass. The pint then forms a handy shield.

the pint glass as a penalty. (Note of caution: As with any 'slamming' activity, make sure the glasses are of the thick, durable type. There's nothing more irritating than a lengthy trip to your local Accident & Emergency Department in the middle of an exciting and frenzied drinking game. It tends to disrupt the flow.)

After this bout of nervous excitement, all the glasses are refilled and the coin passes to the next player. Repeat the game until drowsy. If the room starts spinning, it's probably a good idea to give up. You've gone too far.

Drunken factor...

DICE GAMES

Like cards, money and TV programmes, the use of dice in a drinking game is principally to generate that random element that keeps the competition exciting. Unlike more rigidly-structured pub and word games that rely on a constant degree of concentration, card-, money-, and dice-based games are great levellers. So you don't have to be good at thinking of celebrity names or at throwing coins into strategically-placed ice cube trays. Playing with dice randomizes the dangers and the drinking penalties, creating drinking entertainment where the only thing you can rely on is faith and a large helping of blind luck. In the pages that follow, we've collected the 16 best dice games known to mankind, a jamboree bag of dice-based mania that ranges from the simple (**Just Dice**) to the more involved (**Bunko**), taking in the wildly imaginative (**Dice Man**) and the seemingly stupid (**Boxhead**) along the way. And all you need are a couple of those familiar numbered cubes...

CHEAT DICE

⚠️ **A slow-starter, but this game is an addictive blend of truth and dare.**

You will need:

Five dice. A table. Beer. The ability to lie, cheat and scheme.

All you have to do is lay your hands on five dice. That'll be enough for you to enjoy the drinking game **Cheat Dice**; an irresistible mix of luck and bare-faced cheek. Like its card-based variant, **Cheat**, the rules are simple.

Player one rolls the five dice (WITHOUT letting the other players see how they land) and, leaving the dice hidden on the table, announces the result. He/she may, of course, 'cheat' and lie about the result. The other players must then decide whether they believe the player is telling the truth, i.e. whether he/she has actually thrown three 4s, a 2 and a 1 or if his/her roll is actually lower and far less impressive.

If the first player is believed, the next player takes his/her turn to roll the dice, aiming to score a higher total (see **Scoring**) than the previous dice-tumbler. Again, he/she should roll the dice WITHOUT letting the other players see the result. And, naturally enough, he/she has the option to 'cheat'. If the total is not higher, the player must drink a forfeit (decided by the playing group beforehand). However, if at any time another player believes that the dice-chucker is lying about their score, he/she may challenge the total by shouting **'Cheat'**. The player in control of the dice must then reveal the true roll. If his/her claim is false, the dice-rolling player must drink a forfeit. If the claim is true, the challenging player must drink the forfeit. Play then passes on to the next player.

Hints & Tips

If you always lose money at Poker, don't try playing this game. Unless, that is, you WANT to get so drunk you can't even fall over properly.

Scoring Cheat Dice: Five Of A Kind beats Four Of A Kind beats A Full House (i.e. three 4s and two 3s) beats Three Of A Kind beats a Pair. Naturally, five 6s beat five 5s, five 4s and so on.

Variant: You can change this game most easily by adding to the number of throws allowed. Players may re-roll as many dice as they like up to, say, three times. A more twisted variant is **Cumulative Cheat Dice**. In this game each player gets one roll more than the previous player to try and beat the last total. That's the good news. The bad news is that the forfeit is multiplied by the number of rolls allowed.

Drunken factor...

DICE MAN

⚠ **Embarking on a Dice Man journey might be the best (and last) thing you ever do...**

You will need:

One die. A wild imagination. The world...

Inspired by the cult novel of the same name (in which a man makes all the decisions in his life by simply assigning numbers to the options and rolling a dice), the **Dice Man** game is not only deadly, but immensely portable, variable and exciting.

The idea behind the game is simple, but highly effective. A player is nominated to be the proverbial **Dice Man** or **Woman** and the only rule he/she has to observe is that the **Dice Man** MUST abide by the law of the die. He/she rolls a dice, and away you go.

The laws of the die are thus:

The '1' shall always mean that the die is to be immediately passed onto the next player.

The '6' shall be an action invented by the dice-chucker (usually an easy one, obviously).

The numbers '2', '3', '4' and '5' shall be actions invented by the other players. These actions or tasks can be anything — buy the next round of drinks, chat up a girl in the corner, chat up a guy in the corner, spill someone's pint and get away with it, steal someone's pint, etc. The only limit is your imagination (tempered by a certain degree of morality and ethics, although don't go too far: 'Tidy up your room' is hardly going to lead to an action-packed drinking night to remember) and a desire

Hints & Tips

Don't pick actions that are too difficult. The dice-chucker will go for a drink forfeit AND remember your unkindness when it's your throw.

to obey the will of the die. So if the action for '3' is catch a train to Glasgow, you should do exactly that. If the die comes to a stop on a '2' (leave the pub and go for a curry) then the die should be obeyed.

The actions shall be assigned BEFORE the dice are rolled.

Anyone who fails to obey the die, is subject to a drinking penalty. Let's say a pint. Downed in less than a minute.

Drunken factor...

DROP DEAD

⚠️ **A twisted, beer-soaked game similar to Yahtzee. But with beer.**

You will need:

Five dice. A table. Beer.

Like **Cheat Dice, Drop Dead** involves throwing five dice to amass the highest total possible. Play is taken in turn, and if there are a lot of you it's a good idea to get pen and paper from behind the bar so that you can keep track of the scores.

Each player throws the dice and then adds up the total. As long as the numbers '2' and '5' are not part of the roll's total, the player can collect the dice up again and roll anew, adding the subsequent score (again, unless there is a '2' or a '5' in the roll) to the first score. The player can continue, taking a drink between each roll, until either of the two bogey numbers appear.

If a **'2'** is thrown then the unfortunate player scores a big fat zero for the roll and the dice that showed the '2' are left out from the next roll.

Likewise, if a player reveals a **'5'** in his roll, the score doesn't count and the dice that showed the number is also excluded.

For example, if a player throws three 6s, a 3 and a 1 on his first roll, he can boast a total of 22. If on the second roll the dice reveal two 4s, one 3 and two 2s, the player doesn't score any additional points. Having faltered with two 2s, these dice are removed from play and on the next roll only three dice can be used.

Hints & Tips
If you can find a table that adjoins a wall,
much fun can be had rolling your dice
'Craps' style with forfeits for any that fall off.

Play continues like this, with the player drinking between each dice roll, until a '5' or a '2' is rolled on the last die. When this happens, the player's turn ends, the score is totalled up and control of the dice passes onto the next player. The winner is the player with the highest total after two rounds of play, and he/she can laugh while the losers drink a suitable forfeit.

Drunken factor...

THREE MAN

⚠ **The drinking game equivalent of 'you're it'.**

You will need:

Two dice. A table. Beer.

Gather a group of players together, and let everybody roll the two dice until one player reveals a '3'. When this happens, the player who rolled '3' becomes the **'Three Man'** and the game can begin.

Each player in the group rolls the two dice in turn, whereupon the gathered players must quickly add up the total on the two spotted cubes and perform the relevant action/task (as detailed below). The last person to compete the specified action must drink a forfeit – i.e. two fingers/sips, half-a-pint, etc. If, however, somebody rolls a **three** (in total) then the **Three Man** must drink a four-finger/sip or some similar nasty forfeit. As for the dicey tasks that have to be performed, they are as follows:

If the dice show **'1' & '3'**: everyone touches their glass to edge of the table. The last one to do this incurs the usual drinking forfeit (say, two fingers/sips from their pint) If the dice show **'1' & '4'**: everyone puts their thumb on their forehead. The last one to do so incurs the drinking forfeit. If the dice show **'1' & '5'**: a social drink, everyone drains some beer from their glasses. If the dice total **'7'**: the person to the right of dice-chucker takes a penalty drink. If the dice total **'11'**: the person to left of dice-roller takes a penalty drink. If the dice roll is a double: the dice-flicker adds up the total number of spots on the dice and gives that many penalties away

Hints & Tips

Keep a particularly close eye out for the
'1 & 3' and the '1 & 4'. A little alertness
will save you from a lot of grief.

to the rest of the group. Apart from the **Three Man**. If the penalty is given to the
Three Man by mistake, then the current dice-roller becomes the new **Three
Man**. If the dice roll off the table: the dice-roller incurs a drinking penalty for his
carelessness. If someone spills their drink: the guilty party incurs a drinking penalty for their lack of coordination.

Note: any dice roll not listed here is to be considered a 'null' or 'dead' roll, causing the dice to be passed onto the next player.

Drunken factor...

669

BOXHEAD

⚠ **A simple, effective game of chance played with unusual headgear.**

You will need:

Two dice. An empty cardboard box. Beer. Spirits.

Developed, so it is said, at the University of Victoria in Canada, the **Boxhead** drinking game is loosely based on the old **Three Man** game that you should now be familiar with. Like most drinking games, it's easy to pick up, yet the random nature of the game makes it impossible to master. Gather your players around a large table, nominate somebody to go first and then roll the two dice in turn, noting the result and applying the rules listed below.

If the dice total '**2**': everybody takes a drink (usual penalty of two fingers/sips) If the dice total '**3**': the person sitting to the left of the dice-roller drinks. If the dice total '**4**': nothing happens. Move onto the next player. If the dice total '**5**': roll another die. The result equals the number of fingers/sips everyone at the table must drink. If the dice total '**6**': the dice-roller can make up a new rule. Further rolls of '6' will activate this new rule although the dice-roller can make up a new one afterwards if he/she wishes. If the dice total '**7**': players slap their hands down on the table. The last one to do this drinks. If the dice total '**8**': roll another die. The result equals the number of fingers/sips that are poured into a glass for the dice-roller to drink. If the dice total '**9**': the person sitting to the right of the dice-roller drinks. If the dice total '**10**': toilet break. Unless you can roll a '10' you won't be allowed to leave the table. If the dice total '**11**' or '**12**': **Boxhead!** The dice-roller must wear the cardboard box on their head (this is particularly effective in pubs) until he/she rolls another '11' or '12' to remove it. However, if another player rolls an '11' or '12', the box is automatically transferred to them. And, worse than the indignity of wearing

670

Hints & Tips

On no account hit the cardboard box while it is on someone's head. They won't know who's doing it and may become agitated.

a box on your noggin, the **Boxhead** must also drink whenever anybody else in the game drinks. With some difficulty, obviously.

Variations:

Double Boxhead: Unsurprisingly, you'll need two cardboard boxes for this version. **Double Boxhead** follows **Boxhead** rules to the letter, the only real difference being that there are two boxes in play. So, the first player to roll an '11' or '12' wears one box, the second player to do so gets the other one. The same rules apply to get rid of the box. Players cannot wear two boxes on their head (unless the boxes are different sizes and it is funny).

Oracle Boxhead Played in the same way as normal **Boxhead**, the difference here is that before each dice roll, you get to ask the **Boxhead** one question. Just as in the old party game **Truth Or Dare**, the wearer of the box must give a truthful answer to the question. If anybody at the table can prove that the **Boxhead** has lied, the wearer faces triple the usual drinking penalty.

Triple Death Boxhead: Imagine normal **Boxhead**, but played with THREE dice instead of two... Yet there aren't an extra six rules to add onto the 12 already covered in the original game. Instead, **Triple Death Boxhead** dares you to carry out all possible combinations of the three dice rolled. For example, if a player rolls a '3',

Drunken factor...

a '6' and a '2', all of the following actions apply: 3+6=9 (the person sitting to the right of the dice-roller drinks); 3+2=5 (roll another die. The result equals the number of fingers/sips everyone at the table must drink); 6+2=8 (roll another die. The result equals the number of fingers/sips that are poured into a glass for the dice-roller to drink). Three times the fun...

Pinball Boxhead Every time a player finishes a drink, he/she should place the empty cup/glass/can in front them on the table. After a while, each player should have built up a sizeable wall of empties. With these walls in place, the dice are rolled one at a time... The only thing is, the aim now is to bounce the dice off of the other players walls, just like a pinball bouncing around a table. If you manage to bounce it off two walls, you can double the eventual penalty. Off three walls, then triple it. When both dice have landed, the usual **Boxhead** rules apply, modified by the pinball bonus. Note: if the dice should leave the table at any time during an enthusiastic throw, the dice-roller concerned must finish his beer in one go.

MAGIC DICE

 Another random drink-a-thon, and perfect for loudmouths everywhere.

You will need:

One die per player. A table. Beer.

Before every round of **Magic Dice**, pick a player to be the **'mouth'** and then give everybody in the group one die. The rules are simple – in a fit of choreographed recklessness, all of the players roll their dice onto the table simultaneously. At the same time, the designated **mouth** calls out a number between 1-6 and the players incur a forfeit (the usual two-fingers/sips will suffice) if the number yelled matches the spots shown on their tumbled dice. The **mouth** can also mix things up a bit by calling either **'even'** or **'odd'**, whereupon anybody who has an even or odd number on their dice, incurs **double** the usual penalty. There's an added risk, however, because if the **mouth** calls even and ends up with a '2', '4' or '6' showing on his/her own die, or calls odd and is unfortunate enough to get a '1', '3' or '5', he/she must drink **triple** the two-finger/sip penalty.

 **Hints & Tips**

Avoid playing this game with maiden aunts and visiting clerics. This game is going to get dirty-mouthed in a hurry.

Drunken factor...

THRESHOLD

⚠ **Heads or tails? Guess the orientation of the coin or pay the liquid penalty.**

You will need:

A die. A cup. A coin. A table. Beer.

How simple can a game be? Even after seven pints of lager, a couple of gins and a curry, the rules for this game remain crystal clear and addictively simple. (**1**) Get a cup. (**2**) Put the dice and the coin in the cup. (**3**) Each player gets a chance to shake the contents of the cup and to ask the player next to them to guess whether the coin will land on 'heads' or 'tails'. (**4**) The shaker of the cup then empties the dice and the coin hopefully onto the tabletop, noting the orientation of the coin and the number shown on the dice. (**5**) If the guessing player gets the 'heads/tails' forecast correct, the shaker of the cup is forced to drink X fingers/sips of beer – where X is the number shown on the dice. (**6**) If the guessing player gets the 'heads/tails' forecast wrong, however, he/she must drink as many fingers/sips at the upturned die has spots.

Variations: Stupid Threshold Essentially the same as **Threshold**, but played with two coins.

Bloody Stupid Threshold: Essentially the same as **Stupid Threshold**, but played with two coins and two dice.

Hints & Tips

To avoid confusing yourself, write 'heads' or 'tails' clearly on a beermat in front of you and shout it when someone asks.

Drunken factor...

TWENTY-ONE ACRES

 Simple to learn, but very difficult to give up.

You will need:

Five dice. Beer. Spirits.

Another tiny but effective game that's easy on a beer-addled brain and a breeze to learn. Unlike other dice games which count all of the numbers on a dice, **Twenty-One Acres** is only interested in the number of '1's that are rolled by the participating players.

Here's how it works: each player takes it in turn to roll the five dice. If a '1' is rolled then the players either make a mental note of it or scribble it down on a handy piece of paper, beermat or cigarette packet. The player that rolls the seventh '1' of the game is the player who gets to pick what drink will be consumed later in the game (beer, vodka, gin, whatever your poison). The player who rolls the 14th '1' of the game is the player who gets to pay for the drink specified earlier. Finally the player who rolls the 21st '1' is the lucky soul who gets to drink the chosen (and now paid for) drink in one.

 Hints & Tips
It's wise to limit the size of the drink that's picked, to avoid the evening becoming uncontrollably expensive.

Drunken factor...

BUNKO

⚠ **A game for the early evening, when players can still string thoughts together.**

You will need:

Six dice. Two tables. Eight players. Beer. Some paper. A pen.

A game that can only be played with groups of four people, **Bunko** is a slightly complex dice game that's played in rounds. Simply put, the aim of **Bunko** is for your team (two players) to amass 21 points before the opposing team (two players) does.

If there are eight players involved (that's two teams of four), these are split between two tables – two play two on table 1 and two play two on table 2. Team partners sit opposite each other and, rolling three dice in turn, each player tries to get as many '6's as possible. Each **6** rolled is worth **one point**, and the player in control of the dice keeps rolling until none of the three dice rolled shows a 6. When this happens, play passes to the next player on the opposing team, and so on around the table. The winners are the first partnership to make it to the magical 21 point total with their combined scores.

However, there are some finer points to the gameplay. Firstly, if a player rolls **three '1's** at any time, the team loses all their points – this is termed a **'wipeout'**. If a player manages to roll **three '6's**, the proverbial **'Bunko'**, the rolling player gets three points, while both teams get the chance to earn a bonus. Whenever a **Bunko** appears, the table becomes free and anyone, from either team, can try to pick up the dice from the table. Each dice recovered is worth an extra point – so if the **Bunko**-rolling team manage to retrieve all three dice, they get an extra three points to add to their score. But if the opposing team manage to grab the dice, they

Hints & Tips

You have to be poised to be quick off the mark when a 'Bunko' occurs. This should be the responsibility of the non–dice-thrower.

score the extra points despite the fact that it is not their go at the table. Winning partnerships then swap tables, playing the other team members.

And where exactly does the excessive drinking come in? Glad you asked. While **Bunko** can certainly be played for fun, a lot of the fun comes from adding an alcoholic element to the proceedings. For example, **'wipeouts'** (when a dice roll serves up three '1's) could also be punished with a drinking forfeit; **Bunko** rolls are given an extra edge by penalizing the rolling team if they don't retrieve at least two of the three dice after a trio of sixes. Add to that the fact that you can make up penalties for most losses, most wipeouts, or if a team rolls three '2's, '3's, '4's or '5's. The possibilities are endless. Why not try a couple of games for yourself?

Drunken factor...

SIX PACK

 **A fast-paced game of glass-filling and glass-emptying.**

You will need:

Six glasses. Beer.

Arrange six glasses (half-pint tumblers for amateurs, pint-glasses for the pros) in a row and number them from 1-6. Half-fill glasses '1', '3' and '5' with beer and leave the others empty. Now take your trusty die, pick somebody to go first and begin as follows:

Each player rolls the die and, on seeing the result, picks up the corresponding glass. If it's **a full glass** then the player drinks the beer and then passes the die onto the person to his/her left. If it's **an empty glass**, the player is obliged to pour some of his own drink into it, before passing the die onto the next player. This process continues around the table until people are either (a) drunk or (b) annoyed that they've given away too much beer. Drunkenness or penniless sobriety rests on the throw of the die…

 **Hints & Tips**

This is a game that becomes much more fun if everybody's drinking something different. Variety is the spice, etc.

Drunken factor…

JUST DICE

⚠ **A relatively simple game. As long as you jot down the string of penalty rules.**

You will need:

Two dice. Beer. Spirits.

Similar to **Three Man, Just Dice** is a much simpler, quicker game, but still one that gets you sloshed out of your brain in under two hours. The rules are straightforward – each player rolls two dice and notes the numbers that come up. Rolls that **add up to a '6'** (1&5, 2&4) or **have a '6'** in them (6&1, 6&2, 6&3, 6&4, 6&5), incur the traditional beer-down-the-hatch penalty. In addition, rolling a **double '2', double '4'** or a **double '5'**, incurs an X finger/sip penalty (where X is the number of the double thrown). A **double '3'** incurs two separate penalties, the usual two-finger/sip penalty for having two numbers that add up to '6', plus a three-finger/sip penalty for the double. Worse still, roll a **double '1'** or a **double '6'** and the player to your left gets to pour you a shot of your least favourite spirit. You, naturally, must down it in one.

Hints & Tips

When asked what your least favourite spirit is you MUST tell the truth. To do otherwise would be unprincipled. Ahem.

Drunken factor...

MEXICAN

⚠️ **A game of Mexicans,
Scumbags and point scoring.**

You will need:

Two dice. A pen. Some paper. Beer.

Slightly more involved than most drinking games, **Mexican** can nevertheless lead to a long and competitive evening of drunkenness. Again, like **Three Man** and **Boxhead**, the game involves rolling two dice and performing the tasks (drink-related, of course) that are associated with them. In this case, however, **Mexican** is also about amassing a decent score over your opponents. Dice rolls are subject to the following punishments and penalties:

If the dice show '1' & '2': this is called a **'Mexican'**, the lowest possible roll and so the most nasty. Every time a **Mexican** is thrown, the standard drink penalty (let's say, one finger/sip of beer) is doubled. If the dice show '1' & '3': this is known as a **'Scumbag'**. The dice-roller must immediately finish his current drink, whether it's a quick shot of Tequila or a full pint of lager. If the dice show **a double**: the dice-thrower's score increases by the number of the double multiplied by 100, i.e. if a double '2' is thrown, the player's score increases by 2 x 100=200. **Any other throw**: another scoring roll. Simply take the highest number on the two dice and multiply it by 10 + the smallest number, i.e. 6&4 scores 64, 3&2 scores 32.

The player that starts the game has a choice of taking **up to three** rolls to get the highest score possible. However many you decide to take, the final score is always the total amassed on the last throw, whether it's the first, second or third attempt. Once the starting player has decided on how many dice rolls he/she is going to make, the other players must follow suit, i.e. if the starting player decides to take

Hints & Tips

There are enough Mexican games in this book to make a theme night: Moustaches, stupid accents; the fun is probably endless.

only one dice roll, everybody else in the game can only take one roll too. However, the two dice do NOT have to be thrown at the same time. If a player has more than one throw available, he/she can elect to only roll one of the two dice the second time around, i.e. if a player has two throws available, and rolls a 5&1 on the first go, he/she may decide to only pick up the '5' and to throw that die again (thereby increasing the chances of a **Mexican** or a **Scumbag**). But, as the object of the game is to amass the highest score, the player may want to rethrow the '1' to increase the points total. The loser is the player who scores the lowest and so he must incur the penalty drink as a result.

Variations:

Mega-Mexican: For real masochism, try adding a third die; one that's a different colour to the two point-scoring dice. Thus, when drinking penalties occur, the player must not only drink the traditional finger/sip punishment (and this may have been increased by **Mexicans** during the game), but he/she must repeat the penalty X times (where X is the number on the third die).

Drunken factor...

MEXICO

⚠ **No Mexicans or Scumbags in this dice-based variant of Cheat.**

You will need:

Two dice. A cup. A pen. Some paper. Beer.

As another version of the **Mexican** game, the unadventurously titled **Mexico** not only refines the rules, but makes the gameplay slightly more dangerous by introducing an element of bluff.

Again, **Mexico** revolves around the chucking of two dice onto a table, but this time the dice are rattled around in a cup which is slammed down on the table to hide the dice roll from the other players. The dice-roller is allowed to take a look at the result and, like **Mexican**, the highest number gets multiplied by 10 and added to the lower number. Rolling a '5' and a '6', for example, would give you a score of 65. But, as you always have to roll a bigger, better score than the previous player, you may have to lie about it. Dice rolls are ranked in the following order: 1&1; 2&1; other doubles (6&6, 5&5, etc.); 6&5; 6&4; 6&3; 6&2; 6&1 and so on.

Once the dice-rolling player has **announced** his score, he waits for somebody to challenge him or call him a **liar**. If nobody does, the roll stands and the dice move onto the next player. If, however, the dice-roller IS challenged, the challenger can lift up the cup to see if the dice-roller is telling the truth. If he/she was telling the truth, the challenger must drink half-a-pint of beer. If the dice-roller is proved to be a liar, he/she downs the penalty half.

Hints & Tips
Make sure you understand the ranking system of the different rolls before you start bluffing, otherwise you'll definitely come a cropper.

Special rules apply for rolls of **1&1** (tell any opponent to drink half-a-pint... if they **don't believe you** but you have rolled a true 1&1, this penalty is **doubled**) and rolls of **1&2** (which changes the direction in which the dice are passed around the table).

Extra rules: if you drop a die (and someone notices), drink one finger/sip. If you drop both dice, drink two fingers/sips. If you slam the cup down on the table and one die sneaks out, drink one finger/sip. If you lose a die, drink a whole pint.

Drunken factor...

SPEED DICE

Roll the dice, drink the beer. What could be simpler?

You will need:

Two dice. Beer.

Short and sweet, all you need for a passport to oblivion is a pair of dice and a table to chuck them on to. Everybody in the group rolls two dice and adds up their score. The loser is the player with the lowest combined score from the two dice and must drink the **difference** between the highest score and the lowest score in fingers/sips. If there is a tie for the lowest score, both losers must drink the hefty forfeit.

Variations:

If any player rolls a **six**, they get to roll that die again adding the extra number to the total. Larger totals = bigger differences. And ultimately this means **more drinking.**

 **Hints & Tips**

The only advice we can offer when playing this game is to wear a helmet. It'll help when you fall over.

Drunken factor...

FORFEIT DICE

⚠ **A dice-based version of Russian Roulette.
With more than one bullet in the gun.**

You will need:

Three dice. A table. Beer.

Before play starts, take some time out to decide on six individual forfeits (i.e. drinking two fingers/sips of beer, downing your pint, buying the next round, etc.) and to **assign each** one a number from **1-6**. Set one of the three dice aside – this will be known as the **'forfeit die'** and will be used to decide which one of the six penalties you have created will be applied to losing players. Now for the game itself – each player in turn takes the two remaining dice and rolls them in full view of the other players. The next player must then guess whether his dice-roll will have a higher total than the previous players. When he/she has plumped for **'higher'** or **'lower'**, the dice are rolled and result examined. If the player is right, then he/she gets to roll the dice for a second time, again guessing whether the total will be **'higher'** or **'lower'** than the first. If the player is correct again, then play passes onto the next player in the group. **Two correct guesses** in a row and **play passes** onto the next player in the group. If, however, a dice-rolling player gets two guesses wrong back-to-back, then he/she must pay a forfeit which is decided randomly by rolling the **'forfeit die'**.

Hints & Tips

Students of odds will tell you that a '7' is the most common total with two dice. That may help you.

Drunken factor...

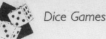

7-11-DOUBLES

⚠ **A fast-paced game with lots of booze that requires a minimum of brainpower.**

You will need:

Two dice. A table. An empty pint glass. Beer.

Another simple dice game, heavily laced with the possibility of extreme drunkenness. Each player takes two dice and rolls them, taking careful note of the result. If the dice-chucker comes up with a **7**, an **11**, or any **double**, then he can pick somebody at random to drink a forfeit.

The forfeit: Whoever is chosen must first locate the empty pint glass (making sure NOT to touch it with their hands) and then fill it half-full with beer.

The aim of the game, is for the forfeiting player to drink the contents of the pint glass BEFORE the player with the dice manages to roll another **'7'**, **'11'** or **double**. The player with the dice cannot roll them until the forfeiting player has **touched** the pint glass.

If the forfeiting player manages to drink the beer in the glass before the dice show any of the relevant bogey numbers, then play passes onto the next player. If, however, the forfeiting player does not manage to drain the amount of penalty booze before a **'7'**, **'11'** or **double** is rolled, then another half of beer is added to the glass and the process begins again. This continues until the player beats the dice-roller.

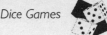

Hints & Tips

If you have to pay the forfeit, make sure you've got everything planned BEFORE you touch the pint glass. Or suffer the consequences.

Note: Any form of abuse of the dice by anybody involved with the game – throwing them wildly off of the table, clattering them into other people's drinks, seeing if you can bounce them down the corridor and through the toilet doors – incurs a **hefty** one-pint penalty.

Also note: if the penalty beer glass is ever filled, a fresh glass shall be sought out and the excess penalty deposited therein.

Drunken factor...

TONGUE-TWISTERS & WORD GAMES

Highly portable (all you need is your mouth, your brain and a couple of useful limbs), drinking games based on word association, spelling and name-calling, are amongst the most popular boozy entertainment you can find. And here you'll find the best of the bunch. It's the definitive collection of the old (**Fuzzy Duck, Ibble Dibble**) and the new (**Drink Don't Think, Sentences**), all games designed to briefly challenge the mind and, the longer you play them, to lead you by the hand into the welcoming arms of alcohol-powered amusement. They can be played anywhere too – in the pub, at home, at the station while you're waiting for a train, because most of them don't require any props. So pick a game (we recommend **Drink Don't Think** or the anarchic **Fizz Buzz**) and try your luck.

I NEVER DID

⚠️ **A game that requires a keen mind and a low embarrassment threshold.**

You will need:

Beer. Spirits.

A simple, alcoholic version of the party-favourite **Truth Or Dare** – a game that will undoubtedly start off slow and cautious, but that just as inevitably gets better the longer you play and the more you drink…

Gather a group of friends around a table, or in a circle on the floor. Select one player to begin. This player kicks off the game by saying **'I never did…'** followed by something that the player actually has done. Everybody around the table who also has done the exploit mentioned by the speaking player then drinks an appropriate drinking fine. Then the next player announces that he/she **'never did'** something and play continues around the circle. As the inhibitions start to crumble due to excessive alcohol consumption later in the game, the deeds mentioned will alter from the largely innocent ('I never did go to the supermarket'), to the risky ('I never did lie and say I was busy') to the downright confrontational, ('I never did sleep with Dave's wife').

 **Hints & Tips**
Don't ever play this game with anyone you've really done something terrible, and secret, to. It'll come out…

Drunken factor…

FUZZY DUCK

⚠️ **Fuzzy Duck? Reverse the D and the F and giggle at the rudeness of it all...**

You will need:

Beer. Spirits.

Herd your favoured friends into a circle and spin a coin to decide who goes first (preferably somebody who knows how to play the game). Player one starts the game by saying: **'Fuzzy Duck'.** The person to the left, player two, follows this opening gambit by either announcing: **'Fuzzy Duck'** or **'Does he?'** If the player plumps for saying **'Fuzzy Duck'**, the game continues and moves onto player three, who also has the opportunity to say **'Fuzzy Duck'** or **'Does he?'** If, however, a player decides to say **'Does he?'** play is reversed (moving anticlockwise) and instead of **'Fuzzy Duck'**, players have to say **'Ducky Fuzz.'** If a player says **'Does he?'** again, the direction changes back and **'Ducky Fuzz'** returns to the original **'Fuzzy Duck'**.

Players drink a penalty if they say **'Fuzzy Duck'** when they should say **'Ducky Fuzz'** (and vice versa) or if they speak out of turn. Or indeed if they accidentally say something rude.

Hints & Tips

Somebody may latch on to the idea that it's clever to say 'does he' a lot. Well, it's not if everyone else does.

Drunken factor...

ACTOR AND MOVIE

⚠ **A simple game of movie knowledge enlivened by a smattering of lovely booze**

You will need:

Beer. Spirits. A loose tongue.

Another simple knowledge game, where 'you either know it or you don't' and if 'you don't' you'll get into alcoholic trouble quicker than everybody else. This game's theme is the movies and although the rules of play are simple, an extensive knowledge of films, actors and actresses is a distinct advantage.

Here's how it works: gather a group of players and select somebody to go first. This player then names an **actor or** an **actress** and the rest of the players, in turn around the group, attempt to **name a film** that the named actor/actress has been in (30 seconds are allowed for deep thought), i.e. if player one says **'Bill Pullman'**, player two could mention **'Independence Day'**, player three might say **'Lost Highway'** and so on. The first person who can't guess a movie that the relevant star has appeared in, or says a movie that the star did NOT appear in, has to a drink a penalty.

And there's a neat twist – when somebody can't think of a movie the actor/actress has appeared in, the other players get 60 seconds to try and think of some extra ones. The total of these films is counted up after the minute has passed and the player paying the penalty must then **drink for X seconds** (where X is the number of films that the other players managed to think of).

Hints & Tips
Watch lots of Wim Wenders films and buy
the Time Out movie guide if you want to be
any good at this diabolically difficult game.

Unsurprisingly, a keen knowledge of little-known Euro-actors and arthouse is a distinct advantage. Everybody can name some movies that **Bruce Willis** has been in. But how many people will be able to list the filmography of **Koji Yakusyo?**

Drunken factor…

CATEGORIES

Think drink. Think drink. Repeat until 'sober' sounds like sofa.

You will need:

Beer. Spirits.

Another relatively simple game, worth learning because it can be used as part of the **Multi** card-based drinking game. Gather people together in a rough circle and select an eager player to go first. He/she must think of an appropriate category, e.g. Division I football teams, and then each subsequent player must name an item/thing that fits into the category – so player two could say **Birmingham City**, player three might mumble **Wolves** and so on. Hesitation is punishable with a drinking penalty, as is the player who can't think of a new item/thing to add to the category. This player then drinks the penalty and chooses a new category. Then the game begins anew. Told you it was simple.

Variants: A Ship Came Into the Harbour

The same game, but with a salty, nautical spin. The first player announces that: 'a ship came into the harbour carrying... **a cargo of beer**', then the players around the table must name different brands of beer or lager (Heineken, Kronenbourg, Carlsberg, etc.) Whoever can't think of a new kind of beer, then **pays the penalty** and picks a new category, i.e. 'a ship came into the harbour carrying... a cargo of cigarettes.' (Marlboro, Camel, Silk Cut, etc.)

Hints & Tips
Try and choose relatively easy categories, because the game is more fun played like that. 'Mongolian Cheeses' is not clever.

Drunken factor...

BUZZ

⚠ **Think, drink. Think, drink. Then repeat, until 'sober' sounds like 'sofa'.**

You will need:

Beer. Spirits.

This well-known game may sound easy to play, but its simplicity is merely a smokescreen for a devilish word game that's actually much trickier than it first appears. Start the game, by sitting everyone down in a circle and by picking one player to start. This player then begins to count, saying the number '**1**'. The person to their immediate left then says '**2**', the next player says '**3**', and so on around the group.

Things start to get interesting, however, when the count gets to either 7, 11, a multiple of 7 or 11, or a number that features 7 in its digits. As soon as this happens, the player must say '**Buzz**' instead of the number, i.e. 1, 2, 3, 4, 5, 6, Buzz, 8, 9, 10, Buzz, 12, 13, Buzz, 15, etc.)

Also, as soon as someone says **Buzz** you switch directions – so if the game was rolling to the left, it now stops, reverses and moves around to the right. Again, if anybody hesitates, says a 7, 11, multiple of 7 or 11, or a number with 7 in it, or says **Buzz** when they don't have to, the usual drinking penalty (for example, two fingers/sips per mistake) applies. Easy to learn, difficult to master, repeat the game, getting faster and faster, until the participants can no longer stand, let alone from 1-10.

Hints & Tips

We can't help you here. All we suggest is that you try and work a little bit ahead so that you have some idea what's coming. It won't last long.

Variants: Fizz Buzz

This version plays in the same way as **Buzz** above, only that instead of numbers containing or divisible by 7 and 11, the game challenges players by changing the magic number to 3. That means that no number that's a multiple of 3 or features a 3 can be said. Instead the player must substitute the numeral with either **'Buzz'** or **'Fizz'** – i.e. 1, 2, Fizz, 4, 5, Buzz, 7, 8, Buzz, etc. Simply put, if a player says **'Buzz'** the direction of play reverses, but if the player says **'Fizz'** the play continues in the same direction. Any mistake is penalised by a drink. Believe it, this can get incredibly confusing.

Bizz Buzz Bang

Now it gets really tricky. **Bizz Buzz Bang** takes the obvious step and introduces different words for different numbers and their multiples. In this case, **Bizz** equals 3, **Buzz** represents 5 and **Bang** takes the place of 7. So whenever a 3 or a multiple of 3 comes up during the count you say **'Bizz'** (3, 6, 9, 12, 13, 15, etc.); whenever a 5 or multiple of 5 comes up you say **'Buzz'** (5, 10, 15, 20, etc.); and when a 7 or multiple of 7 comes up you say **'Bang'** (7, 14, 17, 21, 27, 28).

Finally, if you have a number that has more than two properties, you say both words – i.e. 15 is divisible by 3 and 5 so you would say **'Bizz-Buzz'**; 35 contains a 3, and is divisible by 5 and 7, so this warrants a **'Bizz-Buzz-Bang'**. Thus, a game would unfold like this: 1, 2, Bizz, 4, Buzz, Bizz, Bang, 8, Bizz, Buzz, 11, Bizz, Bizz, Bang, Bizz-Buzz, 16, and so on. As usual, anybody who makes a mistake, drinks. If anyone can work out that they have.

Drunken factor...

697

DRINK DON'T THINK

⚠️ **By far this author's favourite drinking game. Fun, demanding and deadly...**

You will need:

Beer. Spirits.

Typically simple yet addictively playable, **Drink Don't Think** is one of the easiest/trickiest drinking games ever devised. And that's just the start of the seriously twisted thinking that this game is going to inspire in you.

Here's how it works: gather your group of friends and select a player to go first. This player then kicks off the game by saying the name of a famous person, either a **celebrity** (Johnny Depp, Bruce Forsythe) or a well-known **cartoon character** (Donald Duck, Mickey Mouse).

The next player to go can then say the name of another celebrity, a name that must begin with the first letter of the previous celeb's surname, i.e. player one might start with **Emma Thompson**, so player two would have to say a name beginning with **'T', Terence Stamp**. Player three therefore has to think of a name that begins with an **'S', Steve McManaman**, and so on.

Hints & Tips
Panic is the enemy in this game, above all else
just try and stay completely, utterly calm.
Otherwise you're going to lose it big-time.

The extra rules are simple: while a player thinks of a name he/she has to con-
tinually sip from their drink; if a player says a name that has a surname and a fore-
name that begin with the same letter, i.e. **Charlie Chaplin**, the direction of play is
reversed. Names cannot be reused or repeated, if this happens the offending player must down the rest of their drink. Finally, players that cannot think of a name,
must drink a two-finger/sip penalty.

Drunken factor...

🍾🍾🍾🍾🍾🍾🍾

CHEERS!

IBBLE DIBBLE

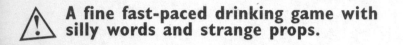

⚠ **A fine fast-paced drinking game with silly words and strange props.**

You will need:

Beer. Spirits. A cork. A lighter (or box of matches).

Arrange a gang of players around a table, and assign each one of these players **a number**. So, assuming there are four players, assign numbers **1-4** to the people around the table in a clockwise direction.

Make sure everybody has at least one large drink, then take the cork and blacken one end of it by burning it with the lighter or the matches. **Now for the game...** First of all, it's vital that you understand these two basic concepts – an **'ibble dibble'** is a player who wants to get drunk; a **'dibble ibble'** is a black mark on a player's face made by the cork. Once you understand this, you can start to play the game.

Whoever has been assigned the number **1** kicks off the game and can pass the play onto anybody else in the circle by **naming himself** (i.e. **'number 1 ibble dibble'** – player one who wants to get drunk), **identifying how many marks he has (**i.e. **'with no dibble ibbles'** – no cork marks), and then **calling another player and identifying the number of marks they have** (i.e.**'calling number 3 ibble dibble with 1 dibble ibble'** – player three who wants to get drunk and has one mark).

Hints & Tips

Try not to have too far to travel home after you've been playing this. No cab is going to stop for someone covered in dibble-ibbles.

So, a sample game might go something like this: player one says: 'This is number 1 **ibble dibble** with no **dibble ibbles** calling number 3 **ibble dibble** with no **dibble ibbles**'; player three would then quickly respond with: 'This is number 3 **ibble dibble** with no **dibble ibbles** calling number 4 **ibble dibble** with no **dibble ibbles**'. If player three had paused, he/she would have a sooty mark added to their face and has to drink a penalty. Then the player can continue; 'This is number 3 **ibble dibble** with 1 **dibble ibble** calling number 2 **ibble dibble** with no **dibble ibbles**'. And so on. Drinking penalties are incurred for hesitation, or for getting your number of marks (**dibble ibbles**) wrong, or for getting your **dibble ibbles** and your **ibble dibbles** mixed up.

Drunken factor...

CHEERS!

SERGEANT MAJOR GENERAL

⚠️ **A fast-paced, name-calling game with a macho military theme.**

You will need:

Beer. Spirits.

Another simple word game which involves calling people names for amusement. Specifically, once you've gathered a sizeable group of friends around (say about six), these players are given ranks. Nominate a starting player and, moving clockwise around the group, dub player 1 the **'General'**, player 2 the **'Major'**, player 3 the **'Sergeant'**, player 4 **'1'**, player 5 **'2'**, and player 6 the **'Dunce'**. The game is kicked off by the General who calls out his own rank, followed by the rank of another player, i.e. General 1, or General Major. Quickly, the player referenced in the previous player's call must pass the play onwards by calling out their own rank followed by somebody else's number. For example:

The General: General 1

Player 1: 1 Major

The Major: Major Sergeant

And so on...

Hints & Tips
Try and decide what you're going to say before your rank is called out. Boy scouts should find this game particularly easy.

The only real rule is that the game cannot be passed on to a player that is (a) sat either side of the caller, or (b) to the player that just gave the game to you. Anybody who speaks at the wrong time, or hesitates when called, drinks an appropriate forfeit. This loser then becomes the **Dunce** who must sit in the **Dunce's seat**, and the rest of the players swap seats and ranks accordingly.

Drunken factor...

SENTENCES

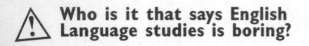

⚠ Who is it that says English Language studies is boring?

You will need:

Beer. Spirits.

Circle of friends in place, leading player nominated, a game of **Sentences** (a tricky word game that's much more difficult than its simplistic rules suggest) can begin. Player one kicks things off by saying a **random** word. The next player must then say a word that helps form a sentence but doesn't finish it. The next player must do the same and so on around the group.

For example in a four-player game: player one says **'Fish'**; player two says **'love'**; player three says **'swimming'**; player four says **'in'**, player one says **'the'**; player two says **'deep'**; player three says **'blue'**; player four says **'sea'** and the game ends.

Play continues around the circle until somebody either: **(a)** says a word that actually doesn't make sense in the context of the sentence, **(b)** hesitates too long, **(c)** is the third person to add an adjective or **(d)** accidentally finishes the sentence. When this happens, the losing player drinks a suitable boozy forfeit. Play then begins with a new word.

Hints & Tips
'And' can become such a useful and eventually irritating word that you may want to ban it from the start.

Drunken factor...